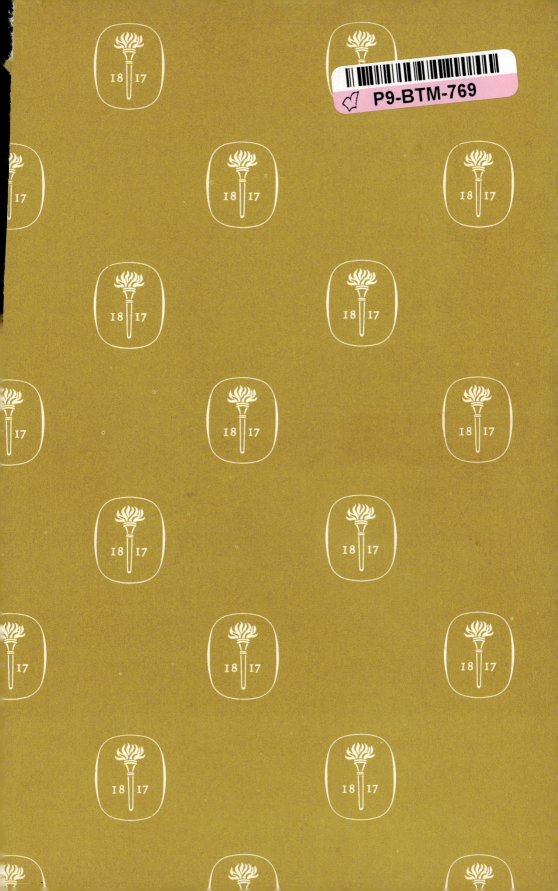

WHEN WOMEN LOOK AT MEN

WHEN WOMEN

LOOK AT MEN

An Anthology

Edited by

John A. Kouwenhoven

and

Janice Farrar Thaddeus

Harper & Row, Publishers

New York, Evanston, and London

ACKNOWLEDGMENTS

Grateful acknowledgment is made to the following for permission to reprint selections included in this book:

Anonymous, excerpt from a letter received by Lynn White, Jr., in "Educating Our Daughters," *Harper's Magazine,* 1950.

Atherton, Gertrude, "Man of the World," from *Adventures of a Novelist.* Copyright © R-1960 by Muriel Atherton Russell. Reprinted with the permission of Liveright, Publishers.

Barr, Amelia E., excerpt from an article in the *Ladies' Home Journal,* 1891.

Benson, Sally, "He'll Outgrow It," from *Women and Children First.* Copyright 1942 by the F-R Publishing Corporation. This material originally appeared in *The New Yorker,* and is reprinted with the permission of Random House, Inc.

Benton, Frances, excerpt from *Etiquette.* Random House, Inc., 1956.

Berriault, Gina, "The Stone Boy," from *The Houses of the City.* Copyright © 1958 by Gina Berriault, *Short Story 1.* Reprinted with the permission of Charles Scribner's Sons.

Bogan, Louise, "The Meeting." Copyright © 1957 by The New Yorker Magazine, Inc. Reprinted with the permission of Farrar, Straus & Company, Inc.

Boothe, Clare, Act I from *The Women.* Copyright 1937 by Random House, Inc. Reprinted by permission.

Bouton, Emily S., excerpt from *Social Etiquette.* F. T. Neely, 1894.

Boyle, Kay, "Effigy of War." Copyright 1940 by Kay Boyle. Originally published in *The New Yorker.* Reprinted with the permission of the author.

Buchwald, Emilie Bix, "Jupiter and Io: These Older Nights." Reprinted with the permission of the author and *The Kenyon Review.*

Buck, Pearl S., "Fighting Angel," from *Fighting Angel,* the John Day Company, Inc. Copyright 1936 by Pearl S. Buck. Reprinted with the permission of Harold Ober Associates, Incorporated.

——, "I Am Glad I Am Not a Man in America," from *Of Men and Women,* the John Day Company, Inc. Copyright 1941 by Pearl S. Buck. Reprinted by permission of Harold Ober Associates, Incorporated.

iv ❧

Calisher, Hortense, "In Greenwich There Are Many Graveled Walks," from *In the Absence of Angels*. Copyright 1950 by Little, Brown and Company. Originally appeared in *The New Yorker*. Reprinted with the permission of the publisher.

Cather, Willa, "Paul's Case," from *Youth and the Bright Medusa*. Reprinted by permission of Alfred A. Knopf, Inc.

Chase, Ilka, excerpt from *In Bed We Cry*, Doubleday & Company, Inc., 1943.

Cooke, Maud C., excerpt from *Social Life*, Cooperative Publishing Company, 1896.

Cudahy, Sheila, "They Met by Chance in the Park at the Zoo," from *Poems*. Published by Harvill Press, London, 1961, and reprinted with their permission.

Currie, Ellen, "Moses Supposes," from *New World Writing* #14. Copyright © 1958 by New American Library of World Literature, Inc., and reprinted by permission of the author.

Davis, Bette, "Glamour Boys" and "Should Men Be Men?," from *The Lonely Life*. Copyright © 1962 by Bette Davis. Reprinted by permission of G. P. Putnam's Sons.

De Lima, Sigrid, "A Seedy Husband," from *Captain's Beach*, Charles Scribner's Sons. Reprinted by permission of the author.

De Mille, Agnes, excerpt from *And Promenade Home,* Little, Brown and Company, 1958.

Deutsch, Babette, "The Dispassionate Shepherdess," from *Coming of Age*. Reprinted by permission of Indiana University Press.

Deutsch, Helene, M.D., excerpt from *The Psychology of Women*. Grune & Stratton, Inc., 1944.

Dix, Dorothy, pseudonym (Elizabeth Gilmer), excerpt from an essay published by the Political Equality Association, 1912.

Duncan, Isadora, excerpt from *My Life,* Boni and Liveright, 1927.

Dunham, Katherine, "A Touch of Innocence," from *A Touch of Innocence*. Copyright © 1959 by Katherine Dunham. Reprinted by permission of Harcourt, Brace & World, Inc.

Eliot, Charlotte C., "William Greenleaf Eliot," from *William Greenleaf Eliot*, Houghton Mifflin Company, 1904. The poem by T. S. Eliot quoted in the introduction is from "A Song for Simeon" in *Collected Poems of T. S. Eliot*, copyright 1936 by Harcourt, Brace & World, Inc., and reprinted with their permission.

Gale, Zona, excerpt from *Mister Pitt*, D. Appleton and Co., 1925.

Gardner, Isabella, "A Loud Song, Mother," from *The Looking Glass*. Copyright © 1961 by the University of Chicago. Originally appeared in *The Minnesota Review*.

Gildersleeve, Virginia Crocheron, "Committee Men," from *Many a Good Crusade*, The Macmillan Company, 1954.

Glasgow, Ellen, "General Archbald," from *The Sheltered Life,* Doubleday & Company, Inc. Reprinted with the permission of First and Merchants National Bank, Richmond, Va., executor of the Estate of Ellen Glasgow.

Goldman, Emma, "Johann Most," from *Living My Life*. Copyright 1931 by Alfred A. Knopf, Inc. Reprinted with the permission of Alfred A. Knopf, Inc.

Hahn, Emily, excerpt from *Spousery*, Watts, 1956.

Hardwick, Elizabeth, "The Life and Death of Caryl Chessman," from *A View of My Own*. Copyright © 1960, 1962 by Elizabeth Hardwick. Reprinted by permission of Farrar, Straus & Company, Inc.

Harriman, Margaret Case, "Mr. Miller and Mr. Hyde: Gilbert Miller," from *Take Them Up Tenderly*. Copyright 1944 by Margaret Case. This story first appeared in *The New Yorker*. Reprinted with the permission of Alfred A. Knopf, Inc.

Herschberger, Ruth, excerpt from *Adam's Rib*, Pelligrini and Cudahy, 1948.

Holt, Felicia, excerpt from "Marriage and Money," *The Ladies' Home Journal*, 1889.

Housepian, Marjorie, "Levon Dai in Council Bluffs," from *A Houseful of Love*. Copyright © 1957 by Marjorie Anais Housepian. Reprinted by permission of Random House, Inc.

Hurston, Zora Neale, "The Frizzly Rooster," from *Mules and Men*. Copyright 1935 by Zora Neale Hurston. Reprinted by permission of J. B. Lippincott Company.

Jackson, Shirley, "Life Among the Savages," from *Life Among the Savages*. Copyright 1949, 1953 by Shirley Jackson. Reprinted by permission of Farrar, Straus & Company, Inc.

Janeway, Elizabeth, "The Third Choice," from *The Third Choice*. Copyright © 1959 by Elizabeth Janeway. Reprinted by permission of Doubleday & Company, Inc.

Jewett, Sarah Orne, "The Taking of Captain Ball," from *Harper's New Monthly Magazine*, December, 1889 to May, 1890.

Jones, Mary Harris, "A Human Judge," from *Autobiography of Mother Jones*. Reprinted by permission of Charles H. Kerr and Company.

Komarovsky, Mirra, "Lords of Creation?," from *Women in the Modern World*, Little, Brown and Company, 1953.

Kumin, Maxine W., "Poem for My Son," from *Halfway*. Copyright © 1957, 1958, 1959, 1960, 1961 by Maxine W. Kumin. Reprinted by permission of Holt, Rinehart and Winston, Inc.

Laing, Dilys, "Once Upon an Eternity," from *Walk Through Two Landscapes*. Reprinted by permission of Twayne Publishers, Inc.

Learned, Mrs. Frank (Ellin Craven Learned), excerpt from *The Etiquette of New York Today*, Frederick H. Stokes Company, 1906.

Livermore, Mary A., excerpt from *Woman's Work in America*, Annie Nathan Meyer, ed., Henry Holt and Company, 1891.

Lowell, Amy, "A Communication," from *Ballads for Sale*. Copyright 1927 by Houghton Mifflin Company. Reprinted with the permission of the publishers.

Luhan, Mabel Dodge, excerpt from *Intimate Memories*, Harcourt, Brace & World, Inc., 1936.

McCarthy, Mary, "The Genial Host," from *The Company She Keeps*, Harcourt, Brace and World, Inc. Copyright 1941 by Mary McCarthy. Reprinted by permission of the author.

McCullers, Carson, "A Tree, A Rock, A Cloud," from *The Ballad of the Sad Café*. Copyright 1946 by Carson McCullers. Reprinted with the permission of Houghton Mifflin Company.

McGinley, Phyllis, "The 5:32," from *Times Three*. Copyright 1941 by Phyllis McGinley. First appeared in *The New Yorker*. Reprinted by permission of The Viking Press, Inc.

McNeal, Violet, "Medicine Men," from *Four White Horses and a Brass Band*. Copyright 1947 by Violet McNeal. Reprinted by permission of Doubleday & Company, Inc.

Magid, Marion, "The Innocence of Tennessee Williams," from *Commentary*, January, 1963. Copyright © 1963 American Jewish Committee.

Mannes, Marya, "If I Were a Man," from *More in Anger*. Copyright 1958 by Marya Mannes. Reprinted by permission of J. B. Lippincott Co.

Marshall, Lenore, "Flashlight," from anthology *Cross-Section*, edited by Edwin Seaver, 1944. Rights reserved and copyright 1944 by L. B. Fischer Publishing Corp. Reprinted with the permission of the author.

Mead, Margaret, "Sex and Achievement," from *Male and Female*. Copyright 1949 by Margaret Mead. Reprinted by permission of William Morrow and Company, Inc.

Meyer, Annie Nathan, excerpt from "Woman's Assumption of Sex Superiority," *North American Review*, 1903.

Millay, Edna St. Vincent, "Time does not . . ." from *Collected Poems* by Edna St. Vincent Millay. Copyright 1917, 1945 by Edna St. Vincent Millay. Harper & Row, Publishers, Inc. Used by permission of Norma Millay Ellis.

———, "Well, I . . ." "Sonnet XLVII of *Fatal Interview*, reprinted in *Collected Poems* by Edna St. Vincent Millay. Copyright 1931, 1958 by Edna St. Vincent Millay and Norma Millay Ellis. Harper & Row, Publishers, Inc. Used by permission of Norma Millay Ellis.

Miller, Alice Duer, "Evolution," from *Selected Poems* (1949). Reprinted with the permission of Coward-McCann, Inc.

Nicolson, Marjorie Hope, "Gentlemen and Scholars," from *The Rights and Privileges Pertaining Thereto*. Reprinted with the permission of the author and the Hampshire Bookshop.

Paley, Grace, excerpt from *The Little Disturbances of Man*. Doubleday & Company, Inc., 1959.

Parker, Dorothy, "A Valentine for Mr. Woollcott." By permission of The Viking Press, Inc.

———, "Men," from *The Portable Dorothy Parker*. Copyright 1926, 1953 by Dorothy Parker. Reprinted by permission of the Viking Press, Inc.

Perkins, Frances, "He Liked People," from *The Roosevelt I Knew*. Copyright 1946 by Frances Perkins. Reprinted by permission of The Viking Press, Inc.

Porter, Katherine Anne, "A Day's Work," from *The Leaning Tower and Other Stories*. Copyright 1940 by Katherine Anne Porter. Reprinted by permission of Harcourt, Brace & World, Inc.

Post, Emily, excerpt from *Etiquette*, Funk & Wagnalls Company, Inc., 1922.

Rich, Adrienne Cecile, "An Unsaid Word," from *A Change of World*. Reprinted by permission of Yale University Press.

Roosevelt, Eleanor, excerpt from *This Is My Story*, Harper & Brothers, 1937.

Saarinen, Aline B., "Charles Lang Freer," from *The Proud Possessors*. Random House, Inc., 1958. Copyright © 1958 by Aline B. Saarinen.

Sanford, Marcelline Hemingway, "Ernest Had Enough to Bear . . . ," from *At the Hemingways'*, Copyright © 1961, 1962 by Marcelline Hemingway Sanford. Reprinted by permission of Little, Brown & Co.–Atlantic Monthly Press.

Sanger, Margaret, "Planned Fatherhood," from *Woman and the New Race*. Brentano's, 1920.

Sarton, May, "A Celebration," from *Cloud, Stone, Sun, Vine*. Reprinted with the permission of W. W. Norton & Company, Inc.

Scott, Adelin White, excerpt from *A Professional Woman in a Man's World*. By permission of Vantage Press, Inc.

Seabury, Florence Guy, "The Sheltered Sex," from *The Delicatessen Husband*. By permission of Harcourt, Brace & World, Inc.

Slayden, Ellen Maury, "Washington Wife," from *Washington Wife: Journal of Ellen Maury Slayden.* Copyright © 1962 by Harper & Row, Publishers, Incorporated.

Stanton, Elizabeth Cady, excerpt from *The History of Woman Suffrage,* Susan B. Anthony and Ida Husted Harper, eds., 1902.

Stein, Gertrude, "Men All Write About Themselves," from *Everybody's Autobiography.* Random House, Inc., 1937.

Tarbell, Ida M., excerpt from *The Business of Being a Woman.* The Macmillan Company, 1913.

Teasdale, Sara, "Four Winds," from *The Collected Poems of Sara Teasdale.* Reprinted with the permission of The Macmillan Company.

Thorp, Margaret Farrand, "A Cinema Husband," from *America at the Movies.* Copyright 1939 by Yale University Press.

Vanderbilt, Amy, excerpt from *Amy Vanderbilt's Complete Book of Etiquette.* Garden City, 1952.

Van Doren, Dorothy, "Manly Men and Womanly Women," from *Men, Women, and Cats.* Reprinted with the permission of Appleton-Century-Crofts.

Welles, Winifred, "White Valentine," from *The Shape of Memory.* Copyright 1944 by Holt, Rinehart and Winston, Inc. Reprinted by permission of Holt, Rinehart and Winston, Inc.

Wertenbaker, Lael Tucker, "This Is How He Was," from *Death of a Man.* Copyright © 1957 by Lael Tucker Wertenbaker. Reprinted by permission of Random House, Inc.

West, Jessamyn, excerpt from *To See the Dream,* Harcourt, Brace & World, Inc., 1957.

Wharton, Edith, "His Father's Son," from *Tales of Men and Ghosts.* Copyright 1910 by Charles Scribner's Sons. Copyright 1938 by William R. Tyler. Reprinted with the permission of A. Watkins, Inc.

Wylie, Elinor, "The Puritan's Ballad," from *The Collected Poems of Elinor Wylie.* Copyright 1928 by Alfred A. Knopf, Inc. Reprinted with the permission of Alfred A. Knopf, Inc.

To

Millicent Carey McIntosh

President Emeritus

and

Rosemary Park

President of Barnard College

in honor of the 75th anniversary

of the college

"The most interesting study of womankind is man;

it ever has been, ever will, and ever should be so."

—Ella Wheeler Wilcox, 1891

Contents

III ✌ FATHERS, SONS, AND BROTHERS

IV &ebony; LOVERS

Preface
by
John A. Kouwenhoven

What do American women think—or say they think—about men?
And what changes, if any, have there been in the way they look
at those who used to be called their lords and masters?

Mrs. Thaddeus and I make no claims for ourselves as historians or
scholarly analysts of women's views, but we do make some claim
as pioneers. For this anthology is, so far as we know, the first to
present a representative selection of writings that reveal, overtly
or by implication, the way American women think and feel about
men.

Oddly enough, the historians and sociologists who might have
been expected to look into such matters have apparently overlooked
them. There have been many studies of women's role in our culture,
and of women's ideas about themselves, and even of men's ideas
about women. The last, in fact, have been assembled and displayed in at least two anthologies: one called *Men Against Women*
and the other *With Malice Toward Women*—titles which, we suppose, must reflect the anthologists' biases, since neither of us has
reason to think they reflect men's general attitude toward the
opposite sex.

Certainly our sampling of the things women have written about
men does not warrant a title that implies any such unanimity of
attitude, hostile or friendly. We have surveyed, and selected our
material from, fiction and nonfiction, prose and poetry, and from

writers of diverse backgrounds and temperaments. Some of the
authors are professional writers; others are better known in less
verbal occupations or professions. Some are college educated; some
had little schooling. All had something to say, or some feelings they
could not help betraying, about men. But the images of man that
emerge from these portraits and perspectives do not average out
to any "majority view."

The idea of making such a survey arose in connection with
plans for celebrating the seventy-fifth anniversary of Barnard College, the women's undergraduate unit of Columbia University.
In the three-quarters of a century since Barnard opened its doors
there have been profound changes in the social and intellectual
position of women in the United States. It was in 1890—the year
after Barnard was founded—that Wyoming became the first state
in the Union that granted equal suffrage to women and men.[1]
Three years later women won the ballot in Colorado, and by 1912
they had won full suffrage in nine western states. Not until 1920,
however, did the ratification of the nineteenth amendment establish equal suffrage throughout the nation.

In these same years, women have won equal educational rights.
Seventy-five years ago there were few institutions offering women
higher education equivalent to that available to men, none at all
in New York City, the nation's metropolis. Out West, where frontier
conditions had favored equality of the sexes, coeducation had been
making headway ever since Oberlin College admitted women as
well as men in 1833, and a few women's colleges with high academic
standards had been established in the East since the Civil War. But
as the struggle of those who founded Barnard witnesses, higher
education for women, on a parity with men, was in 1889 still a
novel and by no means universally approved experiment.

The president of Columbia College had been trying for ten years
to persuade Columbia's trustees to admit women as undergraduates.
But despite President Frederick A. P. Barnard's support, women
were not admitted, and the women's college that bears his name
had to be set up as a separate corporation, with its own trustees,
faculty, endowment, and buildings. Its academic standards were,
however, coordinated with those of Columbia College, and women
who successfully completed the course received (as they still do)
Columbia's Bachelor of Arts degree. As it has turned out, this rather

---

[1] Women had had equal political rights in Wyoming Territory since 1869, but
no other territory and no state had followed Wyoming's lead.

odd setup has been a continuing source of strength to Barnard (except when people who are not aware of it give, or leave, money to Columbia for women's education and Barnard receives none of it). It has, for example, permitted the college a degree of autonomy in developing a curriculum adapted, in certain areas of study, to women's special interests, while augmenting the established interdependence of the college and the great university of which it is a part. But the original reasons for the college's separate-though-equal status are a reminder that the notion of equal educational rights for women was almost as novel as that of equal political and legal rights seventy-five years ago. Even now, anyone who closely studies this anthology will discover that only two-thirds of its major contributors were graduated from—or even attended—a college or university. This probably would not be the case if our authors were men, or if a similar anthology were to be collected seventy-five years hence.

With this and other changes in women's status in relation to men, it would be strange indeed if women's attitudes toward men had not changed considerably since 1889. But the changes reflected in the things Mrs. Thaddeus and I have read are subtler than might at first be supposed. For one thing, women of the 1880's and 90's seem seldom to have regarded men as their oppressors (though you will find on page 3 a couple of excerpts from the suffragettes that prove they could be testy). In general they seem to have shared the complaisant attitude of Sarah Josepha Hale, author of a monumental tome with the unabashed title *Woman's Record; or, Sketches of All Distinguished Women, from the Creation to A.D. 1868,* which Harper & Brothers published in 1870. Mrs. Hale had dedicated her book "To the men of America; who show, in their laws and customs, respecting women, ideas more just and feelings more noble than were ever evinced by men of any other nation. . . ."

Of course there have always been some women who care little, one way or the other, about men. My own favorite, of this breed, is the anonymous British spinster who wrote a book published in London in 1857, entitled *Unprotected Females in Norway: or, the Pleasantest Way of Travelling There.* This doughty creature, who traveled with her mother through the wildest parts of Norway in carriages, on horseback, and a-foot, "found out and will maintain," as she rather aggressively put it, that "the only use of a gentleman in travelling is to look after the luggage, and we take care to have no luggage." She must have had her American counterparts in the eighties, as she does today.

But most American women, if our unsystematic research is trust-worthy, cannot so easily dispense with luggage, or with gentlemen. Early in our period a more widely shared attitude was expressed by Ella Wheeler Wilcox, author of *Poems of Passion,* who might long since have been forgotten if she had not mothered these lines:

> Laugh, and the world laughs with you;
> Weep, and you weep alone.

"The most interesting study of womankind," she wrote in the *Ladies' Home Journal,* "is man; it ever has been, ever will, and ever should be so."

Whether or not the young ladies then studying at newly estab-lished Barnard thought man was their *most* interesting study we have no way of knowing. But our impression is that the subject ranks high in interest among their successors now in college, how-ever unlikely it is that, in the changed cultural climate, they would be interested in any poems called *Poems of Passion.* The mood of the 1960's seems to be better expressed by the title of Babette Deutsch's poem, "The Dispassionate Shepherdess" (p. 309).

Mrs. Thaddeus and I have not made our selections to "prove" some theory of ours about woman's changing view of man and its relation to changing circumstance. We have in fact, no theory about that. Each of us has some impressions, based on the reading we have done, but our impressions often differ, and we expect that each reader will have his own.

It is, after all, very difficult even to determine whether the things women say about men tell us more about men than about women. Quite often in the course of our work on this book something that struck Mrs. Thaddeus as being "about" men would strike me as being "about" the woman who wrote it. And readers may well dis-agree, as we do, about such a story as Katherine Anne Porter's "A Day's Work" (p. 390). Mrs. Thaddeus reads it as a story about Mr. Halloran; I read it as a story about Mrs. Halloran as her husband's destroyer; perhaps it is about both. Similarly, Gertrude Atherton's description of her "man of the world" (p. 307) can be read as a vignette about a man (in the sense that it shows how easily men can be made asses of by a dispassionate woman), but can also be read as a vignette about a woman (in the sense that it shows how fiendishly a detached one enjoys taking advantage of an enamored man).

So we have left it to the reader to draw his or her own conclusions on such matters. Our aim has been to gather a readable selection of good fiction, poetry, and nonfiction written about men by women of varied backgrounds, and to garnish the whole with some brief excerpts of historical, if not always of literary, interest. For convenience, we have arranged the selections chronologically within five groups, beginning with a group on "Men in General" and ending, as most women (happily for the other sex!) do, with "Husbands."

Here, then, is a preliminary survey of a neglected area of American experience. Hitherto, as Professor David M. Potter of Stanford University recently pointed out, historians and sociologists (amateur and professional) have habitually derived their generalizations about the American character from the experience of only half the population—the male half. If they find evidence, for example, that modern industrial conditions provide fewer and fewer opportunities for men to develop varied skills and resources, they are likely to generalize that the American people are becoming more and more specialized, yet modern conditions have not by any means turned women into specialists. On the contrary, American housewives—who comprise the largest occupational group in the nation—are required by modern conditions to be increasingly versatile. If we based our social generalizations upon women's experience, rather than upon men's, we might, as Professor Potter says, "quite justifiably affirm that the modern age is an age of diversified activity rather than an age of specialization."[2]

Perhaps some of the generalizations habitually made about education are as fallacious as those Professor Potter discusses, and for the same reason: that we too readily assume men's experience is the norm by which to measure our resources and our needs. Certainly the history of Barnard's coordinate relationship with Columbia College proves that equality of education for women and men need not mean identity of curriculum. It also suggests that the importance of independent colleges for women will be more clearly understood when we remember that the character of the American people is, as Professor Potter justly admonishes us, "the composite of the character of its men and of its women," and not alone of its men.

To Barnard, in any event, Mrs. Thaddeus and I herewith express our thanks for the opportunity to assemble this book in honor of its seventy-fifth anniversary. I am especially grateful to the several

[2] David M. Potter, *American Women and the American Character* (Stetson University Bulletin, January, 1962), p. 9.

trustees, faculty members, administrators, and students with whom I have served on the Seventy-fifth Anniversary Committee for the past three years—first under President Millicent McIntosh, now President Emeritus, and more recently under President Rosemary Park. To them, and to the Department of English, I am indebted for the arrangement by which Mrs. Thaddeus was relieved of part of her teaching in order to do research and reading, and to attend to the many details involved in preparing such a book for the press, including the writing of the introductory notes for the selections.

She and I bear joint responsibility for the selection and arrangement of the material. But many of our colleagues and friends have made valuable suggestions, and the students in Mrs. Thaddeus' English A section turned up some nuggets we might otherwise have overlooked. By allowing Mrs. Thaddeus to use the Frederick Lewis Allen Room, the New York Public Library greatly eased the job of research. Neither of us can imagine a publisher's editor who could have been more helpful than Genevieve Young, of Harper & Row.

Finally, we wish to thank the authors and copyright owners who have given permission to reprint the various selections, with a special word of gratitude to those who have disdained the usual permission fees for anthology use, in order that Barnard College—as sole beneficiary of the royalties derived from the book—might derive maximum benefit from its publication.

I   MEN IN GENERAL

Blasts and Counter-Blasts

For fifty years we have been plaintiffs in the courts of justice, but as the bench, the bar and the jury are all men, we are non-suited every time. Some men tell us we must be patient and persuasive; that we must be womanly. My friends, what is man's idea of womanliness? It is to have a manner which pleases him—quiet, deferential, submissive, approaching him as a subject does a master. He wants no self-assertion on our part, no defiance, no vehement arraignment of him as a robber and a criminal. While the grand motto, "Resistance to tyrants is obedience to God," has echoed and re-echoed around the globe, electrifying the lovers of liberty in every latitude and making crowned heads tremble on their thrones; while every right achieved by the oppressed has been wrung from tyrants by force; while the darkest page on human history is the outrages on women—shall men still tell us to be patient, persuasive, womanly?

—ELIZABETH CADY STANTON, in an address
to the National Suffrage Convention of 1890

The long past has denied to women the possession of souls, and they have been relegated to the ignorance and injustice to which men have always doomed those regarded as their inferiors. . . . All through these ages the history of woman has been disastrous. Her physical weakness, and not alone her mental inferiority, has made her the subject of man. Toiling patiently for him, asking little for herself and everything for him, cheerfully sharing with him all perils and hardships, the unappreciated mother of his children, she has been bought and sold, petted or tortured, according to the whim of her brutal owner, the victim everywhere of pillage, lust, and war.

—MARY A. LIVERMORE, in "Woman in the State," 1891

In the very charge of inferiority launched against men by the women, they present the strongest possible indictment of their own sex. These men, who are so weak, so corrupt, so far below the standard of the women—had they no mothers?

—ANNIE NATHAN MEYER, in an antifeminist tract, 1903

The great trouble with men, and the source of all their injustice toward women, is that they have never realized that the two sexes are of the same flesh and flavor, and that what is sauce for the goose is sauce for the gander. They act as if women were animals of some peculiar and foreign breed, and were only fit for the human palate when served up in a sweetish sauce à la feminine instead of as just plain, rare humanity.

—DOROTHY DIX, pseudonym (ELIZABETH GILMER), in an essay published by the Political Equality Association, 1912

Men and women are widely apart in functions and in possibilities. They cannot be made equal by exterior devices like trousers, ballots, the study of Greek.

—IDA M. TARBELL, in *The Business of Being a Woman*, 1913

Most men aren't so handsome that they can afford to play fast and loose with the little the good Lord gave them. I suppose when He took one look at Adam and realized what He'd done, He simply had to give women loving hearts to overcome the handicap.

—Matilda Stevens, in ILKA CHASE's novel, *In Bed We Cry*, 1943

ELLEN MAURY SLAYDEN   [1897]

Ellen Maury Slayden (1860-1926), who says of herself that she "never went to a real school" a day in her life, kept a diary with Boswellian mania, sometimes taking notes on the spot. The result is a peculiarly vivid recounting of the men and manners she encountered in Washington while her Texan husband was Congressman from 1897 to 1919.

Washington Wife

San Antonio, January (1897)

This notebook has not been opened since the dog days. The novelty, excitement, and hard work of J.'s [1] brief and hectic campaign for Congress left me no time for recording personal experiences. I am sorry, because so many pleasant and amusing things happened that I would not willingly forget. One constantly hears that politics is an ugly game, but we have seen little but the kindly side of it.

The campaign brought such splendid opportunities to test the friendship of our friends, and of others who we had not dreamed were so much our friends. They were almost without exception loyal and helped us in many odd and unexpected ways. An appreciable amount of money from Republicans for the campaign fund was not the least of our surprises. Help of that sort was most opportune, for our cash in hand the day J. was nominated was little more than $100. My heart was touched to the depths by the fact that J.'s friends and neighbors, those who have known him best and longest, wanted him to represent them, and especially under the peculiar circumstances of his failing in business, making an assignment of all he possessed one day and being nominated for Congress the next morning. I doubt if I shall ever again feel the same thrill of gratitude and pride that I felt when hearing that the men who were thrown out of work by his firm's collapse just in the beginning of the cotton season were the first to organize a Slayden Club and to offer money for the campaign.

Wynne Andrews, not a rich man, offered his time, a pair of fine mules, and a strong buggy. He and J. drove hundreds of miles to places that cannot be reached by rail in this vast twelfth district— thirty-seven counties, and larger by 10,000 square miles than the state of New York. It was cold, wet weather, and stopping places few and primitive, but they made light of the hardships. After the first few days, they said, the mules could recognize a voter afar off; when near enough, they would stop abruptly, J. would stand up and make his argument, the voter would pledge his support, and the mules move on at once.

[1] Author's husband, James Luther Slayden.

Of course J. was away almost constantly, and if sentimental people had not already convinced me that woman's sphere is in the home, the conviction would have been forced upon me by the exigencies of those ten weeks. We could not afford clerical help, so I spent many long days at the typewriter, addressing campaign literature, writing letters and sometimes speeches for supporters who wanted to speak and did not know what to say. I was flattered when a friend quoted her coachman as saying that my colored boy made the best political speech they had had at the Coachmen's Union.

Ed is the son of our colored cook, and when we employed him last summer, we little thought that his services would be so largely political and clerical. He is amazingly educated for his age—about sixteen years—and writes such a good hand that J. said reproachfully, "It makes me ashamed to see a colored boy write better than my wife." "And spell better than my husband," I retorted, after which passage at arms we settled down to make use of his gifts. We found him unfailingly loyal, trustworthy, and best of all, cheerful under every trial.

Only once did he mope or neglect his various duties. The election was close, the result in doubt for several days, and during that time he let the house get very dusty, but one night the good news came that J. had won. When we went down to breakfast the next morning, Ed was waiting for us all smiles, and writ large in the dust on the tables and piano was the one word "Elected."

McKinley has let it be known that he will call an extra session in March, so we shall be breaking up, and I dread it, but except for that the outlook is pleasant. Sometimes I feel a little irritated by the idea some of our friends have that we must feel socially elevated by the new position. How could we be socially elevated? I cherish the good old American belief that if you are born gentlefolk, no amount of worldly honors can make you anything more, and only your own conduct make you anything less. There are others who seem to think that Washington is almost entirely peopled with diplomats and discuss my fitness for diplomatic society, or say, "When you get up there among those foreigners—" Happily, so much of my youth was spent in Washington that I have no delusions of grandeur as to the status of a new Congressman's wife, but renewing old friendships and being so near my parents in Virginia are pleasant things I look forward to.

*   *   *

Our first experience of the obligations of congressional life was in entertaining W. J. Bryan, our defeated candidate for President. San Antonio thinks it the crowning glory of our hitherto obscure career, but it was really only a visit from a simple, cultivated gentleman of the kind—barring a few Western touches—that I have always been accustomed to.

Elected by Bryan's party, J. thought he should be our guest while he was here on his lecture tour, but when he accepted the invitation only two days before he was to arrive, I was a bit upset. We were dining at Jane's.[2] Good sister that she is, she offered to have mince pies, cake, and jelly made for me; and I drove at once to market to buy venison, quail, and wild duck, so as to be prepared for much coming and going and feeding of hearty Democrats. Coming home through the back gate I ordered the killing of a big gobbler bought weeks before and named "W.J.B."; paused in the kitchen to put a Virginia ham in soak, and then sat down to think "What next?"

It was bitter cold, and this, like most Texas houses, all doors and windows, is a cave of the winds in winter. The largest fires are only ornamental. My good cook was away; Ed was gone back to college, alas!; the best long tablecloth was soiled, and the water pipes frozen. I wondered if our Virginian ancestors who entertained Washington and Lafayette ever had more to contend with. Bryan himself didn't appall me, but the people who would come to see him would look around to see how the new Congressman's wife was doing things.

Besides Bryan, we were to have Governor Culberson, ex-Governor Jim Hogg, and several local magnates, and a later telegram, saying that they could not get here to dinner Thursday but would come to breakfast Friday and to dinner that evening, did not make the situation easier.

Snow was falling when they all arrived, but the house was almost warm. Bryan was easy to get acquainted with, and we had a pleasant breakfast and a good one—thanks to Mrs. George Maverick, who lent me her cook, the best one in town. Could such a simple kindness be thought of in any society more formal than our frontier?

I have always liked and admired Governor Hogg. For all his roughness (some of it assumed, I think) he is a stimulating companion, wise, kind, and sincere, and full of homespun humor. Among other hot breads, we had some very small biscuits, and apropos of J.'s asking him to take two at a time, he launched out in his tremen-

2 Jane Maury Maverick (Mrs. Albert Maverick).

dous voice, "When I was a gre't big water-jointed boy, used to eatin'
at the blowin' of the horn, my sister moved to town, and one day she
had some o' these biscuits, and I'd take one and they wouldn't get
'round the table before I'd want another, and I felt so foolish, and
got so mad that I never would let one be made in my house." I assured him there was a "free and unlimited coinage" of them going
on in the kitchen at a ratio of "sixteen to one," and I think he ate his
allowance. I had a plateful kept by him, but didn't know until that
night that he had noticed it.

Before breakfast was over the gallery and front rooms were full of
people waiting to see the lion, but Hogg was in some respects more
the center of attraction than Bryan. Our biggest chair creaked under
his weight, but he made Rena and Jessie Maverick sit on the arms
and held little Mary Wilson in his lap. When I introduced him to my
most punctilious friend, he reached around the children to shake
hands with her, and said, "Howd'do, Mrs. Moore, I'm glad to know
you," so heartily that she quite forgot his failure to rise.

The dinner party strained the capacity of our dining room. Bryan
never insisted upon leading but followed any person who introduced
a subject worthwhile. His talk was easy, unpretentious, and amazingly humorous for such a dead-in-earnest person. He discussed his
defeat without embarrassment or bitterness, told funny stories of the
campaign, and read newspaper jokes at his own expense. His hair is
too long—the usual weakness of Western statesmen—and his clothes
of smooth black cloth and eccentric cut are queer, but I didn't notice
them until he was on the stage. I saw only his clear, steel-blue eyes
with black brows and lashes, very Irish, his straight uncompromising
mouth, and well-kept teeth.

From dinner we hurried to Beethoven Hall, where the mass of
people shouting for Bryan, Hogg and Slayden almost carried us off
our feet. When Bryan began to speak, I realized for the first time
that he was a big man, not just a pleasant one.

He has the most perfect voice I ever heard. The audience went
wild. When he finished people swarmed around him, shaking his
hands, touching his shoulders, almost kissing the hem of his garment.
How can a man retain his sanity amid such adulation?

I was standing in a stage box looking down at the ovation when
Governor Hogg, who was beside me, called out to a dignified-look-
ing gentleman almost across the hall, "Jack Dunkin, Jack Dunkin,
come here! I want you to meet Mrs. Slayden." When Judge Duncan
came near enough, he went on, "She's little, but, I tell you, she's a

whizzer. She kept me a whole plate o' hot biscuits to myself this mornin'." I felt as if I were being dangled before the crowd by the back of my neck.

Home again sitting around the fire, Bryan was only a quiet, genial guest, talking of his wife and children, of books and poetry. He repeated the "Ode to the Waterfowl" so beautifully that I felt as if I had never heard it before.

Privately Governor Hogg told me to prepare to stay a long time in Washington, giving some expert political reasons and some personal estimates of J. that almost brought tears to my eyes, but the future is in the lap of the gods. I shall not look too far forward.

Bryan was immensely taken with my sister and Albert Maverick and their eleven children. After his address to working men on Alamo Plaza at noon, J. took him to lunch with them, and the children hung around him with delight. My house is littered with queer presents people brought him, rare bits of stone, historical letters and documents, and old books of dubious interest. If he accumulates such stuff everywhere, I hope his house has an ample attic.

Washington, March 28

J. came up before the 15th for the Democratic caucus. I spent a few days in Virginia and arrived here late on a cold, rainy night. I have rarely felt so profound a sense of homesickness and depression as when we came splashing up the gleaming avenue in a sprawling old hack to the Oxford Hotel where J. has found a place for us to live. We have left a pleasant way of life for a future full of turmoil and uncertainty, and sometimes my heart sinks, but I never let J. know it. We have four rooms on the first floor at the corner of 14th and H. They are a little apart from the rest of the hotel, fortunately, but woefully ugly and ill arranged. However, they are large and airy, with big gilt mirrors and marble mantels in the grand old-Washington manner, and since I have banished the folding beds and marble washstands from the front room, and put out my own belongings—table covers, books, and flowers (so expensive here compared to Texas)—it is quite presentable. The house was once the home of a Kentucky Senator of philandering memory, and from the look of some fair ones in the dining room I think a few of his light o' loves must hang round it still, but on the whole it is dull and respectable.

Our first caller was a blond, curly-haired young man, "Governor" Osborne of Wyoming, newly elected to the House. He talked politics all the time. Art, literature, religion and weather were unconsidered trifles to him. We are inundated with cards of people we never heard of, and who, I strongly suspect, never heard of us until they saw our names in the Congressional Directory.

It is a distinct advantage to have known Washington before. An invitation came from a "Baroness" something, and instinct prompted me not even to send a card of acknowledgment. I have heard since that she took the title from the given name of a departed husband who made a fortune keeping a bar, and that new Congressmen's wives are her favorite prey. Some Texas girls told me that I "missed a lovely time" at the tea; that the Baroness was "real elegant" and "was coming to call"—just as I feared.

My many sweet "cave dweller" Maury relatives have been most kind, and Mrs. Sayers of the Texas delegation, a pretty and graceful woman with twelve years' experience here, has led me gently in the way I should go officially. The Texas delegation is splendid. Thirteen of the fifteen men sworn in were over six feet. J.'s six feet two inches, and white hair (it grieves him no little, but I admire it), his strong, firm lines, a very Anak rejoicing in his strength, filled me with content. He has the chance now to do justice to himself and be a credit to his state.

ALICE DUER MILLER   [1914]

Although Alice Duer Miller was a skilled mathematician, she became a professional writer soon after her graduation from Barnard College in 1899. Her most popular book was The White Cliffs, *a long, narrative poem which had sold upwards of 200,000 copies by the time of her death in 1942.*

Evolution

Said Mr. Jones in 1910:
"Women, subject yourselves to men."
Nineteen-Eleven heard him quote:
"They rule the world without the vote."
By Nineteen-Twelve, he would submit
"When all the women wanted it."

By Nineteen-Thirteen, looking glum,
He said that it was bound to come.
This year I heard him say with pride:
"No reasons on the other side!"
By Nineteen-Fifteen, he'll insist
He's always been a suffragist.
And what is really stranger, too,
He'll think that what he says is true.

FLORENCE GUY SEABURY   [1926]

Florence Guy Seabury, who died in 1951 at the age of seventy, was born in New Jersey and raised in Boston. Active in the feminist movement, she often published articles on the subject of women's needs and rights, and for a time she edited The Woman Voter. *In addition to her writing activities, she taught modern applied psychology at Briarcliff Junior College.*

The Sheltered Sex

By the time a boy is ten, he knows the whole truth about women. He makes no secret of the news that they are too nervous to manage motor cars, too feeble to drive nails, too dull for political office, and far too emotional for general social life. The conductor on the car line that takes him to school has an equal understanding of femininity. If a woman gives him pennies for fare, forgets to signal at her street, or steps from the car backward, he winks at the male passengers and murmurs, "Ain't that just like a woman?" The minister and the dentist; the clerk in the drug store, creator of marvelous sundaes drowned in whipped cream and cherries; the undertaker, are all up on the subject. In fact, every man, from the down-and-outer on the park bench to the fur-lined gentleman in his limousine, is woman-wise.

The odd thing is that while all the information about women is an open secret, the truth about men has remained vague and unspoken. There is supposed to be a vast body of androcentric wisdom which mothers whisper to their daughters, who in turn pass it on to their feminine young. Sometimes, when little groups of women are gathered together, opinions on masculinity become joint property, but for the most part, lore on the subject of the male and his ways is scattered and almost impossible to find. One of the difficulties lies in the fact that men, with a clannish camaraderie, say little about themselves, either in literature or in fact. They have a desire to maintain their status as an enigma, and to perpetuate the age-old secrecy, men are constantly liberating a smoke screen as to the elusiveness of the female. She is a sphinx, they say, a riddle, and Mona Lisa, with her inscrutable smile, is a symbol of the sex.

Of course, everybody knows that there is nothing in the mystery stuff about femininity. Woman's make-believe is only on the skin— not under it. Man, on the other hand, plays the astute game naïvely. Tell him he is a perpetual boy and he tumbles over himself to admit the charge that he has never grown up. Picture him as a sort of baboon in accidental captivity, he smiles benignly and rubs imaginary whiskers. Give him the wise head of a Moses or a Solomon on the body of an innocent cherub, and he is satisfied. All he asks is to remain unknown, apparently simple, easily explained, while woman is camouflaged as the eternal puzzle.

In the faraway days of long ago, when national woman suffrage was at stake, the Men's Patriotic Association issued the following statement:

The noblest democracy should see to it that woman suffrage is defeated, because non-woman suffrage conditions give man the best opportunity and encouragement to maintain his present superior standing politically, commercially and professionally and he needs these conditions to make good; and, maintaining a slightly superior earning power, he is enabled to assume the ennobling position of being the head of the family, where he is a more important support than women in the family. By this and other means he is enabled to maintain a certain amount of pride in himself, a characteristic of the male, the gratification or realization of which is essential to his mental and physical well-being. It is more necessary to him than it is to women.

Undoubtedly, this manly profession reveals the secret which has been kept so deeply hidden through the centuries. Man isn't really sure of his masculinity. He wants to live up to the cave idea, he thinks he should strut and fume, take initiative, be dominant. But all the time he is worried for fear he really can't keep on with the masquerade. He is wobbly. Women probably sense this fact, which accounts for their protection of him, even from himself. It's almost impossible to find any record of their real opinion about men. One woman, named Mary Astell, broke the silence in 1721 in *A Letter to a Lady by a Lady,* where, with brutal candor, she divided men into groups of braggards and bullies, dandies and squires, and showed how, whatever their outward appearance, all were dependent upon women for daily comfort and happiness. This lone instance is proof of women's desire to shield men from discovery, for the book remained unknown and unread. Between then and now is stillness, vast, discreet and abysmal.

In contrast to this delicacy, although women are eternally mysterious, whole libraries are filled with criticisms, analyses, and interpretations of them by men, while during the crusade for suffrage they were obliged to listen for hours to public discussions of their abilities and disabilities. It is doubtful if men could have survived such a series of campaigns for enfranchisement. They would probably have succumbed at the first general discussion of their frailties and weaknesses, and the universal weighing and measuring of their capacities. Brutal broadsides on masculine limitations, comparable to the pronunciamentos of male antisuffragists about women, would have made them lie down from sheer dismay at the thought of living under such handicaps.

DOROTHY PARKER   *[1926]*

A representative selection from Dorothy Parker might itself be called When Women Look at Men. *Born in 1893, she was educated at Miss Dana's school in Morristown, New Jersey, and the Blessed Sacrament Convent, New York City. After working on* Vogue, Vanity Fair, *and* The New Yorker *she launched her own stories and poems against both sexes.* "Men" *reveals her in one of her most exasperated moods.*

Men

They hail you as their morning star
Because you are the way you are.
If you return the sentiment,
They'll try to make you different;
And once they have you, safe and sound,

They want to change you all around.
Your moods and ways they put a curse on;
They'd make of you another person.
They cannot let you go your gait;
They influence and educate.
They'd alter all that they admired.
They make me sick, they make me tired.

GERTRUDE STEIN [1937]

Born in Pennsylvania in 1874, Gertrude Stein specialized in psychology for four years at Radcliffe College and then went on to Johns Hopkins University, where she studied medicine for four years more, though she did not take a degree from either institution. In 1903 she went to France, and lived there as an expatriate until her death in 1946. Her writings are full of comments about various men, ranging from Picasso to the American G.I. What she has to say in Everybody's Autobiography *about male novelists is one of her most intriguing and perceptive comments.*

Men All Write About Themselves

I said to [Dashiell] Hammett there is something that is puzzling. In the nineteenth century the men when they were writing did invent all kinds and a great number of men. The women on the other hand never could invent women they always made the women be themselves seen splendidly or sadly or heroically or beautifully or despairingly or gently, and they never could make any other kind of woman. From Charlotte Brontë to George Eliot and many years later this was true. Now in the twentieth century it is the men who do it. The men all write about themselves, they are always themselves as strong or weak or mysterious or passionate or drunk or controlled but always themselves as the women used to do in the nineteenth century. Now you yourself always do it now why is it. He said it's simple. In the nineteenth century the men were confident, the women were not but in the twentieth century the men have no confidence and so they have to make themselves as you say more beautiful more intriguing more everything and they cannot make any other man because they have to hold on to themselves not having any confidence. Now I he went on have even thought of doing a father and a son to see if in that way I could make another one.

MARJORIE HOPE NICOLSON [1937]

Marjorie Hope Nicolson's position as distinguished Professor Emeritus of the Graduate English Department at Columbia University belies her contentions in the following excerpt, but her statements may still give pause to the rest of us. A graduate of the University of Michigan, class of 1914, she was a professor and dean at Smith College when she delivered this address in 1937.

Gentlemen and Scholars

Here is the matter in a nutshell: it is entirely possible to be a scholar and a gentleman; it is intensely difficult to be a scholar and a lady! Long ago in a certain periodical I uttered these words, which wasted their sweetness on the desert air. Yet I have found no reason to change them. The fundamental reason that women do not achieve so greatly in the professions as do men is that *women have no wives.* Until such time as science or economics corrects this blunder of nature, we shall remain, I fear, the "inferior sex." Society puts upon women pressure which men hardly feel. Who really objects to the absent-minded professor of caricature and of legend, his clothes awry, his hair unkempt, his socks undarned, his shortsighted eyes peering blandly if unseeingly upon the current scene? Every campus owns him; we should be poorer without him; and in their hearts his colleagues are often proud of him, for he is a "campus character," a well-known authority upon this or that. But look here upon that portrait and on this; translate the description into the feminine world and shudder at those women who deny their sex. The undarned sock, I am sure, is the ultimate barrier between the equality of the sexes; in a man it moves to pity, in a woman to disrepute. Yet the darning of stockings takes time from more important work. The difficulty is not, as Virginia Woolf suggested, in finding "a room of one's own"; many women have such a room, but they find little time for staying in it, and during that little time they must keep that room in order!

There are men who have risen high in the academic profession less through their own qualifications than through their social contacts. Who makes those contacts? Often the hand that rules the cradle and the hand that rules their world. In any normal society, such contacts are often important and even definitive. The man of prominence who has gone on to further and further contacts has often his wife to thank. He does his part, to be sure; he performs his duties consistently and well; but that in itself is often not enough. After a difficult day in an administrative office, dealing with personalities, or in the study attempting to "settle Hoti's business," he returns at dusk, nerves frayed, mind intent upon the problem of the moment or of eternity. He finds that a dinner party is in progress, of considerable importance to his ultimate advancement. If his wife has done her part, he has nothing to do but to retire temporarily into the silence, and then to don his well-pressed evening clothes, and descend into the life of the present. Every hair is in place, every garment correct; his mood, if not enthusiastic, may at least be acquiescent. The fight is o'er, the battle won. And in the meantime, what of his feminine colleague? She too has returned from an office where she has done man's work, from a study where she also deals with Hoti's business; she too is absent-minded, and remembers only at the last moment that tonight's the night; guests are invited whose word is law. She finds herself faced in the kitchen with Irish or Polish temperaments, which must be "adjusted"; she must survey the table, write the place-cards, remember who does not speak to whom. She rushes at the last moment to the room of her own, dons the only possible garment, finds the last pair of stockings—perhaps undarned. To be sure, she should have made her plans well ahead, but so should her masculine colleague. And she wonders during the next week or month when the coveted advancement is given to her brother professor. She wonders; but in her heart she really understands. She has no wife!

Not only in such social relationships do wives again and again aid the advancement of their husbands. I have seen my masculine colleagues at great libraries in Europe and America, all of us engaged on what seems to us immortal work. Scholarship, we all know, consists of both tedium and exaltation. There is no day like that day on which one discovers something, hidden from the eyes of man. But between those days lie routine and tedium. One must copy, and read, and check, and reread, and copy again. In the British Museum, in the Bodleian, in the Cambridge University Library, in the Huntington Library, I have found myself surrounded again and again by a cloud of witnesses. The days of routine and tedium I must spend alone, grimly copying, sadly checking; this is the inexorable law. But in the meantime I look about and see those colleagues of mine who have had the intelligence to bring their wives with them, who turn over the tasks of copying and checking and of typing to them. I do not blame them; I honor them. History will show, I believe, that the greatest contributions to knowledge (at least quantitatively speaking) have been made by those men who had acumen enough to marry students whom they themselves had trained, students young enough to appreciate the honor, old enough to accept the responsibility. I have no resentment; but in passing, I salute them!

KAY BOYLE [1940]

Kay Boyle, who was born in St. Paul in 1903, and attended Columbia University, from the start wrote prolifically and successfully about social conditions and political tensions. And this story is no exception, for here we see men tyrannized by their own political beliefs.

Effigy of War

The barman at the big hotel on the sea front had been an officer in the Italian army during the last war, and somehow or other the rumor began to get around. Whether it was that he said too much to people who spoke his own language with him, saying late at night that the vines in Italy were like no other vines and the voices more musical and the soldiers as good as any others, no matter what history had to say about them, or whether it got around in some other way, it was impossible to know. But the story came to the director of the hotel (Cannes, it was, and the people just as gaudily dressed as other years, and the shops on the Croisette as fancy), and because of the feeling that ran high against the foreigner and against the name of Italy, the director stepped into the lounge bar about eleven one morning to tell the barman what he'd better do. He was a dressy, expensive-looking little man, the director, who could speak four languages with ease, and he had been a Russian once, a White Russian, so that France was the only country left to him now. He came into the bar at a quiet hour, just before the idle would begin wandering in out of the eternally springtime sun, and he jerked his cuffs inside his morning coat and screwed the soft, sagging folds of his throat from his collar wings and started speaking quietly over the mahogany-colored bar.

"Maestro," he said to the barman who had been ten years with them, "with all this trouble going on the management would quite understand your wanting to go back to Italy."

"Italy?" the barman said, and it might have been Siberia he was pronouncing as a destination and the look in his eyes was as startled. He stopped whatever it was he had been doing, setting the glasses straight or putting the ash trays out or the olives, and he looked at the director. He was a slight, dark man and his face was as delicate-boned as a monkey's, and the hair was oiled down flat upon his monkey-fragile skull.

"A lot of Italians are going back," the director said, and he swung himself up onto the stool as elegantly and lightly as a dwarf dressed up for a public appearance, the flesh hairless and pink, and the hand on the wood of the bar as plump as a child's. "Give me a glass of milk," he said, and he went on saying in a lower voice: "In times like these everyone wants to avoid all the trouble they can. Everybody likes to feel he's in his own country." He said it with a slight Russian accent, and the barman waited while the director took the cigarette out of the silver case, and then the barman snapped the lighter open and held the flame to the end of the cigarette in his dark, monkey-nervous hand. "We're perfectly willing to discuss things with you," the director said, and as the first bluish breath of smoke drifted between them, their eyes met for a moment across it, and the director was the first to look away.

"Ah, if we should all go back to the places we belong to!" the barman said as he put the lighter into the pocket of his starched white coat. He turned aside to take the bottle of milk off the ice, and he went on saying in strangely poetic sorrow: "If we all returned to the waters of our own seas and the words of our own languages, France would be left a wilderness—"

"Of course, there are some national exceptions," the director added quickly. "There are some nationalities which cannot go back." He took a swallow of milk and looked rather severely at the barman. "In countries where there have been revolutions, economic upheavals," he went on, his hand with the cigarette in it making the vague, comprehensive gestures of unrest. "But with Italians," he said, and the barman suddenly leaned forward and laid his small bony hands down flat upon the bar.

"Well, me," he said, "I've been fifteen years in this country. I'm too old to go back now. For me, Mussolini was an economic upheaval," he said. He picked up the bottle of milk again and filled the director's glass, pouring it out a little too quickly. "I've never gone back, not since fifteen years," he said, the words spoken sharply and rapidly, almost breathlessly across the bar. "I'm like a refugee, like a political refugee," he said. "I haven't the right to go back."

"That can be taken care of," the director said, and he took out his folded handkerchief and dabbed at the drops of milk on his upper lip. "The management would advance you what you needed to get back, write you a good testimonial—"

"I haven't done military service for them," the barman said, and he was smiling in something like pain at the director, the grin pulled queer and ancient as a monkey's across his face. "I can't go back," he said. "This is my country by now. If I can't go on working here I can't work anywhere. I wouldn't leave this country no matter what anybody said to me or no matter what they did to me."

"You never did very much about getting any papers out," said the director. He was looking straight ahead at the small silk flags of all the nations and at his own immaculately preserved reflection in the glass. "You never did much about trying to change your nationality." he said, and he took another discreet swallow of milk. "You should have thought of that before."

"I might have been a Frenchman today if it hadn't been for my wife," the barman said, and his tongue ran eagerly out along his lip. "My wife—" he said, and he leaned closer, the starched sleeves, with the hairy, bony little wrists showing, laid on the bar. "I haven't seen her for fifteen years," he said, and the director looked at the glass of milk and shrugged his shoulders. "She's in Italy, and she wouldn't sign the papers. She wouldn't do that one thing," he said, the eyes dark and bright, and the face lit suddenly, like a poet's, with eagerness and pain. "Not that she wanted me," he said. "It wasn't that. But women like that, Italian women, they're as soft and beautiful as flowers and as stubborn as weeds." He said it in abrupt poetic violence, and the director stirred a little uneasily and finished the milk in his glass.

"Now, you take a run up to the Italian Consul this afternoon and have a talk with him," he said, and he wiped his upper lip with his folded handkerchief again. "Tell him you're thinking of going back. Put Raymond on duty for the afternoon. And another thing, Maestro," he said as he got down off the bar stool, "don't keep that *Corriere della Sera* out there where everybody can see it. Put it in your pocket and read it when you get home," he said.

It might have passed off quietly enough like that if the Dane hadn't come into it. He was a snub-nosed, sun-blacked, blond-headed little man who gave swimming lessons in one of the bathing establishments on the beach. He had been a long time there, walking season after season tough and cocky up and down the beach with his chest high and his thumbs hooked into the white belt of his bathing trunks. He wore a bright clean linen cap down to his yellow brows, and royal-blue swimming shorts, and the muscles in his shoulders and arms were as thick and smooth as taffy. But after the war came, he didn't parade up and down the esplanade in the same way in the sun, but stayed hour after hour in the water or else in a corner of the beach café. He still gave lessons, but he let the pupils seek him out in the shade of the café, as if the eyes of the mobilized and the uniformed and the envious could see him less distinctly there.

The one who started it all was the Greek waiter in the big hotel who had got his French naturalization papers eight months before and was leaving for training camp in a week or two. He'd lean over the diners—what was left of the English and the American colony, and the dukes and duchesses, and the Spanish who had got their jewels and their pelts and their money out of Spain—and he'd say:

"What nationality do you think I am, eh? What country would you say I come from?" showing his teeth in pride and pleasure at them as he slipped the dishes of *filets de soles bonne femme* or *champignons à la Reine d'Angleterre* down before them, provided the maître d'hôtel was looking the other way. Sometimes the guests would say he looked one thing, and sometimes another: Italian, Rumanian, or even Argentine, and he'd smile like a prima donna at them, leaning almost on their shoulders, with his eyes shining and the serviette flung rather wildly over his arm.

"No, no, oh, *mon dieu*, no!" he'd say. "I'm pure French. What do you think of that? In another two or three months you'll see me coming in here with gold stripes on my sleeve, ordering everything like everybody else has to eat." And then he'd take out his mobilization order and show it to them, balancing the *homard à l'américaine* on its platter in the other hand as he opened out the stamped, signed paper. "I'm French," he'd say, with the garlic hanging on his breath. "I'm going right into the French army to fight. I'm going to fight for everybody sitting here having dinner tonight," he'd say, and he'd give the people at the next table their salad, holding his mobilization order open in his hand.

The Greek waiter had never liked the look of the Dane, and now that he had his military orders he couldn't so much as stand the sight of the cold-eyed, golden little man. In the hours he had off in the afternoons, he took the habit of walking out on the esplanade and stopping just above the bathing place to call the names down to him. There he would be, the Dane, with his white cap on and his royal-blue bathing trunks, talking half naked to the half-naked girls or women on the beach, war or no war, and going on making money just the same.

"*Sale étranger!*" the Greek would call down, with a fine Greek accent to it, and "*Crapule!,*" with his voice ringing out like an opera singer's across the sand and the striped bathing houses and the sea. "France for the French!" he'd roar over the railing, and the little Dane in his bathing suit would go quietly on with his swimming lessons, or if he were alone he'd turn and go into the beach café and sit down out of sight in the shade. There was a week ahead still before the Greek waiter would go, and all those days in the afternoons he'd stand on the esplanade and call the names down. In the end he appealed to the French themselves, exhorting them to rise. "The French for the French!" he'd shout down through the funnel of his hands. "Don't employ foreigners! Give a Frenchman the job!"

The last night of the week the little Dane came into the lounge bar for a drink before he went to bed; coming late, in discretion, when no one else was there. The two of them were talking there together, the Dane sitting on the stool with the glass of beer before him, and the Italian on the other side with his starched jacket on and the wisps of his monkey hair slicked flat across his skull, and in a few minutes the barman would have taken the bottles down and locked the safes and turned the lights out, and then nothing would have occurred. But now the barman was leaning on the counter, speaking the French tongue in a low, rather grievous voice to the swimming teacher, his thin hand rocking from side to side like a little boat as he talked.

"Drinking has ceased," he was saying in faultless pentameter, "in the old way it has ceased. Even before September there was a difference, as if the thirst of man had been slaked at last. To any sensitive eye, the marks of death were to be seen for years on the façades of casinos, palace hotels, luxury restaurants, and on the terraces of country clubs and vast private estates. Even the life of the big bars has been dying," he said. "For years now that I can remember, the lounge bar has been passing through the agonies of death." He made a tragic and noble gesture toward the empty leather armchairs in the half-darkened room, and he said in a low, dreamy voice: "All this is finished. There is no more place in the hearts of men for this kind of thing. The race that insisted on this atmosphere of redundance for its pleasure, that demanded this futility, is vanishing, dying—"

"War levels the ranks," the Dane said quietly. His sun-blacked, sun-withered face under the bright light thatch of hair was as immobile as if carved from wood.

"Ah, before the war even," the barman said softly, and then he stopped, for the men had come into the bar. The Greek waiter walked a little ahead of the others, wearing a gray jersey and a cap pulled down, and they both of them knew him; it was the others behind him they had never seen before.

"Get that one, the one on the stool," the Greek waiter said, and one of the other men stepped past him and walked toward the bar. Just before he got there he lifted his right arm and hit the swimming teacher on the chin. The little, light-crowned head and the strong, small body rose clear of the stool an instant, like a piece of paper lifted and spun sidewise by the wind, and then it sailed into the corner and collapsed there, bent double, by the leather chair. "That's the kind of language he understands," the Greek said, and he crossed the length of thick, soft carpet, jerking his cap up on his forehead. He was smiling with delight when he kicked the swimming teacher's body into another shape. "Walking up and down out there on the beach," the Greek said, and he turned back to the others and the Italian barman behind the bar. "Giving lessons just like men weren't bleeding their guts out for him and people like him—"

"He volunteered. I tell you that man volunteered," the barman began saying, and his bones were shaking like a monkey's in his skin. "I've seen the paper he got. I know he volunteered to fight like anybody else would—" And when he jumped for the bell the Greek waiter reached over and took him by the collar of his starched white coat and dragged him out across the plates of potato chips and the empty beer bottle and the glass the Dane had been drinking and slung him across the elegant little glass-topped tables into the other corner of the room.

"Pick him up and take him along too," the Greek said. "I know all about him I need to know. He was an officer last war, officer in the Italian army, so you'll know what side he'll fight on this time. Take them both out," he said. "This country's not good enough for them, not good enough for either of them."

They did it by moonlight, taking the two men's clothes off on the sand and shingles by the Mediterranean water, and giving it to them in fiercely accelerating violence. They broke the swimming teacher's jaw, and they snapped the arms of the barman behind him like firewood, beating the breath and the life from them with whatever fell under their hands. The Greek carried over an armful of folding iron chairs from the bathing establishment's darkened, abandoned porch and, with these as weapons, they battered the two men's heads down and drove their mouths into the sand.

"So now repeat this after me, foreigners," the Greek began saying in wild holy passion as he kneeled beside them. He had taken the flag out of his jersey and was shaking out its folds. "So now repeat what I'm going to tell you," he said in violent religious fervor against the pulsing and murmuring of the water, and his hands were trembling as he laid the flag out where their mouths could bleed upon the tricolor emblem, the cotton stuff transformed now to the exigencies of a nation and a universe.

SAMPLER: The Compleat Gentleman

When a gentleman is introduced to a lady for the purpose of asking her to dance, a bow is all the preface this [*sic*] is necessary for the question, "Can I have the pleasure of dancing this quadrille (or whatever it may be) with you?" but there may be a great deal of grace or much awkwardness in the way this is done. Should she assent he offers her his left arm and leads her to the place upon the floor. When the dance is over he gives her his right arm and promenades slowly around the room before taking her to a seat or to her chaperon. It is courteous for him to thank her, before leaving her, for the honor she has conferred upon him. Some of these are little things, but they all go to making up the polished gentleman.

It is usual to dance last before supper with the lady he designs to escort to the table. He will there have an opportunity to show his good breeding. If selfish and inclined to "stuff," he will be quite likely to be careless about attending to the wants of his companion. She may be very sure that this disposition extends through everything in life, and if she has any thoughts of becoming his wife, let her hesitate awhile unless she wants to be second always to the gratification of his appetite. Straws show which way the wind blows. No gentleman should ever go to the supper room alone unless he is sure that all the ladies have been attended thither.

A truly courteous gentleman will do all that he can to make the party a pleasant one. If he sees ladies who have rare opportunities to dance, he will not devote himself to a few of his favorites, but invite the "wall flowers" to a participation in the "light fantastic." By so doing he confers a pleasure, helps his hostess and wins popularity. Nor does a truly courteous gentleman, because he cannot dance with the one he wishes to devote himself to, gather with a knot of his cronies near the door and makes [sic] remarks upon those on the floor. He never tangles himself in a lady's train by carelessly attempting to step over instead of going around it. He may wish it and the wearer in Jericho, if he chances to be unfortunate enough, with all his care, to plant his foot upon it, but he must instantly beg pardon, and if it is torn, offer to take the wearer to the dressing room, where it may be repaired. He is always ready to pay attention to any lady, however uninteresting, at the bidding of his hostess. Indeed, in her service he will run the risk of sometimes being bored, since all women do not have the tact to know when they are abusing good nature.

One point more in regard to a gentleman's duty at a large party or ball. Many seem to imagine that it is exceedingly rude to leave a lady to whom one has been introduced until she is joined by someone else. Or if she happens to be standing or sitting alone and he stops by her for a little chat, no matter how much he may want to go away, he must remain on guard until relieved from duty. This may not occur for a half hour or an hour, perhaps not for a whole evening if the lady is a stranger, and though both may be excessively weary of the protracted conversation, they must martyrize themselves because of this false idea of politeness.

The very life and pleasure of such a gathering lies in the free circulation of the guests among each other; the meeting and greeting of old acquaintances and the beginning—it can be nothing more in such a place—of new, and in general a few moments is all that one cares to pass with individuals. Now anything that tends to destroy this freedom diminishes the social enjoyment, and therefore the success of such a gathering. Gentlemen afraid of being "cornered" are chary of giving the opportunity, and are sometimes almost rude in consequence, when it is really the last thing they desire to be. . . . A gentleman's tact and sense of propriety must decide his conduct in such cases.

—EMILY S. BOUTON, in *Social Etiquette,* 1894

A gentleman will not stand on the street corners, or in hotel doorways, or club windows, and gaze impertinently at ladies as they pass by. This is the exclusive business of loafers, upon which well-bred men will not trespass.

Gentlemen unaccustomed to the management of a boat should never venture out with ladies. To do so is foolhardy, if not criminal. Great care should be taken not to overload a boat. The frequent boating accidents that happen are in most instances due either to overloading, or to the inexperience of the man at the oars. Men who cannot swim should never take ladies upon the water. (Also . . .) great care must be taken not to splash the ladies, either in first dipping the oars or subsequently. Neither should anything be done to cause them **fright.**

If one possesses such a commodity as a brother or a husband, he can always be made useful on a cycling excursion. Never is a man better able to show for what purpose he was made than upon such occasions.

The man's duty to the woman who rides might be made the text for a long sermon; but long sermons are never popular; therefore, it may be better to state briefly that he must always be on the alert to assist his fair companion in every way in his power—he must be clever enough to repair any slight damage to her machine which may occur en route, he must assist her in mounting and dismounting, pick her up if she has a tumble, and make himself generally useful and incidentally ornamental and agreeable.

—MAUD C. COOKE, in *Social Life*, 1896

A well-bred man is free from arrogance; he is courteous, unpretentious, natural, simple, unaffected—in a word, true. He is considerate in his feelings, polite and kind to his inferiors as to his equals. He respects himself. He is chivalrous toward women and reverences their sex because he bears in mind his love and respect for his own mother. He protects the weak and is tender toward children and aged persons. He is never self-assertive, pushing, aggressive or familiar, for to possess any of these qualities would indicate a distressing lack of good breeding.

In social life it is taken for granted that a man is indebted to a woman who accepts any attention from him. She is supposed to be like a fair and stately princess accepting the homage of courtiers and rewarding them with a smile.

A man may not ask permission of a lady to call on her. He must wait until she offers him the privilege of calling. This rule is because a woman has the right to choose who may be admitted to her home. But if he has good reason for thinking she might like the suggestion to come from him, he may say, "May I not have the pleasure of calling to see you?" Personal remarks and compliments are not in good taste, and fulsome praise is not acceptable to anyone.

With the exception of flowers, bonbons or books a man may not send gifts to a woman unless she is to become his wife, and then he may not offer anything that could not be returned uninjured, if such a misfortune as a broken engagement should occur.

—MRS. FRANK LEARNED (ELLIN CRAVEN LEARNED), in *The Etiquette of New York To-day*, 1906

A gentleman does not bow to a lady from a club window; nor according to good form should ladies ever be discussed in a man's club!

—EMILY POST, in *Etiquette*, 1922

Too many young men, finding themselves in a girl's bachelor apartment without the steadying presence of other guests, imagine that more than conversation is expected of them.

Swimming in the same ocean does not give a man the right to force his conversation or attentions on other—usually feminine—swimmers or sun bathers. Exhibitions of water-splashing, porpoising, wrestling, and sand-throwing, often engaged in by very young men to attract feminine attention, usually make them offensive in the very eyes of those they seek to attract, and certainly make them loathsome to the run-of-the-beach bather in search of a little peace.

—Amy Vanderbilt, in
Amy Vanderbilt's Complete Book of Etiquette, 1952

Taking a girl on an evening date includes door-to-door service, and you should see her home—right up to her door, unless it's an apartment house with a doorman—before your escorting duties are over. At her door, you thank her for the pleasant (grand, wonderful) time. If she asks you in for a drink or some food, accept or not as you wish, but you shouldn't be the one to ask.

—Frances Benton, in *Etiquette,* 1956

PEARL S. BUCK   [1941]

Pearl S. Buck, who graduated from Randolph-Macon Woman's College in 1914, in 1938 achieved the rare distinction of winning the Nobel Prize. She is a strong defender of the woman's cause and an unusually large proportion of her work is devoted to this defense.

I Am Glad I Am Not a Man in America

Equality, of course, is no easy matter except for talk. Only careful education can make people equal. There is no equality in individuals, that we know. But how can man be persuaded that woman is his equal until he is educated in that knowledge, and how can woman be persuaded that she can and ought to be man's equal except by education in that knowledge?

It is perhaps timely at this moment for men and women to consider this question of their basic relationship to each other, since the actual danger of fascism inevitably is that, in one way or another, with or without war, all the world will be affected by it. Brain touches brain, and emotion stirs emotion; and even in a determined democracy we shall not escape some infusion of fascism. That infusion will run and spread in the channels of traditionalism, and we

Americans are nowhere so traditional as in the relationship between men and women.

My own anxieties about fascism have less to do with women than with men. For when woman goes back to medievalism she never goes back alone. She always takes man back with her. In proportion as she becomes a slave, he becomes a slave owner, and of the two the slave is less harmed. Slaves develop great qualities of character, endurance, philosophy, diplomacy, humor, secret strength of resistance, and the ability to keep their own counsel even to the point of slyness. Out of all this they learn to rule, and they gain, if they have any wits, the real ascendancy over their masters.

Thus the consequences of fascism for men are very serious, and the more serious because there are so many American women who look with longing at the comfortable restrictions of fascism which would take beyond woman's power of decision the difficult question of whether or not her place is in the home. For women have long had to be devious creatures, as we all know, and many a woman would welcome the possibilities for power which slavery gives her, and secretly many a woman would enjoy the power joined with total lack of responsibility which a slave has. A slave need not worry about improvements in society or in the community. She can leave all that to her owner, man. She need not worry even about her food and drink, her clothing, or the roof over her head. These are provided to slaves as a matter of course. She has her little labors well defined each day, but there are no laws for slaves to compel them to speed or to standards of production; and, above all, in slavery woman has entire mental leisure. The world is not her affair. She can devote all her powers to thinking up new means to have her own way and so to become man's ruler.

I am alarmed for American men in this approaching wave of fascism because they have been so foolish as to grant all the privileges of freedom and democracy to women without compelling them to share any of the practical responsibilities in return. Here society requires no real service from women, though it extends to them in fullest measure its advantages and protection, even to the point of giving them education. All this ought to terrify any thinking man, for when the wave of fascism hits him and he succumbs to it, probably unaware for the moment that he has done so, he will have in the nursery, the kitchen, the church, no ignorant peasantlike creature sharpening her few wits as best she can, but a clever, subtle being whose development, body and mind, has long been the equal of his own and whose energies are often superior to his. I am glad I am not a man in America.

The truth is that under no form of government and in no civilization has the relationship between men and women been entirely satisfactory to man. One of woman's most hateful qualities has been that she can make the best of anything and somehow emerge to be an annoyance, and man suffers. I have never seen a country, and I have seen many, where man was not in some way or another annoyed by woman, by her inferiority and by her superiority. The one possible solution for the problem of woman has never been tried. It is simple equality with man. This seems never to have occurred to him.

MARGARET MEAD   [1949]

From her first book, Coming of Age in Samoa (1928), *to her current articles counseling against early marriages in the United States, Margaret Mead has frequently and pungently noted that "Different cultures have styled their relationships between men and women differently." Graduated from Barnard College in 1923, with a Ph.D. from Columbia in 1929, she has supplemented her formal education by wide anthropological study among both primitive and presumably civilized peoples.*

Sex and Achievement

There has long been a habit in Western civilization of speaking as if it were possible for men to have a picture of womanhood to which women reluctantly conformed, and for women to make demands on men to which men adjusted even more reluctantly. This has been an accurate picture of the way in which we have structured our society, with women as keepers of the house who insist that men wipe their feet on the door-mat, and men as keepers of women in the house who insist that their wives should stay modestly within doors. There have been a thousand varieties of these demands, from the way a teacup was balanced to the prohibition on a wife's smoking or on daughter's cutting her hair. From one point of view they provided a pleasant tension on which drawing-room etiquette could be based, or by way of which a man could proclaim his natural masculine desire to be free and dirty and careless and un-punctual *if* his wife had not insisted that he be home every night promptly for dinner. The picture can be obsessively elaborated, and girls attempting to plan their own lives may stop every other moment to say, "But men don't like women who . . ." However, it is one thing to recognize these phrasings as cultural devices which maintain a working equilibrium between male and female roles, but quite another thing to take them seriously and talk about a "man-made" world, or to say, as Emily James Putnam does in the introduction to *The Lady*, "Where he put her, there she stays," * and thus deny the far more fundamental fact that both men and women share the same images of what makes a marriageable or an unmarriageable woman, a good husband, a fascinating lover whom any woman would be a fool to marry, or a born old bach-elor. The phrases "a man's man" or "a woman's woman" do not mean a basic disagreement between men and women about which type of man gets on better with men than with women, but a basic agreement between men and women about each kind of man or woman. When a man and a woman get into an argument about some solid, plodding, devoted young woman, and the woman says, "But she'll make some man a very good wife," and the man says "I don't believe any man will want to marry her," there is no real conflict between them. The dissenting man means the same thing as the woman speaker by the words "good wife," only he is saying, "But who wants that kind of a good wife?" In the last century, when the upper-class and middle-class worlds were so neatly pro-tected against bad women who wore bright colors and were filled with allure, this did not mean that good women thought bad women were unalluring. The man who, exhausted by the demands of a wife who had taken permanently to a sofa after the birth of her first child, sought out a glittering lady in a large plumed hat, and his wife who lay on the sofa and imagined the lady in the hat, both agreed that she was alluring, and both also agreed that it was both natural and wrong for the husband to be allured and both natural and right for his wife to resent it. So both father and mother, brother and sister, neighbor and preacher and teacher, future mother-in-law, possible mistress, local Don Juan, and village wise-acre, as well as the comics, the radio, the films, build together the images of the different kinds of men and women who will be loved,

* The footnotes which appeared in *Male and Female*, of which this excerpt formed a chapter, have been omitted here by permission of the author.

valued, hated, and ignored by their own sex, the opposite sex, or both.

So every hesitancy in a woman and every bit of bluster in a man are not to be laid to some male conspiracy to keep women in their place, any more than every bit of blundering shyness in a man or of conceited demandingness in a woman is to be laid to some female conspiracy to dominate men. Different cultures have styled the relationships between men and women differently. When they have styled the roles so that they fitted well together, so that law and custom, ideal and practical possibilities, were reasonably close together, the men and the women who lived within that society have been fortunate. But to the degree that there have been discrepancies in the two roles, to the degree that a style of beauty that was unobtainable by most people, or a style of bravery or initiative, modesty and responsiveness, was insisted upon although the culture had inadequate devices for developing such initiative or such responsiveness, then both men and women suffer. The suffering of either sex—of the male who is unable, because of the way in which he was reared, to take the strong initiating or patriarchal role that is still demanded of him, or of the female who has been given too much freedom of movement as a child to stay placidly within the house as an adult—this suffering, this discrepancy, this sense of failure in an enjoined role, is the point of leverage for social change. One has only to follow the fortunes of the demand for equal political rights for women from one country to another to note how contrasting are the responses from women in different countries, and how slight the overt relationship between low position of women and the eager demands for women's rights. Unfortunately we do not have as good comparative material on attempts to change the status of men—parallel movements such as the abolition of alimony, controversies as to whether family subsidies are to be paid to fathers or mothers, arguments over community-property laws. Attempts to free men from responsibilities and limitations that no longer appear reasonable or just are not neatly summed up under a men's-rights movement, or considered by international subcommissions on the legal status of men. Yet detailed analysis of any of these legal reforms would show quite clearly that there is a continuous movement also to free men from limitations that are out of line with the contemporary calendar. Breach-of-promise cases are a silly excrescence in a world in which women do half the proposing, and alienation-of-affection cases between two men, which assume that the woman is a gently pliant lily, ring just as false. Alimony for a young child-less woman with an education equal to that of her husband, who must postpone his next marriage to support her, is coming to seem glaringly unfair. But the historical trend that listed women among the abused minorities, and which was a natural outcome of the sorts of inspection of legal and social abuses that went with our transfor-mation from a society of status, where rights were inherent, to a society of contract, in which rights have to be established, lingers on to obscure the issue and gives apparent point to the contention that this is a man-made world in which women have always been abused and must always fight for their rights.

It takes considerable effort on the part of both men and women to reorient ourselves to thinking—when we think basically—that this is a world made not by men alone, in which women are unwilling and helpless dupes and fools or else powerful schemers hiding their power under their ruffled petticoats, but a world made by mankind for human beings of both sexes. In this world male and female roles have sometimes been styled well and sometimes badly; sometimes the men have an easier time while the women have recourse to soothsayers, daydreams, autoerotic devices, gigolos, somatic diseases, and downright insanity. Sometimes it is the women whose role has been cast in terms so close to the realities of their fate that they present a picture of relative placidity while the men pursue phan-toms. But there seems little doubt that the relative attainability of either role has its effect on both men and women. Women who seem placid while the men seem erratic and bewitched pay a price for the discrepancies in the men's role; men who appear far more favored and more free than their womenfolk have not yet reached the level of self-realization that would have been theirs had their wives and mothers also had roles that they could attain and enjoy.

Literature in the United States at present is raucous and angry on this whole question of the relationship between men and women. We have had a spate of books that claim women are being mascu-linized, to their ill, to men's ill, to everybody's ill, and another spate, or sometimes the same spate, of books that insist that men are being feminized. When one follows the shrill insistencies of books like *Modern Woman: The Lost Sex,* which end by attacking men as well as women, one realizes that we are passing through a period of dis-crepancies in sex roles which are so conspicuous that efforts to dis-guise the price that both sexes pay are increasingly unsuccessful. Only if we perpetuate the habit of speaking about "the position of women" in a vacuum will we fail to recognize that where one sex suffers, the other sex suffers also. As surely as we believe that the present troublesome problems of sex adjustment are due to the position of women alone, we commit ourselves to a long series of false moves as we attempt to push women out of the home, into the home, out of the home, adding mounting confusion to the difficulties born of a changing world-climate of opinion, a shifting technology, and an increasing rate and violence of cultural change.

It has been fashionable in the last few years to call America a matriarchy, and thus do considerable violence to a useful anthropological concept. A matriarchal society is one in which some if not all of the legal powers relating to the ordering and governing of the family—power over property, over inheritance, over marriage, over the house—are lodged in women rather than in men. So we may speak of matrilineal societies, in which a man inherits his name, his land, and his position, or any one of these from his mother's brother, through his mother. This may not mean a great deal of power for women, although it is a system in which women are sufficiently favored so that polygamy, for instance, does not work well within it. Or we may speak of a matrilocal society, in which house and land are owned by women and pass from mother to daughter, and husbands move in and move out. This system is even less compatible with polygamy, or with the exercise of very much authority by the husband-fathers, who live under their mother-in-law's roof. Then there are a variety of modifications, in which a woman is returned to be buried on her own kin's land, or in which ties through the mother play an important but different role than do ties through the father, or where, as in Samoa, the sister's son retains a veto in the councils of his mother's family. There are very rare systems, such as that of the Iroquois Indians, where political power is in women's hands, since the women elders nominated the holders of titles who also wielded political powers.

When contemporary American society is viewed against such sets of arrangements, it is obvious that the word "matriarchy" not only is not descriptive, but actually obscures the basic issues. In the United States women take their husbands' names and the children bear their fathers' names. Women are expected to live where their husbands elect to live, and refusal to do so is tantamount to desertion. Men are liable for the support of their wives and children, and women are not liable for the support of their husbands, nor are brothers liable for the support of their sisters. The basic legal assumption is that a woman as a minor is dependent upon her father, and thereafter upon her husband. In our legal forms we are a patri-nominal, patrilineal, patrilocal, and legally, for the most part, a patri-archal society. The circumstance that American fathers don't conform to some folklore concept of a patriarch with a long beard and ten children is not relevant. Both men and women are reared within this explicit paternally oriented framework. There are laws against a man's beating his wife, but other concepts have to be invoked when his wife beats him. The female is defined by usage as helpless, in need of protection, especially of support. We are also, of course, a monogamous society in which every form of polygamy, even the most casual, is frowned upon.

This is the framework of the family we have inherited from Europe, but it was brought to this country under exceptional condi-tions. The power of the father over the son was sapped by the weak-ening of the property sanction, and the infinite possibilities in the new country for leaving home. The power of the husband over the wife was altered more subtly. In frontier days, women were few, and sheer competition made it necessary for the man to woo differ-ently than in countries in which he had been able to pick and choose among a dozen girls, each with a dowry thrown in, or at least to relax in self-assurance as some dozen mothers threw their daughters at his head. The dowry disappeared and women were wooed for themselves. The valuation placed on female qualities shifted. Meek-ness, home-abidingness, timorous clinging to the saddle of a hus-band as he rode away for a two-mile journey were all very well in the Old World. But an American frontier woman might have to keep a lonely farm going all by herself for weeks, disciplining the half-grown children, succoring the passing stranger, even fending off the Indians. Strong women, women with character and determi-nation, in fact women with guts, became more and more acceptable. The stereotype of the old maid shifted from the British picture of the manlike spinster who had a tom cat and preferred her nephews to the mild little woman who kept female cats and preferred her nieces. Along with this demand for women who have strength of character and the ability to manage money and affairs, there went no parallel premium on women's looking masculine. A woman was still expected to have womanly qualities, still to be attractive, in fact she was expected to be increasingly attractive as she came to be chosen in marriage for her dowryless self alone. Marriages of choice, phrased as marriages of love, laid increasing demands on both men and women to please the opposite sex openly.

In the hurly-burly of settling a new continent, many tasks were delegated to women in addition to running the farm and disciplining the children and keeping off the Indians while their husbands were away. As rough little frontier settlements assumed the appearance of a real village, the cleaning-up process, closing down the gambling-hell or the saloon, was thought of as coinciding with the arrival of one or more good women. The finer things of life—moral and aesthetic values—were delegated to women in a new and more active form; America was not Europe, where women had been expected to do more praying than the men but not to take any responsibility outside the home. The woman crusader who flouted the dictates of feminine decorum to campaign for the right has been a familiar part of our history since the early days of Anne Hutchinson, and is recognized by both men and women as a valid part of our culture. It is permitted to men to hope that their own wives may not receive the call to reform the world, but this is a hope of the same order as that permitted to a religious mother who still somehow—while she instructs her little son in his prayers—hopes he will be chosen to be a sea captain and not a priest. An ideal arrangement of ethical behavior in the United States would leave good works, those so-necessary good works, to widows and spinsters, thus keeping these two supernumerary classes of women happily occupied in a way that is socially useful. It has been interesting to notice the changes in attitudes toward Mrs. Roosevelt and toward her vigorous, untiring interest in social welfare. As the wife of the President, she was attacked and condemned by men who would be the first to raise their hats in tribute to the long line of noble American women who campaigned, for instance, against slavery. This resentment, however, notably decreased after President Roosevelt's death, when her continued vigorous championing of the right set a pattern for widows rather than wives.

The spinster champion of the right, of education, village improvement, social legislation, freedom for oppressed minorities, has gradually been stereotyped in those occupations in which women are professionally engaged in good works, particularly education and social work. These are both fields that men enter on peril of accusations of effeminacy, unless they enter in an administrative or a financial role. "Where," asks the Englishman who is prominent in social welfare, "are your men? We see their names on the letterheads of organizations, but when we go to international conferences, we meet almost entirely women." "Our men—oh, they are the chairmen of boards, they determine the financial policy of our agencies, but they leave the practice to women. They are too busy to go to conferences."

In such a historical development as this, it is of course impossible to speak of cause and effect. We must speak rather of an endless spiraling process, in which good women were the immediate occasion of some reform, reform became thought of as women's field, this attracted women into it and further styled the field as feminine, and so kept men out. Between the two world wars there was a marked decrease in the willingness of women to enter those fields which had been earmarked as fields of "service"; that is, fields in which the bad pay and heavy work were supposed to be ignored because they gave an opportunity to exercise womanly qualities of caring for the young, the sick, the unfortunate, and the helpless. This whole trend toward the professionalization of service fields means a shift from an occupation to which one gives oneself—as a woman still does in marriage and motherhood—to an occupation to which one gives definite hours and specified and limited duties. It is evident that this ideal for American women is passing as a role both for the woman who expects to marry and for the spinster seeking a way of life. This whole shift is part of the assimilation of female ideal and male ideal to each other. Boys and girls sitting at the same desks, studying the same lessons, and absorbing the same standards alike learn that the two most respectable criteria for choosing one's lifework are that the work should have chances for advancement and that it should be "interesting." Even social workers, every hour of whose working day must, if they are to do their chosen tasks, be devoted to warm helpfulness, will defend their choice of a career because it is interesting, or one in which women can do well. Only with many apologies do they now admit to a simple desire to help human beings.

Meanwhile, during this period of history when styles in women were shifting and changing, a style in men was also being built up. The man had to make a living, he had to deal with the harsh realities of the competitive world, hack and slash at forests and cut corners in a world in which any man could be President. The average American town gave him no education in understanding or enjoying the arts, and conventional aesthetic expressions were closed

to him, and regarded as womanish. To this day, the choice of music or painting or poetry as a serious occupation is suspect for an
American male. Men demonstrated their maleness in the practical
world of business, of farming (where the women were kept indoors
while the men even did the milking), and of politics (the down-to-
earth, corrupt kind as compared with the milk-and-water reform
variety). As our transitional culture made more simplified values
inevitable in order that immigrants from many lands could communicate with one another, so competition increased for these simple
signs of success—money, the things that money could buy, power
over persons and over things. The harsh realities of a competitive
world where each man's pace is determined by the pace of his rival,
and the race is never ended, hit men earlier than they hit women.
The rapidly expanding economy that brought more amenities to the
lives of women made more demands on the lives of men. Finally
we arrive at the stereotypes of today, the tired husband who just
wants to sit at home with this shirt collar open and the wife who
wants to be taken out, the mother who sees too much of the children and is forever importuning the father to see more of them,
while the husband himself feels that if he had a chance he would go
fishing. To receive recognition—from both men and women—a man
in America should be, first of all, a success in his business; he should
advance, make money, go up fast, and if possible he should also be
likable, attractive, and well groomed, a mixer, well informed, good
at the leisure-time activities of his class, should provide well for his
home, keep his car in good condition, be attentive enough to his
wife so that he doesn't give other women an opportunity to catch
his interest. A woman to receive equal recognition should be intelligent, attractive, know how to make the best of herself in dress and
manner, be successful in attracting and keeping first several men,
finally one, run her home and family efficiently so that her husband
stays devoted and her children all surmount the nutritional, psychological, and ethical hazards of maturation, and are successful too;
and she should have time for "outside things," whether they be
church, grange, community activities, or Junior League. A woman
who has time only for her own home is likely to be stigmatized either
as "having too much to do," which means either that she is incompetent, or as having a husband who doesn't make as much as he
should, or that the couple have been shiftless and had too many
children.

But success in their roles rather than the specific qualities of the roles is what is emphasized. Both the successful man and the successful woman will be liked by both sexes, rewarded for their reaffirmation that it is possible for human beings to be what Mother said you must be if you wanted her to love you. It is possible for the public-opinion interviewer to ferret out a great deal of envy among Americans. They find people who listen to programs like "Information Please" in order to hear "college-educated people fail." But this envy, like the detraction of the well-known personality that fills the tabloids whenever some scandal gives opportunity, is still a small component compared with the very widespread pleasure Americans take in someone who is really successful, whether it be shown at the testamentary dinner to the departing executive who is taking a better job, or at the block party for the only family that got into the new housing project. For with the carefully prepared formula that maternal care has placed in its bottle the American child drinks in the admonition to succeed, to be the right weight, to learn to walk at the right time, to go up grade by grade in school, with good marks, to make the team, to make the sorority or clique, to be the one to be chosen by others for success. For the father who disciplined a child who was conceived of as filled with Satan and in need of many beatings, and the mother who succored and comforted the child and taught him how to avoid the beatings, we now have the mother almost alone, not curbing the child's innate wickedness, but yearningly searching for signs that he will make the grade, make good, fail to fail.

This training, which is now so similar for boys and girls, has very different impacts upon them. For the boy, it has two important effects. He is trained by women to be a male, which involves no identification of the self with the mother-teacher. He is to be a boy by doing the things Mother says, but doing them in a manly way. After all, boys grow by eating the right food, they get good marks by studying—in fact by obeying Mother's admonitions—but also they must be manly, they must not be sissies, they must stand up for themselves. All fighting must be defensive, and yet it is being a sissy not to be able to fight, so situations must be arranged that will satisfy the mothers of both little males that each is fighting in self-defense, obeying the highest standards and learning how not to be a sissy at the same time. Only from older brothers and the older brothers of companions does the little boy get any straight-out tutelage in how to be a boy. It was notable how enormously juvenile delinquency increased during the last war when the older boys were withdrawn from the family. But the older brother is himself straining to meet the adult role that his mother and the world have defined for him, and the small boy who tags along imitates and follows someone whose eyes are on future things, a job, a car, a raise.

In enclaves where the newly arrived or the unsuccessful are hemmed in in slum areas this sequence of social development is distorted. The older boys are unable to take their fathers' failures as clues to a remote pattern of male success as reinterpreted by the mothers. They become gang leaders, in turn effectively short-circuiting the development of their younger brothers in the society. This asocial gang life of boys provides a basis for the adult criminal world in America. It high-lights the normal American development, in which a mother who understands the American world can point to a father who, while not a good enough model for the boy merely to imitate, is nevertheless on the right road—whom the boy himself will surpass. In this pattern, older boys, their faces turned not back toward an admiring juvenile audience but forward toward a welcoming, possibly applauding adult world, permit younger boys to tag along and learn—as long as they don't make any trouble. The eyes of the whole family, the whole neighborhood, face ahead, and every male in the group is merely an indication of where and how males should advance.

No one represents a permanent place on the ladder. In peacetime the small boy's heroes, whether his own father keeps a grocery store or is the president of a bank, are policemen, firemen, fliers, cowboys, and baseball players, men who act out in their real life roles the springing active motor impulses of the small boy's body. His mother alternates between letting him jump on the sofa because the books say children shouldn't be restricted and telling him not to break things. And in her voice, in the voice of the radio announcer who introduces his favorite radio program, in the teacher's voice at school, in the voices of everyone around him, the little boy who wants to be a policeman or a baseball player hears that he will grow up to accept some responsible money-making role. He learns that if he wants to argue for choosing the police force or professional baseball, he will have to argue not that this is what he wants to do, but that it is something in which he can make good and make money and advance. He learns that unless he has a job and a car and a wife and kids, he will never be able to respect himself—because his own self-approval, like his mother's now, will be withdrawn, leaving him lonely and unsatisfied. Life is a job at which he can succeed if he tries. All desirable qualities can be acquired if he pays attention to his looks, his skills, his relations to people. And he also learns that the reward of success is love and approval, light in his mother's eyes, bread and jam and an icebox with no rules about raiding it, relief and pleasure in his father's eyes. Here is no mother who thrills to his war-whoop in an Indian suit—although she bought him an Indian suit because children should have some imaginative play, or because all the other children have them—but rather she thrills to his first good grades, his first earned money. Here is no father whose awareness of his own masculinity makes him feel his small masculine son as a threat and a challenge. The father has long since become a parent, and the success of his son is part of his success as a proper husband and father. He is often, in fact, overanxious and overprotective toward his son. So, even in wealthy middle-class suburbs, little American boys still have paper routes, and Chief Justices and presidents of companies take those paper routes when their sons are ill in bed so that the boys will not default in their business obligations. In fact, the rewards are so great for displaying to admiring and helpful parents those qualities of initiative, independence, and assertiveness in the workaday world that will ensure success later that even though there is fear of failure, the American child grows up to be exceedingly optimistic, exceedingly responsive to praise, recognition, and acclaim from others. Failure is stylized as a temporary setback, obstacles are made to be overcome, only a sissy takes defeat as anything but a stimulus to trying harder. "The difficult we do at once, the impossible takes a little longer."

The chief trap for the boy in this pattern of maturation lies in the conditional nature of the whole process. On the one hand he can always win applause by taking the next step, moving from the third team to the second team, from the position of the worst in the class to the position of the next to the worst, by gaining a pound or growing an inch; the applause is hearty and ungrudging from parents who feel they owe their children every chance to succeed and have a right to take their success as a full repayment for parental sacrifice. On the other hand, none of this acceptance and this applause is final. If the next step up is not taken, then the approval becomes only a remembered happiness, now withdrawn, which must be worked for again. Mother loves you *if* you suceed; Father is grinning and proud if you succeed, something a little ruefully comforting when you fail. But at no time in childhood, often at no time in one's whole life, is it possible to arrive, to win love and praise that are not strictly contemporary and conditional and which can never be taken away from one. This is the background of those American attitudes—failure to admit immigrants, ungenerous state laws about welfare settlement for indigent families—that contrast so sharply with American willingness to help others, to give freely of time and goods and services. It is not that Americans learn, as some peoples do, that the supply of goods is limited and so one man's gain is another man's loss. They rather learn that the number of prizes in the race, the number of A's in the class, are more limited than is the number of contestants. If there are more contestants, the endless race for the A's, for the prizes, becomes that much harder. It is not that the boy learns interest in defeating others, but that he fervently hopes he can beat enough others to be counted a success; the others are incidental, not so much rivals to be worsted as entrants to be outdistanced. His upbringing permits him no admitted glee in open battle, and later, in a competitive world that demands harsh and sometimes savage competition, he takes little pleasure in the game itself. He accepts the behest that he must continue and continue and continue to succeed, to advance, to keep his place among others. The methods he has to use are just part of it, to be laid aside in a compensatory good-fellowship that is often mixed right into the distasteful competitive relationships. In those relationships between men when the competition can be laid aside altogether, a delicious game of pretended aggression can be played endlessly, with thrust and counterthrust, harmless and healing.

But the role of sisters and girls and wives is a very complex one in this world in which the boy's whole springing masculinity is diverted into the game of success. Because it is the mother's and not the father's voice that gives the principal early approval and disapproval, the nagging voice of conscience is feminine in both sexes—that voice which says, "You are not being the success you *ought* to be." The man who feels he is failing is a man who is angry with women, and angry with those values for which women stand—social values, social-security legislation, "sentimental schoolmarmish goodness." And it is not only the man who is failing who finds himself angry with women, but also the man who is paying too high a price for his success, and so reiterates over and over how hard he works, how self-made he is, how the modern world is making it too soft for people. The American who is successful without feeling he has paid too high a price will be at ease with himself and his conscience, and give generously to the Community Chest or the union relief fund, and send food to starving Europeans, vote for social legislation, even sit on a board to see that his wife's pet charity gets what it needs. But at any moment this easy good nature may shift to an angry assertiveness against the "do-gooders," those who have set his feet on a path he cannot bear, that path which in ruthless competitiveness seems a long way from the task of maintaining a hospital, or raising the salaries of schoolteachers, to which he is now asked to give help. Any great yielding to the demands of civic virtue is suspect; a man to be a man must go out to prove he is a man, and then, and only then, can he leave a fortune to the orphans' home. The American ideal career is the poor boy who learned his prayers at his mother's knee, worked his way up against fearful odds, used without womanish softness and without enjoyment the methods appropriate to such a battle, and in the end, a millionaire, leaves his money—not to his children to ruin their characters by denying them a gradient on which at least some sort of success is possible, but—to good works, giving to the town or to the nation schools, libraries, art galleries, and orphan asylums. These are the things his mother told him that he ought to respect while he himself puts his whole effort into being a success. Good women made him what he is, and in the end they get the proceeds for their own ends, and in between he worked hard being the man they told him he ought to want to be. So as the mother's love has become more and more conditional upon success, the mother and the schoolteacher have tended to merge in the child's mind, with the teacher taking on some of the aspects of the bad mother that were once given to the stepmother in the fairy tales of another age.

The sister in America has a very special role in the life of the American boy, geared as he is to succeed on a scale in which he is measured by his age and size against others of like age and size, and rewarded by women rather than by men. The sister becomes a double rival as she grows faster than he, does her lessons more dutifully, gets into fewer scrapes, learns the woman-taught lessons more easily. Characteristically, the sister in America is the big sister, whose side the parents always take, who is so slick she always wins, who gets away with murder—that is, gets the same rewards with less effort—and the daydream sister is the little sister, over whom one can win without effort. The habit of American mothers of egging their children on by invidious or challenging comparisons is at its most aggravated in the case of sister, girl-cousin, girl next door. The boy is taught both that he ought to be able to beat her record, as he is a boy, and that it is fair to compare their achievements on the same scale at the same age, because they both ride bicycles or sleep alone on the third floor, or are in the fast-moving section of the fourth grade. They are treated as alike whenever it suits the rest of the world, and as unlike whenever that provides a better goad. If a boy cries, he is scolded more than a girl who doesn't cry; when she out-strips him, he is told it is even worse than if he had been outstripped by a boy, and yet she may be almost twice his size and he has also been told not to hit her because she is a girl. Side by side they sit in the nursery to be compared on table manners, side by side in school to be compared on neatness and punctuality as well as reading and writing and arithmetic. She sits and challenges him, and beats him at least half the time and often more than half, until high school provides the blessed relief of science and shop, where girls aren't en-couraged to succeed any longer. And as he sits and is beaten—at least half the time—he learns both that girls can do most of the things that boys can do for which rewards are meted out and that it is in-tolerable that they should, because it has been made humiliating.

This is expressed in later life in the relatively high accessibility of most occupations to women, but also in the bitter fight that is put up, even in those fields where women are the best trained, as in some government services, against giving women jobs that carry high salaries or administrative powers over people—the two most usual ways in which men demonstrate their success. Many societies have educated their male children on the simple device of teaching them not to be women, but there is an inevitable loss in such an education, for it teaches a man to fear that he will lose what he has, and to be forever somewhat haunted by this fear. But when in addition to learning that at all costs he must not be a girl, he is continually forced to compete with girls at the very age when girls mature faster than boys, and on women-set tasks to which girls take more easily, a sharper ambivalence is established. American men have to use at least part of their sense of masculine self-esteem as men on beating women, in terms of money and status. And American women agree with them and tend to despise a man who is outdistanced by a woman. When American women do rise to positions of power and status, they have great difficulty in treating their male subordinates with any decent sensitivity—for aren't they failures to be there?— and shrink with horror from making more money than their hus-bands to the extent that they wish to feel feminine, or throw their success in their husbands' faces to the extent that their own cross-sexual competitiveness has been developed. So we end up with the contradictory picture of a society that appears to throw its doors wide open to women, but translates her every step toward success as having been damaging—to her own chances of marriage, and to the men whom she passes on the road.

It is just in the middle class, and among those who aspire to middle-class position, that this antagonism waxes strongest, because the middle-class skills are those in which it is easy for women to excel and where men find themelves most fenced in, any rampant masculinity denied and fettered in the interest of saving and postponement of indulgence in impulse. Middle-class mothers, educated and still at home, have a great deal of time to give to molding their growing children, giving and withholding love as the children display the proper attitudes. And middle-class virtues—saving, thrift, punctuality, foresight, hard work, control of present impulse, respect for the opinion of others, conformity to a code of manners—are virtues that can be learned. Those skills in which the body plays a role and in which it is easier for men to attain superiority, such as hunting, riding, or fighting, are absent from the middle-class list. Middle-class virtues learned out of reciprocal relationships between mother and child are patterned originally in the gastrointestinal tract, taking in, keeping, ordered giving out, in which the male child has all the complication of sorting out the control imposed on elimination from the need to keep somewhat available his impulsive masculinity. The female, although her special feminine characteristics are not evoked, has a lesser problem as she learns to observe the rules of time and place. So all through an American boy's childhood he has to compete, at home and at school, with girls who have an edge in almost all the activities for which reward is given, as one is, for example, rewarded for standing up for oneself but not for fighting. Athletics with their close relationship to bodily strength and vulnerability remains almost the only field from which female competition is barred, and they provide through life a thrilling escape, if only in the pages of a newspaper, for American boys and men. And escape is needed from a game in which all the dice are loaded and yet one must not lose—on penalty of losing love and so self-esteem.

Meanwhile, what is the position of the girl whose easy and successful competition with her brother is assured by the conditions of home and the school system? Seen through male eyes, she is big sister who has it easy, who always gets the breaks. Instead of being told that she mustn't do things because she is a girl, that she must cross her legs and lower her eyes and sit on a cushion and sew a fine seam, she is told that she must learn the same things as a boy. The boy is told that he ought to be ashamed to be beaten by a girl, and outworn symbols of sheer male physical superiority are invoked for such routine tasks as remembering to brush one's teeth or do one's lessons. The male's age-old feeling that to be sexually successful he must be strong is invoked in the interest of activities that have lost their immediate relevance. But at the same time the girl is told that she ought to be doing better than her brother, not because she will be humiliated if she fails, but because it is easier for girls to be good. This paradox of boy-girl competition was summed up in Whittier's "In School Days," one of the first poems to celebrate the pleasures and penalties of coeducation, which tells the story of the girl who worsted the boy in spelling:

> "I'm sorry that I spelt the word:
> I hate to go above you,
> Because,"—the brown eyes lower fell,—
> "Because, you see, I love you!"

And it is significant that the poet—a male—while writing so sweetly and wistfully about her, moralizing so nicely on how her attitude contrasts with most people's—

> He lived to learn, in life's hard school,
> How few who pass above him
> Lament their triumph and his loss,
> Like her,—because they love him.—

also very deftly and definitely kills the lady off:

> Dear girl! the grasses on her grave
> Have forty years been growing!

Just so the New Guinea native tells the story of the woman who hands to men the symbols by which they can compensate themselves for their inferiority to her, and then adds that they had better kill her. Love on such terms is unbearable. So there is built into the girl in America a conflict of another order. She too must do her lessons and obey her mother, or she will lose her mother's love, her teacher's approval, and the rewards that are accorded to the successful. She too likes bread generously spread with jam and an icebox that is always open. These are hers, almost for the asking. "For all little girls," reads the sign in a New York candy-shop window, "and for *good* little boys." Hers, by natural right, but at what a price! If she learns the rules well, if she gets good marks, wins scholarships, gets the cub reporter's job, by so much she has done an unforgivable thing, in her own eyes and in the eyes of all those around her. Each step forward in work as a successful American regardless of sex means a step back as a woman, and also, inferentially, a step back imposed on some male. For maleness in America is not absolutely defined, it has to be kept and re-earned every day, and one essential element in the definition is beating women in every game that both sexes play, in every activity in which both sexes engage.

To the extent that the little girl shares the attitudes of Whittier's dead heroine, she rejects the dilemma. True, she may have to spell the word now, in the third grade, for failure is too bitter for her small, success-oriented soul to bear. But later she will shift the field and get out of the unfair competition, go away from the game of loaded dice, and be a success in a different field, as a wife and a mother. The desperate need for success remains; it is not as strong as for the boy, because for the girl success is demanded only as it is demanded of all human beings, and not with a threat that if she does not succeed she will not be regarded as a true female. Boys are unsexed by failure; girls, if they are also pretty, may be more desirable if they need a male Galahad to help them with their lessons. But this is becoming steadily less true. Subtly the demand for the same kind of character structure for men and for women is spreading throughout the country. In a 1946 *Fortune* poll, men were asked which of three girls equally good-looking a man would prefer to marry: a girl who had never held a job, a girl who had held a job and been moderately successful at it, or a girl who had held a job and been extremely successful. The preferences ran: 33.8 percent for the moderately successful, 21.5 percent for the extremely successful, and only 16.2 percent for the girl who had never held a job. The *moderately* successful are still preferred, but with this preference goes increasing pressure on a girl to work before marriage, perhaps to work until the first child comes, and to "begin doing something," if it is only volunteer work or vigorously pursuing a hobby, as soon as her children are in school. Men want their wives both to reassure them by being less successful than they are and to gratify their competitive aspirations, vicariously, by "being successful." It is probably safe to say that the introspective distance between the words "moderately" and "extremely" means "at someone else's expense by playing in another league" as against "beating me at my own game," with the over-all emphasis on success gradually winning out. A girl who has never held a job is becoming increasingly suspect. Maybe she couldn't get a job; maybe if she had tried she would have been a failure, and who wants a wife, however personally pliant and reassuring, who might have been a failure? It is interesting also that in the female replies, 42.2 percent of the women thought men would prefer a moderately successful girl, only 12.1 percent thought a man would prefer the girl who had never held a job, and only 17.4 percent thought they would prefer the exceedingly successful. The *Fortune* commentators go on to say:

Evidently men are not as afraid of capable girls as women think they are. This is especially true of poor men, of whom 25% think that the extremely successful girl would make the most desirable wife. Poor women also give an unusually high vote for the extremely successful girl (24.7%), while women in the upper middle class give her very little backing, only 12.3%.

And note that it is in the upper middle class that girls are treated most like boys in their education, compete with men most directly during childhood, and experience most directly the pressures I have been discussing.

So throughout her education and her development of vocational expectancy, the girl is faced with the dilemma that she must display enough of her abilities to be considered successful, but not too successful; enough ability to get and keep a job, but without the sort of commitment that will make her either too successful or unwilling to give up the job entirely for marriage and motherhood. "Two steps forward and one step back" is the dance-call she must obey. Or take the consequences. And what are the consequences? Failure to marry? If that were all, it might not be so serious. There are more women than men in the world, and societies have found it very possible to stylize vows of celibacy and poverty and still give women dignified lives. The nun who offers her potential wifehood and motherhood to God on behalf of all mankind, and who substitutes prayer and care for the children of God for the creation of particular children, can feel herself a part of God's plan, fulfilling the duty of human beings to "cherish and protect the lives of men and the life of the world." In the crowded bus or cars of the subway, where men now let women stand with children in their arms—because women make money, don't they?—seats are still given to Sisters of Charity and Mercy.

But the woman in the United States who chooses a career instead of marriage is accorded no such satisfying and accredited place in the world. The same feeling that makes Americans, so often generous almost without parallel in the world, vote against the entrance of a few thousand homeless orphans, plus the feeling that any success in a woman calls men's manliness into account, defeats the possibility of her role's being fully rewarding. If she succeeds in a profession like schoolteaching, men either desert it altogether, or are driven to such appalling expedients as rules that women are incapable of teaching second-year American history, so that the very enactment of the defensive measure further lowers them in their own eyes. No one, neither the men themselves nor the women with whom they compete successfully, thinks it is a good thing for an inadequate man to get the job of principal of a school over the heads of five better-equipped women. Neither sex is made happy by the situation, neither the women, able, conscientious, and hard-working, who may be 80 percent of the contestants, nor the men who may constitute the other 20 percent, a large proportion of whom suspect that the real reason for the promotion was just because "they wanted a man."

Perhaps this situation in which able women see themselves perpetually passed over in favor of a man after spending their lives in a "service" profession, a profession in which the womanly virtues of detailed imagination and patience with children are very heavily called for, is one important reason why women are leaving these professions for factory work and business, where they cannot be passed over so easily. And here they can use other weapons. For where the weapons of the schoolteacher and the social worker are the weapons of mother's voice and the persistent demand that men be good, the weapons of the woman in business in the United States may include those of the woman who uses her sex to attain her ambitious ends. Ilka Chase's *In Bed We Cry* is a tragedy of just this situation, of the menace that the successful business woman is to herself and to the man she loves. The little girl who hears the call of success more sharply than the call of her future wifehood and maternity hears a call to competitive action in which no holds are barred. Her brother has been better schooled than she has been for this expected behavior in a competitive world. Fair play, no bullying, do not throw your weight around, are part of the ethics both she and he learned on the playing fields, but here the pretense that all boys are stronger than all girls was kept up. Some of her very drive for success may come from this comparison, this statement that boys should always outdistance girls; some of her drive may come from doors barred to her because "women always leave and get married," come from a sneer from a brother or a father that "girls have no heads for figures." However this may be, she has been defined as weaker, and there are no rules in American life for the good behavior of underdogs. To the extent that American women—most American women—follow the rules of fair play and give-and-take and no alimony, they do so because they think of themselves as strong human beings, human like the men of whom they refuse to take an advantage. But to the woman who makes a success in a man's field, good behavior is almost impossible, because her whole society has defined it so. A woman who succeeds better than a man— and in a man's field there is no other practical alternative to beating a certain number of men—has done something hostile and destructive. To the extent that as a woman she has beauty or attractiveness of any sort, her behavior is that much more destructive. The mannish woman, the ugly woman, may be treated as a man in disguise, and so forgiven her successes. But for the success of a feminine woman there are no alibis; the more feminine she is, the less can she be forgiven. This does not mean that every woman who enters business or fields where she is in an extreme minority is hostile and destructive. But it does mean that any woman who in the course of her childhood had an extra amount of destructiveness developed and repressed is in psychological danger when she is placed in a role that is so destructively defined. To the woman whose maternal attitudes are highly developed, the position may be wholly intolerable.

So brother and sister, boy and girl, educated together, learn what each wishes from what each can give to the other. The girl learns to discipline and mute an ambition that her society continually stimulates, as all girls working in white-collar jobs are said to have "careers," and careers are glamorous, while most men with similar skills merely have jobs. And we have the situation that looks so strange on the surface, that as more and more women work, women seem on the whole less interested in the battle that permits them to succeed professionally. A half-century ago the eyes of the specially able girl who went to college faced ahead toward a profession, toward a career. The idea of marriage was often pushed aside as a handicap. Today, the girl of the same ability is usually willing to admit that she wants to marry, and seems more willing to sacrifice her career to marriage than to sacrifice a chance for marriage to her career. Because it is now more and more accepted that girls should work until they marry—and if one is unlucky, this means all one's life—girls work hard at acquiring skills and professions. If they have brains and ability, sheer virtuosity plus the need to succeed may lead them to become engrossed in their work, but seldom so engrossed that the desire for marriage is blocked out.

Nor will society today treat the woman who is not chosen with the simple pity accorded the wallflower of a century ago. Less kindly verdicts—"She must be neurotic," "She doesn't pay attention," "She hasn't made the most of her chances"—come all too easily to the lips of the young unmarried woman when she speaks of the older one. Success for a woman means success in finding and keeping a husband. This is much more true than it was a generation ago, when men were still supposed to do the seeking, and some women found their new freedom outside the home so intoxicating that they could abandon themselves to their work. Nor is this surprising in a world where the unmarried man is also looked upon as a failure in human relations, a queer bird who, in spite of all the girls there are to marry, never succeeded in finding one, some one who is just too lazy, too do-less, to make an effort. But the more successful a man is in his job, the more certain everyone is that he will make a desirable husband; the more successful a woman is, the more most people are afraid she may not be a successful wife. The *Fortune* survey summarized the reasons people gave why men should prefer extremely successful girls—their greater efficiency and understanding of money and their ability to help their husbands—and it adds: "Very few look upon her intelligence as an asset, and practically none say that she would be easier to get along with." The well-worn phrase "even the best cooks are men" should be footnoted by a recognition that American men are not reared to enjoy being the husbands of successful chefs.

MIRRA KOMAROVSKY [1953]

Are men the lords of creation? Mirra Komarovsky, who graduated from Barnard College in 1926 and now teaches there, gives a sociologist's point of view in Women in the Modern World.

Lords of Creation?

When it comes to truly great cultural innovations, the record of women is unimpressive. While for some this slender yield constitutes prima-facie evidence of women's limited capacity for creative achievement, the inference is by no means conclusive. We are reminded that many male geniuses were not deterred by poverty, discouragement, and even persecution and that, consequently, women who had it in them would have also surmounted environmental handicaps. But the environment that counts is not merely the external one of favorable laws and opportunities. It is the inner environment, the self-image and the level of aspirations, which is at the root of motivation. This self-image, subtly molded by society, has been, and still is, inimical to the full development of whatever creativity women may possess.

Creation of a high order requires a fierce concentration. A man need not have always paid for it by the sacrifice of other goals normally desired, such as love or marriage. But even when supreme sacrifices were entailed, the man in making them need not have suffered the added penalty of corroding self-doubt. Any woman who was prepared to make such sacrifices was condemned as a "freak" and, being a child of her society, inevitably suspected that the verdict was just. Self-doubt at this sensitive core of one's being, apart from external handicaps, tended to block creativity in women. . . . The surprising thing is not the absence of women geniuses but the great number of highly competent women in the arts and in professions. We must remember that men geniuses are rare, too, and that thousands of men are stimulated and trained in various spheres before one genius emerges.

VIRGINIA CROCHERON GILDERSLEEVE
[1954]

Virginia Crocheron Gildersleeve, whose latest book, A Hoard for Winter, *was published in 1962, was Dean of Barnard College from 1911 to 1947, presiding brilliantly over the college from which she had graduated in 1899. The following excerpt is from* Many a Good Crusade, *her memoir of her years as Dean of Barnard.*

Committee Men

Over the years, while sitting as the one woman on committees of men at Columbia, I developed a technique of dealing with such situations which proved satisfactory in my University and useful in later years on other councils and commissions. Men dread the prospect of having a woman around. Their worst fear is that she will talk too much and often irrelevantly, that she may get emotional in seeking to have her own way. My natural instinct was to begin very gently. I spent hours and hours just sitting quietly, listening to discussions of the University budget or whatever was before us, speaking rarely and briefly, to comment on the business, to ask intelligent questions, occasionally to make a suggestion. If a woman just sits quietly and says nothing at all, then the men will think she is timid or stupid and uninterested. If she is to gain any influence, she must establish herself as a pleasant, amiable, but intelligent human being, no trouble but rather a help. The men can then turn to her in any puzzling questions involving women, perhaps enjoy her protection in warding off attacks by militant feminists from outside, and in time will lend an attentive ear to her own projects.

DOROTHY VAN DOREN [1960]

Dorothy Van Doren, who graduated from Barnard College in 1912, has since published many novels, stories, articles, and reviews. Her distinguished career eminently qualifies her to speak for the professional writer on the question of whether or not men are the lords of creation, and she does so in this excerpt from Men, Women, and Cats.

Manly Men and Womenly Women

I do not believe that men are exclusively like men or women like women. I doubt that men are always brave and strong, clearer-headed than women, more apt to understand mathematics, better cooks, and less able to bear pain. Neither do I admit that women are always less romantic than men, more unscrupulous, cattier, or more patient with young children. These categorizations are familiar to all of us, and many more like them. Women are the mothers of the race and as such are fitted to bear and forbear, to suffer, to defend their young against all comers, which they do if necessary with tooth and claw. Men are the creators, the artists, the painters, the poets, the continent builders. Was Homer a woman (there is, of course, a theory that he was), was Plato or Chaucer or Michelangelo or Leonardo, was Mozart or Beethoven, was Tolstoi or Freud or Einstein? Who have you women got except possibly Sappho and Jane Austen and Emily Dickinson, Joan of Arc, St. Theresa, and Eleanor of Aquitaine—and a sadly assorted lot they are!

To all this it is possible simply to say phooey, but that is not a proper answer. It is just like a woman.

Consider how we apply adjectives. We say that a man is woman-ish to mean that he is weak; it is a derogatory description. Yet when we say a woman is like a man we do not mean that she is strong, we mean that she is unwisely imitating a man, and not his worthier qualities. A womanly woman is a man's favorite kind, tender, wise, but in an unobtrusive way, patient, gentle. A manly man is also man's favorite; he is big, muscular, kind to animals, probably smokes a pipe, and can carry his liquor. Women do not care much for "womanly" women and some of them do not even like manly men. These adjectives which ought to be simply descriptive are often enough controversial; which means to me that they are not truly descriptive. There is something wrong with them.

We all know men who are gentle, kind, and patient; men who are great gossips; men who talk too much, who backbite, who can't ham-mer a nail straight (yes, I do), who are so stoical when they are ill that they become a nuisance to the women who have to nurse them. We know women who are first-rate at business, women who can keep books competently, who hold their tempers under provocation, who do not chatter, and woman, alas, who will smack an offspring for apparently no reason at all. If it is said that no living woman is a poet like Shakespeare, no living man is either, nor has been since Shakespeare died. Of the greatest artists there are only a handful in our history. It is true that they are all men. I am not sure it will always be true. Perhaps our modern industrial society is freeing women from certain of the obligations to everyday living that used to hamper them. If that is not what hampered them, if when gadgets get them out of the kitchen and the nursery women do not then become great artists, then somebody will have to reconsider my premise. It will not be me, because I shall have long since departed to another world.

BETTE DAVIS [1962]

Bette Davis began her motion picture career in 1931 at the age of twenty-three. Now, after four marriages and two Academy Awards, she has chosen what she calls "the lonely life," and the men she knows best are the phenomenon she calls "glamour boys."

Glamour Boys

Most of Hollywood's glamour boys spent their lives ensuring their place in the safety of the producers' arms and the hearts of the public. The masculine ego, outsized at birth, takes on gargantuan proportions in the actor. As his box-office power grows, his self-adoration has all the obscenity of a Krafft-Ebing fetish. He is so taken with himself that there really isn't room for a third part.

His world is a small one bound on the north by his own Polaris, on the south by his own twinkling toes. His longitude can be measured by the distance between his reach and his grasp. If he likes women at all he must be careful. He is, in all fairness, a target for every troublemaker alive. The most harmless flirtation holds the promise of scandal. One or two of the more enterprising males have built their reputations on satyrism and they have their own set of problems; but they are different. Most of the men, especially in the 30's and 40's, had stricter moral clauses in their contracts and found it difficult to play around. The amount of money forced out of the town's gentlemen for indiscretions has always been staggering. Whether or not the public would necessarily boycott the typical American lad who was simply caught acting like one is neither here nor there. The studio officials sincerely believed they would. Hence, the restrictions were great. The Hollywood male had his choice of female limited.

It eventually boiled down to the women in his profession or the local debutantes. Pasadena proved an excellent showcase. There were always countless pretty girls with "nice backgrounds" and low striking power. It always amused me. As far as Hollywood was concerned, a debutante was evidently a girl who owned an evening wrap and knew who her father was. But there was always the danger that she was a hysterical fan who would drive him mad. A man was far less fortunate than a woman in this department. Male fans are in much better control of themselves. At any rate, the actor's understandable fears and working hours usually drove the actor to intramural romance. Like a headwaiter he gravitated to the biggest names. Actors and actresses! All-star casts assembled for no one's benefit. The competition was absurd and the amount of flunkies in the no-man's land between them absolutely forbidding.

Most of the male stars, like kings, demanded partners of equal rank. It was safer and their status was guaranteed. Arrival at a premiere with a beautiful and perfectly groomed Queen of Films was essential to their notion of protocol. And beneath the medals and epaulets and plumed helmets, the men who *were* men weren't either. They were so busy parading their virility onscreen and in lobbies that they folded up like gilt party chairs only brought out for special occasions.

Their values shocked me. Their intellects evaded me. For all their cynicism, expediency and patina, they were the most provincial of all Americans. There wasn't a fistful I could even have a conversation with, and with the solitary exception of the powerhouse who would have threatened my career, not one could I look up to in respect. They were on the whole a lot of weak sisters who were attracted to sovereignty and were frightened by it. Like the rock 'n' roll music and Coca-Cola one now finds in Sorrento, Hollywood seems to have exported its handsomely packaged impotence. *O tempus, O mores*—oh men, oh women. Where have they both gone? Is it truly the end of the West? Where are the men who are stronger than women? I lost one Ham and was presented with a townful. It has been said that an actor is something less than a man, an actress more than a woman. It should come out even. It doesn't.

Their vanity is effete, their self-involvement intellectually limiting and their life's work, to the best of them, ignoble. I have never known the great actor who wasn't aware of this and didn't plan eventually to direct, or produce. If he has no such dream, he is usually bitter, ungratified and eventually alcoholic.

There are and always have been a few whose gift is so great and whose perspective so blessed that their virility is preserved. But the majority of actors strut about like the cocks of the walk they wish they were. I have always found it extremely difficult to find a man attractive when he's wearing curlers in his hair. I have always found it impossible to respect man when he is patting his throat. I find it impossible to be excited by a man who becomes hysterical because his better profile has been sacrificed to the advantage of a scene. The glamour boys have always bored me, and always will.

SAMPLER: Should Men Be Men?

"I have come to realize that I was educated to be a successful man and now must learn by myself how to be a successful woman."
—Quoted from a letter received by LYNN WHITE, JR., in *Educating Our Daughters*, 1950

The men who have most enthralled women are those who combine an exterior which is extremely masculine with a psyche which has much femininity. No man without this admixture would be able to be with a woman as much as she wants him to be, or would have the tact, the intuition, the tenderness which, finally, enthrall her beyond all derring-do.
—JESSAMYN WEST, in *To See the Dream*, 1957

Happiness isn't so bad for a woman. She gets fatter, she gets older, she could lie down, nuzzling a regiment of men and little kids, she could just die of pleasure. But men are different, they have to own money, or they have to be famous, or everybody on the block has to look up to them from the cellar stairs.

A woman counts her children and acts snotty, like she invented life, but men *must* do well in the world. I know that men are not fooled by being happy.
—GRACE PALEY, in *The Little Disturbances of Man*, 1959

During the postwar years, man changed in many ways. Following World War I, he came back from the front, believing in free love, and argued about broad-mindedness in sexual relations. And it didn't take long for the older men to imitate the younger.

With his own interpretations of the theories of Freud, the man moved on. He even left off his never-ending conversations about himself to lecture the girl friend on the new psychology, which, of course, was to his advantage, in the hope of persuading her to his way of thinking. He analyzed and called her abnormal if she did not agree with him and fall for his charms and pseudo theories, although he might be mistaken in both his interpretations of charms and theories. Following the Second World War, the man set forth with the Kinsey Report as his Bible. No more double standards because both men and women had the same urges and the age of the single standards was a thing of the past. And you spinsters and widows, why do you punish yourselves so? Again, all these arguments were an effort of the man to get things his way and to clear him of responsibilities. Those women who continued to be themselves, according to their ideas of moral standards, did not lose their foothold or have to pay out as much money to the medical profession for physical and emotional ills as did their gullible sisters.

Along with this attitude of something for nothing, a man began to look for women who could offer him financial help for marriage. In Washington, after the Second World War, it was said that the most popular girl and the one most likely to get married was the one with the best job. According to present-day magazine articles, the man of today has deteriorated, with his wife making the living along with bearing the children, thus wearing the pants. He is no longer head of the house but just a sidekick of the children. But who is to blame for such a condition? No one but the man himself. He has truly sold his manhood for a mess of pottage. Today, as always, a woman continues to be overcome by the great big masculine man who is capable of doing things and who expresses his confidence in himself. One who shoulders responsibilities, and at the same time gets real joy out of his undertakings—never a dependent man or one who wants a woman to carry the load.

Some schools of psychiatry believe firmly that the mothers have caused all the frailties in the present-day man. The man wants, so the psychiatrists say, to be waited on and freed of responsibilities as he was as a child with a mother (now the wife) to protect him. So the man often needs treatment to bring him to an adult level. Naturally many jokes have been made about this theory and plenty of suggestions, not always approved by the theorists, have been offered as to the treatment needed.

Yet we have all heard some women call their husbands little boys, with their husbands ever ready to act in an infantile manner. Why wouldn't a normal woman want a normal husband, one who is mature and capable of acting grown-up and running the household, and

not having a breakdown in a crisis? A most disgusting sight is that
of the show-off tendencies (Look at me, Mama) in a grown-up man.
Even a little bit at cocktail parties sometimes gets very boring.

—ADELIN WHITE SCOTT, in
A Professional Woman in a Man's World, 1962

LOOKING AT MEN

ROSE O'NEILL LATHAM   [1899]

WHAT STOPPED HIM

Sunday-School Teacher—"Now, Joshua, did you learn the forty-second verse of the thirty-fourth chapter of the sixteenth epistle of St. John to the Philippians, as I told you last Sunday?"

Small Boy—"No'm; Ma's pressing out Autumn leaves in that chapter, and I dasn't monkey with it, at all."

"You're so adventurous, Alfred, when it comes to ice cream!"

Copr. © 1936 The New Yorker Magazine, Inc.

"There is no Santa Claus. Gimbel's always tells the truth."

"It's time you faced facts, Rodney."

"Comfy?"

"And I say to you without fear of contradiction . . ."

Reprinted with the permission of The Village Voice, Inc.

"This is his muse speaking."

ANNE CLEVELAND
AND
JEAN ANDERSON

[1960]

"Two f's in 'ineffable'?"

II   MEN IN PARTICULAR

CHARLOTTE C. ELIOT   [1904]

*T. S. Eliot's mother, Charlotte Champe Eliot, said in her dedication to
the biography of her father-in-law that the book was "written for my
children 'lest they forget.'" Her children did not forget. The book was
published when the poet was sixteen years old, and the image of his
brave and godly grandfather, as described by his mother, haunts several
of his mature poems, notably "A Song for Simeon," with its recollection
of one who could say:*

> I have walked many years in this city,
> Kept faith and fast, provided for the poor,
> Have given and taken honor and ease,
> There went never any rejected from my door.
> Who shall remember my house, where shall live my children's children
> When the time of sorrow is come?

*Mrs. Eliot, who was born in 1843 and died in 1930, had seven children,
of whom T. S. Eliot was the youngest. William Greenleaf Eliot was pastor
of a Unitarian Church in St. Louis from 1834 to 1872, then for fifteen
years chancellor and president of Washington University.*

William Greenleaf Eliot

At that period in the older cities of the East, earnest men and their
measures were upborne on the wave of sympathetic enthusiasm. In
the West they must *create* the public opinion and sympathy which
would later assist them. The difficulties and achievements of the
lonely workers in the West were scarcely understood and appreciated in the East. After reading the life of Dr. Channing, Mr. Eliot
wrote:

> I cannot help being struck by the great difference between the life of
> a Boston minister and my own. There the constant help and incitement
> of friends and of books, here a lonely working. Every measure for which
> I work, I must originate. My library is almost nothing, and if it were
> more, pastoral care consumes all my time.

It was not long before Mr. Eliot's ministration within and without his church was to be greatly needed in St. Louis. The year 1849 was the most disastrous in the history of St. Louis, a year of pestilence, fire, and flood. At the very beginning of the year, in January, Asiatic cholera made its appearance. The origin of the disease was very apparent, and demanded quarantine regulations, which were not for some time enforced. In an article published in one of the daily papers in June, appeared this statement:

It is a well-known fact that nearly every New Orleans boat that lands at our wharf brings hundreds of foreign emigrants taken directly from the ships at New Orleans, in which they have been pent up for weeks or months—in the same clothing, without the opportunity of washing or purifying their stores, and in this condition they are brought here, as much or more crowded, and as completely deprived of the means of cleanliness as upon the ship, and in this condition they are scattered through the city.

It was suggested then that some method of quarantine be enforced. No wonder that three-fourths of the mortality from cholera was confined to the emigrants themselves.

Dr. Eliot's church suffered severely, yet, as he said, it was "regularly kept open for its usual religious services, and no one having either direct or indirect claims upon it was permitted to suffer for want of proper ministration or for decent burial." One of the first victims in the city, Haven Henderson, was a member of the church, and his funeral took place from there in January, 1849. At the communion service a few months later, the names were read of nine church members who had died since the previous communion day. "It was a year of fearful trial," Mr. Eliot said at a later period, "and the value of Christian faith, with a steadfast reliance upon God's providence, was fully proved."

Slowly and surely, from the beginning of the epidemic, it claimed its victims in ever increasing numbers. Mr. Eliot wrote in April: "I keep busy, but do nothing with a relish—the urgency of the moment is needed for each action." And again, in May, he wrote: "All plans were made and notice given that I would go to Chicago for a week or two's absence. But Monday the cholera was evidently increasing so fast that I feared to go." Yet he continued thus: "I must present to my people the claims of Meadville Theological School with hope of raising some six or eight hundred dollars for them." On account of the continued prevalence of cholera, this appeal was not made, and on Tuesday, May 15, Mr. Eliot made this entry in his journal: "Cholera increases—was busy from morning till night visiting the sick."

May 17, at nine o'clock in the evening, a fire broke out in the steamer White Cloud moored at the Levee, and quickly spread to other boats, twenty-three of which were consumed. It extended up into the best business portion of the city; fifteen blocks of buildings were consumed or injured, and property to the value of five million dollars destroyed. To a city of the size of St. Louis, the loss seemed almost irreparable, and the presence of the pestilence added to the horror. Dr. Eliot recorded that on the night of the fire he was up all night getting sick people from the Monroe House to their own safe abode. It was a fearful fire!

Soon after the fire the river rose to an unprecedented height, overflowing the low lands; and heavy rains fell, making some parts of the city almost uninhabitable. This hastened the spread of disease. At that time there was no system of drainage in St. Louis.

During the entire continuance of the epidemic Mr. Eliot was under intense physical and nervous strain. He went from the bedside of the dying to the funeral service of the dead, with little opportunity for rest. On Sunday, June 17, he wrote: "Things are very gloomy and becoming worse; but one subject engrosses all minds. In one family five persons have died since Wednesday, and like cases I hear of daily. We keep well, with careful, cheerful, and prayerful hearts." On Tuesday he recorded for himself a comparatively quiet day, yet he went twice to visit Mr. C., who died at one o'clock. At seven in the evening he christened a baby whose mother had died, and at eight o'clock went to a school directors' meeting. At half past nine he received a message from Mrs. G., whose husband he had previously visited. He found her alone with Dr. G., who was not expected to live through the night. The neighbors were all sick, and he persuaded the tired wife to sleep, while he remained during the night with the sick man. These people lived in a small one-story brick house, on low ground, with a bed on the floor. With careful nursing Dr. G. got through the night very well; and when Mr. Eliot left him, there was hope of his recovery. He returned to his home in the morning, and sending a physician to the sick man he had left, went to bed and slept three hours, when he was summoned to Mrs. H. and her child, both ill. At three in the afternoon she sent for him a second time, and as soon as he saw her he "knew that she must die." He spent most of the afternoon with her, and returned in the evening. At midnight he was again summoned to her bedside, and remained until three in the morning. On coming home he met at his door a gentleman who told him his next neighbor, Mrs. C., was very ill. At half after seven the previous evening she had been to Mr. Eliot's door. He had discouraged her from returning to nurse a cholera patient. At nine o'clock she was violently ill, and at half after four in the morning, when he reached her bedside, she was in a dying condition.

And so the record continues. Mr. Eliot's ministrations were not confined to his own parishioners—he went to any one who sent for him. In this season of trial St. Louis had reason to be proud of her citizens. "Many hundreds of persons of both sexes," wrote Mr. Eliot, "devoted themselves to the care of the sick. There was no panic. Very few were left to suffer unrelieved. The clergy, equally Catholics and Protestants, kept faithfully at their posts, and the physicians worked night and day. The greatest mortality in one day was two hundred and five."

On Sunday, July 8, Mr. Eliot preached on "Suffering Considered as Discipline." Many clergymen had proclaimed that God's anger was in the pestilence and fire, a point of view not entirely obsolete, from which Mr. Eliot very decidedly dissented.

On Sunday, the 22nd of July, the number of deaths from cholera the previous week was two hundred and ninety-nine, and it was announced that the epidemic was abating. On that day Mr. Eliot wrote:

I am inexpressibly shocked today to hear of the death of Rev. Mr. Vancourt. Nothing has brought me so strongly to a sense of the danger to which I have been and am exposed, or of the mercy of God by which I have so far been preserved. He came to see me ten days since, and we talked over our several trials and labors. He has been very faithful as a pastor, and very useful. . . . Yesterday at four P.M. he was apparently well, and died at three this morning. It is a further warning to me, and as far as duty will allow, I shall take it to myself.

As to the theory of contagion: I have tried it, I think, very thoroughly, not only in the ordinary exposure of nursing and doctoring, but sometimes I have held the hand of the suffering, an hour at a time, throughout the whole sickness, conversing with him when so feeble that in order to hear the words I have had to lean over and breathe the same breath, even in the last hours of life,—and after death, in kneeling near the coffin, have incurred the further risk of post mortem contagion. This over and over again, by night and by day, when tired and unwell myself, but without harm.

Living as he did in the shadow of death day after day, Mr. Eliot had previously written: "If I am taken away, I leave my own affairs in good condition. My church also is in good order, and would prosper, I think, even without me. My wife and children would find friends everywhere, and a helper in God. Yet I pray to be spared to them."

The first week in August there were only thirty-four deaths from cholera, yet there was still much sickness. Mr. Eliot wrote: "When will it all end? I do now so long for freedom from care and anxiety that I am almost sick at heart." On the last day of July he had counted the children over whom he had some degree of supervision, and there were *twenty-six* besides his own. The responsibilities thus incurred, in some cases, extended over a period of years.

The second week in August there were but twelve deaths from cholera, and the end of the pestilence seemed near. Out of a population of about sixty thousand, nearly one-tenth had succumbed to the prevailing epidemic. Mr. Eliot notes that under all the accumulated trials of that year, the business of the city had gone quietly on. "The citizens had borne their own burden without asking aid from abroad, and declined what was offered. . . . The church and society came out of the trial as men and women always do come out of trials if well and bravely endured, stronger, more vigorous, more self-reliant, and more hopeful than ever before. . . ."

Prayer Dr. Eliot regarded as the sublimest expression of religious feeling of which the human soul is capable. To Dr. Clarke, evidently in response to some remark from him, he wrote:

You cannot pray! It is strange—very strange—that when the mind is so exhausted that it cannot think one sentence, it should be unable to engage in the most powerful exercise of which it is capable. . . . When I came from Peoria two weeks since I was fresh. "I will pray earnestly every day," but I cannot. I could "say prayers," but that I will not. For a few minutes daily I pray, and for the rest I try to live and think and feel in the spirit of prayer. It is the highest effort of the whole mind; to realize the Presence—to feel the Love—to trust implicitly, yet not idly, in God. I am perhaps too lenient to myself, but I will no longer harass myself because my soul will not work in the traces which Richard Baxter wore. He was a good man and prayed by the hour. I will be a good man by God's help, and pray as much as I can.

For a very few special occasions Dr. Eliot wrote prayers, of which several exist in manuscript form. One of these, written under the strain of a great sorrow, is given for the sake of other parents who have suffered the loss of children. On the 20th of February, 1865, Dr. Eliot's daughter Ada, a young girl then sixteen years of age, was drowned while skating with two companions, only children of Mr. and Mrs. Stephen Salisbury. The first shock of the news of this terrible event completely overwhelmed Dr. Eliot, but he soon recovered himself. Mindful of his duty as a pastor, and sympathizing with the parents who were more completely bereaved than himself, he attended the funeral of the Salisbury children, and from the depths of his own sorrow thus addressed the mourners present:

"You who are parents know full well that there is no strength, no hope, no consolation except in God. Thanks be to God who giveth us the victory through our Lord Jesus Christ. It is *given* to us; we do not accomplish it. We can fight the good fight, we can keep the faith. But the victory over death and the grave is given to us by God, through our Lord Jesus Christ. They cannot return to us, but we shall go to them. All of them are together now, dear friends, the children whom God gave to you. 'The Lord gave, and the Lord hath taken away; blessed be the name of the Lord.' Even Jesus prayed, 'Let this cup pass from me.' May God help us also to say, 'Thy will be done.'

"And to you who are young and full of life and hope as they were, I entreat you to be also as pure and religious and good. They always lived near to God and to his holy child, Jesus. They had given their hearts to him who died for them. They were with him here on earth, they are with him now in heaven. You cannot secure length of life, but by God's help you may secure its blessedness. You may consecrate your hearts, your lives, your all, in the Christian service, as those who have been taken from us have done."

On the following day, at the funeral service of his own daughter, Dr. Eliot prayed:

"Almighty and most merciful God, who has taught us to call thee our Father, we thank thee for this, that as a Father pitieth his children, so thou dost pity us. Most sorely do we feel the need of a Father's sympathy and love. Our hearts are bruised, they are broken; but the broken and contrite heart thou wilt not despise.

"We try to say it: 'Thy will, not ours, be done.' We struggle with ourselves, with groanings not to be uttered. The spirit is willing but the flesh is weak. Thou knowest our weakness. Thou rememberest we are dust. Have pity upon us, God our Father! Out of the depths of sorrow we cry out to thee, the Living God. Give us strength;

withhold not from us thy consolation. Our hope is in thee; let us not be confounded.

"For this blessed one, O God, and for all our family in heaven, we thank thee. They still belong to us, for they are with thee. The joy of our lives is fading away by the loss of their daily presence, and our beloved homes seem desolate and our hearts are bereaved. O God, pity our bereavement! pardon the unreasonableness of grief! The dark waves of trouble have so often gone over us, we are cast down, almost destroyed. Yet we thank thee for them. All that remains of life is not more precious than their memory. Thou alone knowest how we loved them. But we would not call them back. Our souls faint within us when we say it, for they were dearer than our life. But thou art giving us the victory. We are dumb with silence, because it is thy doing. Thy will, not ours, be done."

Not only at this time, but always, Dr. Eliot sympathized in the sorrows of his people, as he also rejoiced with them. There seems to be a popular delusion that a man cannot be both a faithful pastor and a good preacher. If one regards a sermon simply as a literary production, an essay with well-rounded period and graceful simile, this may be true; but if its purpose be rather to rouse the conscience than delight the ear, to quicken the spiritual life and engender hope and faith rather than merely to stimulate the intellectual powers, then that minister who has had the largest and deepest human experience, who has been nearest to his people in their joys and sorrows, ought to be able to move and influence them as could no theorist of the study.

In the summer of 1886, on his seventy-sixth birthday, August 5, 1886, Dr. Eliot wrote the poem "Nunc Dimittis," which voiced his own consciousness of his approaching end, and his desire of release from suffering and disability, while ready to live or die "as the Lord willed."

> Fain would I breathe that gracious word,
> Now lettest thou thy servant, Lord,
>   Depart in peace.
> When may I humbly claim that kind award,
>   And cares and labors cease?
> With anxious heart I watch at heaven's gate—
>   Answer to hear;
> With failing strength I feel the increasing weight
>   Of every passing year.

Hath not the time yet fully come, dear Lord,
   Thy servant to release?

Be still, my heart! In silence God doth speak,
Here is thy place; here, not at heaven's gate;
Thy task is not yet finished; frail and weak,
Doing or suffering, steadfast in thy faith,
Thy service is accepted, small or great;
His time is thine—or soon or late,
If daylight fades, work while the twilight lasts.

Dr. Eliot, very frail and feeble, returned in the fall of 1886, from Jefferson, New Hampshire, to his home in St. Louis. With indomitable will he continued to struggle against increasing weakness, longing to achieve purposes still unaccomplished for which he would gladly have lived. At the beginning of the new year he was taken south to the milder climate of Pass Christian, Mississippi, where he died January 23, 1887. His active mind remained clear and conscious to the last moment of life.

WILLA CATHER [1905]

Born in Virginia in 1873 and raised in Nebraska, Willa Cather viewed a wide spectrum of American culture. Her education was austere and individual, since there were no schools nearby, and her grandmothers taught her Latin and the classics at home. She went on to the University of Nebraska, graduating in 1895. She is best at depicting lonely men, such as the heroes of Death Comes to the Archbishop *and* The Professor's House, *and, most tenderly, the driven adolescent in "Paul's Case." She died in 1947.*

Paul's Case

It was Paul's afternoon to appear before the faculty of the Pittsburgh High School to account for his various misdemeanors. He had been suspended a week ago, and his father had called at the Principal's office and confessed his perplexity about his son. Paul entered the faculty-room suave and smiling. His clothes were a trifle outgrown, and the tan velvet on the collar of his open overcoat was frayed and

worn; but for all that there was something of the dandy about him,
and he wore an opal pin in his neatly knotted black four-in-hand,
and a red carnation in his buttonhole. This latter adornment the faculty somehow felt was not properly significant of the contrite spirit
befitting a boy under the ban of suspension.

Paul was tall for his age and very thin, with high, cramped shoulders and a narrow chest. His eyes were remarkable for a certain
hysterical brilliancy, and he continually used them in a conscious,
theatrical sort of way, peculiarly offensive in a boy. The pupils were
abnormally large, as though he were addicted to belladonna, but
there was a glassy glitter about them which that drug does not produce.

When questioned by the Principal as to why he was there, Paul
stated, politely enough, that he wanted to come back to school. This
was a lie, but Paul was quite accustomed to lying; found it, indeed,
indispensable for overcoming friction. His teachers were asked to
state their respective charges against him, which they did with such
a rancor and aggrievedness as evinced that this was not a usual case.
Disorder and impertinence were among the offenses named, yet
each of his instructors felt that it was scarcely possible to put into
words the real cause of the trouble, which lay in a sort of hysterically
defiant manner of the boy's; in the contempt which they all knew he
felt for them, and which he seemingly made not the least effort to
conceal. Once, when he had been making a synopsis of a paragraph
at the blackboard, his English teacher had stepped to his side and
attempted to guide his hand. Paul had started back with a shudder
and thrust his hands violently behind him. The astonished woman
could scarcely have been more hurt and embarrassed had he struck
at her. The insult was so involuntary and definitely personal as to be
unforgettable. In one way and another, he had made all his teachers,
men and women alike, conscious of the same feeling of physical
aversion. In one class he habitually sat with his hand shading his
eyes; in another he always looked out of the window during the
recitation; in another he made a running commentary on the lecture,
with humorous intent.

His teachers felt this afternoon that his whole attitude was sym-
bolized by his shrug and his flippantly red carnation flower, and they
fell upon him without mercy, his English teacher leading the pack.
He stood through it smiling, his pale lips parted over his white teeth.
(His lips were continually twitching, and he had a habit of raising
his eyebrows that was contemptuous and irritating to the last de-

gree.) Older boys than Paul had broken down and shed tears under that ordeal, but his set smile did not once desert him, and his only sign of discomfort was the nervous trembling of the fingers that toyed with the buttons of his overcoat, and an occasional jerking of the other hand which held his hat. Paul was always smiling, always glancing about him, seeming to feel that people might be watching him and trying to detect something. This conscious expression, since it was so far as possible from boyish mirthfulness, was usually attributed to insolence or "smartness."

As the inquisition proceeded, one of his instructors repeated an impertinent remark of the boy's, and the Principal asked him whether he thought that a courteous speech to make to a woman. Paul shrugged his shoulders slightly and his eyebrows twitched.

"I don't know," he replied. "I didn't mean to be polite or impolite, either. I guess it's a sort of way I have, of saying things regardless."

The Principal asked him whether he didn't think that a way it would be well to get rid of. Paul grinned and said he guessed so. When he was told that he could go, he bowed gracefully and went out. His bow was like a repetition of the scandalous red carnation.

His teachers were in despair, and his drawing master voiced the feeling of them all when he declared there was something about the boy which none of them understood. He added: "I don't really believe that smile of his comes altogether from insolence; there's something sort of haunted about it. The boy is not strong, for one thing. There is something wrong about the fellow."

The drawing master had come to realize that, in looking at Paul, one saw only his white teeth and the forced animation of his eyes. One warm afternoon the boy had gone to sleep at his drawing-board, and his master had noted with amazement what a white, blue-veined face it was; drawn and wrinkled like an old man's about the eyes, the lips twitching even in his sleep.

His teachers left the building dissatisfied and unhappy; humiliated to have felt so vindictive towards a mere boy, to have uttered this feeling in cutting terms, and to have set each other on, as it were, in the gruesome game of intemperate reproach. One of them remembered having seen a miserable street cat set at bay by a ring of tormentors.

As for Paul, he ran down the hill whistling the Soldiers' Chorus from *Faust*, looking wildly behind him now and then to see whether some of his teachers were not there to witness his lightheartedness. As it was now late in the afternoon and Paul was on duty that evening as usher at Carnegie Hall, he decided that he would not go home to supper.

When he reached the concert hall the doors were not yet open. It was chilly outside, and he decided to go up into the picture gallery—always deserted at this hour—where there were some of Raffelli's gay studies of Paris streets and an airy blue Venetian scene or two that always exhilarated him. He was delighted to find no one in the gallery but the old guard, who sat in the corner, a newspaper on his knee, a black patch over one eye and the other closed. Paul possessed himself of the place and walked confidently up and down, whistling under his breath. After a while he sat down before a blue Rico and lost himself. When he bethought him to look at his watch, it was after seven o'clock, and he rose with a start and ran downstairs, making a face at Augustus Cæsar, peering out from the east room, and an evil gesture at the Venus de Milo as he passed her on the stairway.

When Paul reached the ushers' dressing room half-a-dozen boys were there already, and he began excitedly to tumble into his uniform. It was one of the few that at all approached fitting, and Paul thought it very becoming—though he knew the tight, straight coat accenuated his narrow chest, about which he was exceedingly sensitive. He was always excited while he dressed, twanging all over to the tuning of the strings and the preliminary flourishes of the horns in the music room; but tonight he seemed quite beside himself, and he teased and plagued the boys until, telling him that he was crazy, they put him down on the floor and sat on him.

Somewhat calmed by his suppression, Paul dashed out to the front of the house to seat the early comers. He was a model usher. Gracious and smiling he ran up and down the aisles. Nothing was too much trouble for him; he carried messages and brought programs as though it were his greatest pleasure in life, and all the people in his section thought him a charming boy, feeling that he remembered and admired them. As the house filled, he grew more and more vivacious and animated, and the color came to his cheeks and lips. It was very much as though this were a great reception and Paul were the host. Just as the musicians came out to take their place, his English teacher arrived with checks for the seats which a prominent manufacturer had taken for the season. She betrayed some embarrassment when she handed Paul the tickets, and a *hauteur* which subsequently made her feel very foolish. Paul was startled for a moment, and had the feeling of wanting to put her out; what business had she here among all these fine people and gay colors? He looked her over and decided that she was not appropriately dressed and must be a fool to sit downstairs in such togs. The tickets had probably been sent her out of kindness, he reflected, as he put down a seat for her, and she had about as much right to sit there as he had.

When the symphony began Paul sank into one of the rear seats with a long sigh of relief, and lost himself as he had done before the Rico. It was not that symphonies, as such, meant anything in particular to Paul, but the first sigh of the instruments seemed to free some hilarious spirit within him; something that struggled there like the genie in the bottle found by the Arab fisherman. He felt a sudden zest of life; the lights danced before his eyes and the concert hall blazed into unimaginable splendor. When the soprano soloist came on, Paul forgot even the nastiness of his teacher's being there, and gave himself up to the peculiar intoxication such personages always had for him. The soloist chanced to be a German woman, by no means in her first youth, and the mother of many children; but she wore a satin gown and a tiara, and she had that indefinable air of achievement, that world-shine upon her, which always blinded Paul to any possible defects.

After a concert was over, Paul was often irritable and wretched until he got to sleep—and tonight he was even more than usually restless. He had the feeling of not being able to let down; of its being impossible to give up this delicious excitement which was the only thing that could be called living at all. During the last number he withdrew and, after hastily changing his clothes in the dressing room, slipped out to the side door where the singer's carriage stood. Here he began pacing rapidly up and down the walk, waiting to see her come out.

Over yonder the Schenley, in its vacant stretch, loomed big and square through the fine rain, the windows of its twelve stories glowing like those of a lighted cardboard house under a Christmas tree. All the actors and singers of any importance stayed there when they were in the city, and a number of the big manufacturers of the place lived there in the winter. Paul had often hung about the hotel, watching the people go in and out, longing to enter and leave schoolmasters and dull care behind him forever.

At last the singer came out, accompanied by the conductor, who helped her into her carriage and closed the door with a cordial *auf wiedersehen*—which set Paul to wondering whether she were not an old sweetheart of his. Paul followed the carriage over to the hotel, walking so rapidly as not to be far from the entrance when the singer alighted and disappeared behind the swinging glass doors which were opened by a Negro in a tall hat and a long coat. In the moment that the door was ajar, it seemed to Paul that he, too, entered. He seemed to feel himself go after her up the steps, into the warm, lighted building, into an exotic, a tropical world of shiny, glistening surfaces and basking ease. He reflected upon the mysterious dishes that were brought into the dining room, the green bottles in buckets of ice, as he had seen them in the supper party pictures of the Sunday supplement. A quick gust of wind brought the rain down with sudden vehemence, and Paul was startled to find that he was still outside in the slush of the gravel driveway; that his boots were letting in the water and his scanty overcoat was clinging wet about him; that the lights in front of the concert hall were out, and that the rain was driving in sheets between him and the orange glow of the windows above him. There it was, what he wanted—tangibly before him, like the fairy world of a Christmas pantomime; as the rain beat in his face, Paul wondered whether he were destined always to shiver in the black night outside, looking up at it.

He turned and walked reluctantly towards the car tracks. The end had to come sometime; his father in his nightclothes at the top of the stairs, explanations that did not explain, hastily improvised fictions that were forever tripping him up, his upstairs room and its horrible yellow wallpaper, the creaking bureau with the greasy plush collar-box, and over his painted wooden bed the pictures of George Washington and John Calvin, and the framed motto, "Feed my Lambs," which had been worked in red worsted by his mother, whom Paul could not remember.

Half an hour later, Paul alighted from the Negley Avenue car and went slowly down one of the side streets off the main thoroughfare. It was a highly respectable street, where all the houses were exactly alike, and where businessmen of moderate means begot and reared large families of children, all of whom went to Sabbath school and learned the shorter catechism, and were interested in arithmetic; all of whom were as exactly alike as their homes, and of a piece with the monotony in which they lived. Paul never went up Cordelia Street without a shudder of loathing. His home was next to the house of the Cumberland minister. He approached it tonight with the nerveless sense of defeat, the hopeless feeling of sinking back forever into ugliness and commonness that he had always had when he came home. The moment he turned into Cordelia Street he felt the waters close above his head. After each of these orgies of living, he experienced all the physical depression which follows a debauch; the loathing of respectable beds, of common food, of a house permeated by kitchen odors; a shuddering repulsion for the flavorless, colorless mass of everyday existence; a morbid desire for cool things and soft lights and fresh flowers.

The nearer he approached the house, the more absolutely unequal Paul felt to the sight of it all; his ugly sleeping chamber; the cold bathroom with the grimy zinc tub, the cracked mirror, the dripping spiggots; his father, at the top of the stairs, his hairy legs sticking out from his nightshirt, his feet thrust into carpet slippers. He was so much later than usual that there would certainly be inquiries and reproaches. Paul stopped short before the door. He felt that he could not be accosted by his father tonight; that he could not toss again on that miserable bed. He would not go in. He would tell his father that he had no carfare, and it was raining so hard that he had gone home with one of the boys and stayed all night.

Meanwhile, he was wet and cold. He went around to the back of the house and tried one of the basement windows, found it open, raised it cautiously, and scrambled down the cellar wall to the floor. There he stood, holding his breath, terrified by the noise he had made; but the floor above him was silent, and there was no creak on the stairs. He found a soapbox, and carried it over to the soft ring of light that streamed from the furnace door, and sat down. He was terribly afraid of rats, so he did not try to sleep, but sat looking distrustfully at the dark, still terrified lest he might have awakened his father. In such reactions, after one of the experiences which made days and nights out of the dreary blanks of the calendar, when his senses were deadened, Paul's head was always singularly clear. Suppose his father had heard him getting in at the window and had come down and shot him for a burglar? Then, again, suppose his father had come down, pistol in hand, and he had cried out in time to save himself, and his father had been horrified to think how nearly he had killed him? Then, again, suppose a day should come when his father would remember that night, and wish there had been no warning cry to stay his hand? With this last supposition Paul entertained himself until daybreak.

The following Sunday was fine; the sodden November chill was broken by the last flash of autumnal summer. In the morning Paul had to go to church and Sabbath school, as always. On seasonable Sunday afternoons the burghers of Cordelia Street usually sat out on their front "stoops," and talked to their neighbors on the next stoop,

or called to those across the street in neighborly fashion. The men
sat placidly on gay cushions upon the steps that led down to the
sidewalk, while the women, in their Sunday "waists," sat in rockers
on the cramped porches, pretending to be greatly at their ease. The
children played in the streets; there were so many of them that the
place resembled the recreation grounds of a kindergarten. The men
on the steps—all in their shirt sleeves, their vests unbuttoned—sat
with their legs well apart, their stomachs comfortably protruding,
and talked of the prices of things, or told anecdotes of the sagacity
of their various chiefs and overlords. They occasionally looked over
the multitude of squabbling children, listened affectionately to their
high-pitched, nasal voices, smiling to see their own proclivities reproduced in their offspring, and interspersed their legends of the
iron kings with remarks about their sons' progress at school, their
grades in arithmetic, and the amounts they had saved in their toy
banks.

On this last Sunday of November, Paul sat all the afternoon on
the lowest step of his "stoop," staring into the street, while his sisters,
in their rockers, were talking to the minister's daughters next door
about how many shirtwaists they had made in the last week, and
how many waffles someone had eaten at the last church supper.
When the weather was warm, and his father was in a particularly
jovial frame of mind, the girls made lemonade, which was always
brought out in a red-glass pitcher, ornamented with forget-me-nots
in blue enamel. This the girls thought very fine, and the neighbors
joked about the suspicious color of the pitcher.

Today Paul's father, on the top step, was talking to a young man
who shifted a restless baby from knee to knee. He happened to be
the young man who was daily held up to Paul as a model, and after
whom it was his father's dearest hope that he would pattern. This
young man was of a ruddy complexion, with a compressed, red
mouth, and faded, nearsighted eyes, over which he wore thick
spectacles, with gold bows that curved about his ears. He was clerk
to one of the magnates of a great steel corporation, and was looked
upon in Cordelia Street as a young man with a future. There was
a story that, some five years ago—he was now barely twenty-six—
he had been a trifle "dissipated," but in order to curb his appetites
and save the loss of time and strength that a sowing of wild oats
might have entailed, he had taken his chief's advice, oft reiterated
to his employees, and at twenty-one had married the first woman
whom he could persuade to share his fortunes. She happened to be

an angular schoolmistress, much older than he, who also wore thick glasses, and who had now borne him four children, all nearsighted, like herself.

The young man was relating how his chief, now cruising in the Mediterranean, kept in touch with all the details of the business, arranging his office hours on his yacht just as though he were at home, and "knocking off work enough to keep two stenographers busy." His father told, in turn, the plan his corporation was considering, of putting in an electric railway plant at Cairo. Paul snapped his teeth; he had an awful apprehension that they might spoil it all before he got there. Yet he rather liked to hear these legends of the iron kings, that were told and retold on Sundays and holidays; these stories of palaces in Venice, yachts on the Mediterranean, and high play at Monte Carlo appealed to his fancy, and he was interested in the triumphs of cash boys who had become famous, though he had no mind for the cash-boy stage.

After supper was over, and he had helped to dry the dishes, Paul nervously asked his father whether he could go to George's to get some help in his geometry, and still more nervously asked for carfare. This latter request he had to repeat, as his father, on principle, did not like to hear requests for money whether much or little. He asked Paul whether he could not go to some boy who lived nearer, and told him that he ought not to leave his schoolwork until Sunday; but he gave him the dime. He was not a poor man, but he had a worthy ambition to come up in the world. His only reason for allowing Paul to usher was that he thought a boy ought to be earning a little.

Paul bounded upstairs, scrubbed the greasy odor of the dishwater from his hands with the ill-smelling soap he hated, and then shook over his fingers a few drops of violet water from the bottle he kept hidden in his drawer. He left the house with his geometry conspicuously under his arm, and the moment he got out of Cordelia Street and boarded a downtown car, he shook off the lethargy of two deadening days, and began to live again.

The leading juvenile of the permanent stock company which played at one of the downtown theaters was an acquaintance of Paul's, and the boy had been invited to drop in at the Sunday-night rehearsals whenever he could. For more than a year Paul had spent every available moment loitering about Charley Edwards' dressing room. He had won a place among Edwards' following not only because the young actor, who could not afford to employ a dresser,

often found him useful, but because he recognized in Paul something akin to what churchmen term "vocation."

It was at the theater and at Carnegie Hall that Paul really lived;
the rest was but a sleep and a forgetting. This was Paul's fairy tale,
and it had for him all the allurement of a secret love. The moment
he inhaled the gassy, painty, dusty odor behind the scenes, he
breathed like a prisoner set free, and felt within him the possibility
of doing or saying splendid, brilliant things. The moment the
cracked orchestra beat out the overture from *Martha,* or jerked at
the serenade from *Rigoletto,* all stupid and ugly things slid from
him, and his senses were deliciously, yet delicately fired.

Perhaps it was because, in Paul's world, the natural nearly always
wore the guise of ugliness, that a certain element of artificiality
seemed to him necessary in beauty. Perhaps it was because his experience of life elsewhere was so full of Sabbath-school picnics,
petty economies, wholesome advice as to how to succeed in life,
and the unescapable odors of cooking, that he found this existence
so alluring, these smartly clad men and women so attractive, that
he was so moved by these starry apple orchards that bloomed per-
ennially under the limelight.

It would be difficult to put it strongly enough how convincingly
the stage entrance of that theater was for Paul the actual portal of
Romance. Certainly none of the company ever suspected it, least
of all Charley Edwards. It was very like the old stories that used to
float about London of fabulously rich Jews, who had subterranean
halls, with palms, and fountains, and soft lamps and richly appar-
eled women who never saw the disenchanting light of London day.
So, in the midst of that smoke-palled city, enamored of figures and
grimy toil, Paul had his secret temple, his wishing-carpet, his bit
of blue-and-white Mediterranean shore bathed in perpetual sunshine.

Several of Paul's teachers had a theory that his imagination had
been perverted by garish fiction; but the truth was, he scarcely ever
read at all. The books at home were not such as would either tempt
or corrupt a youthful mind, and as for reading the novels that some
of his friends urged upon him—well, he got what he wanted much
more quickly from music; any sort of music, from an orchestra to
a barrel organ. He needed only the spark, the indescribable thrill
that made his imagination master of his senses, and he could make
plots and pictures enough of his own. It was equally true that he
was not stage-struck—not, at any rate, in the usual acceptance of

that expression. He had no desire to become an actor, any more than he had to become a musician. He felt no necessity to do any of these things; what he wanted was to see, to be in the atmosphere, float on the wave of it, to be carried out, blue league after blue league, away from everything.

After a night behind the scenes, Paul found the schoolroom more than ever repulsive; the bare floors and naked walls; the prosy men who never wore frock coats, or violets in their buttonholes; the women with their dull gowns, shrill voices, and pitiful seriousness about prepositions that govern the dative. He could not bear to have the other pupils think, for a moment, that he took these people seriously; he must convey to them that he considered it all trivial, and was there only by way of a joke, anyway. He had autograph pictures of all the members of the stock company which he showed his classmates, telling them the most incredible stories of his familiarity with these people, of his acquaintance with the soloists who came to Carnegie Hall, his suppers with them and the flowers he sent them. When these stories lost their effect, and his audience grew listless, he would bid all the boys good-bye, announcing that he was going to travel for a while; going to Naples, to California, to Egypt. Then, next Monday, he would slip back, conscious and nervously smiling; his sister was ill, and he would have to defer his voyage until spring.

Matters went steadily worse with Paul at school. In the itch to let his instructors know how heartily he despised them, and how thoroughly he was appreciated elsewhere, he mentioned once or twice that he had no time to fool with theorems; adding—with a twitch of the eyebrows and a touch of that nervous bravado which so perplexed them—that he was helping the people down at the stock company; they were old friends of his.

The upshot of the matter was that the Principal went to Paul's father, and Paul was taken out of school and put to work. The manager at Carnegie Hall was told to get another usher in his stead; the doorkeeper at the theater was warned not to admit him to the house; and Charley Edwards remorsefully promised the boy's father not to see him again.

The members of the stock company were vastly amused when some of Paul's stories reached them—especially the women. They were hard-working women, most of them supporting indolent husbands or brothers, and they laughed rather bitterly at having stirred the boy to such fervid and florid inventions. They agreed with the faculty and with his father that Paul's was a bad case.

The east-bound train was plowing through a January snowstorm; the dull dawn was beginning to show gray when the engine whistled a mile out of Newark. Paul started up from the seat where he had lain curled in uneasy slumber, rubbed the breath-misted window glass with his hand, and peered out. The snow was whirling in curling eddies above the white bottom lands, and the drifts lay already deep in the fields and along the fences, while here and there the long dead grass and dried weed stalks protruded black above it. Lights shone from the scattered houses, and a gang of laborers who stood beside the track waved their lanterns.

Paul had slept very little, and he felt grimy and uncomfortable. He had made the all-night journey in a day coach because he was afraid if he took a Pullman he might be seen by some Pittsburgh businessman who had noticed him in Denny & Carson's office. When the whistle woke him, he clutched quickly at his breast pocket, glancing about him with an uncertain smile. But the little, clay-bespattered Italians were still sleeping, the slatternly women across the aisle were in open-mouthed oblivion, and even the crumby, crying babies were for the nonce stilled. Paul settled back to struggle with his impatience as best he could.

When he arrived at the Jersey City station, he hurried through his breakfast, manifestly ill at ease and keeping a sharp eye about him. After he reached the Twenty-third Street station, he consulted a cabman, and had himself driven to a men's furnishing establishment which was just opening for the day. He spent upward of two hours there, buying with endless reconsidering and great care. His new street suit he put on in the fitting room; the frock coat and dress clothes he had bundled into the cab with his new shirts. Then he drove to a hatter's and a shoe house. His next errand was at Tiffany's, where he selected silver-mounted brushes and a scarf pin. He would not wait to have his silver marked, he said. Lastly, he stopped at a trunk shop on Broadway, and had his purchases packed into various traveling bags.

It was a little after one o'clock when he drove up to the Waldorf, and, after settling with the cabman, went into the office. He registered from Washington; said his mother and father had been abroad, and that he had come down to await the arrival of their steamer. He told his story plausibly and had no trouble, since he offered to pay for them in advance, in engaging his rooms; a sleeping room, sitting room and bath.

Not once, but a hundred times Paul had planned this entry into New York. He had gone over every detail of it with Charley Edwards, and in his scrapbook at home there were pages of description about New York hotels, cut from the Sunday papers.

When he was shown to his sitting room on the eighth floor, he saw at a glance that everything was as it should be; there was but one detail in his mental picture that the place did not realize, so he rang for the bellboy and sent him down for flowers. He moved about nervously until the boy returned, putting away his new linen and fingering it delightedly as he did so. When the flowers came, he put them hastily into water, and then tumbled into a hot bath. Presently he came out of his white bathroom, resplendent in his new silk underwear, and playing with the tassels of his red robe. The snow was whirling so fiercely outside his windows that he could scarcely see across the street; but within, the air was deliciously soft and fragrant. He put the violets and jonquils on the tabouret beside the couch, and threw himself down with a long sigh, covering himself with a Roman blanket. He was thoroughly tired; he had been in such haste, he had stood up to such a strain, covered so much ground in the last twenty-four hours, that he wanted to think how it had all come about. Lulled by the sound of the wind, the warm air, and the cool fragrance of the flowers, he sank into deep, drowsy retrospection.

It had been wonderfully simple; when they had shut him out of the theater and concert hall, when they had taken away his bone, the whole thing was virtually determined. The rest was a mere matter of opportunity. The only thing that at all surprised him was his own courage—for he realized well enough that he had always been tormented by fear, a sort of apprehensive dread that, of late years, as the meshes of the lies he had told closed about him, had been pulling the muscles of his body tighter and tighter. Until now, he could not remember a time when he had not been dreading something. Even when he was a little boy, it was always there—behind him, or before, or on either side. There had always been the shadowed corner, the dark place into which he dared not look, but from which something seemed always to be watching him—and Paul had done things that were not pretty to watch, he knew.

But now he had a curious sense of relief, as though he had at last thrown down the gauntlet to the thing in the corner.

Yet it was but a day since he had been sulking in the traces; but yesterday afternoon that he had been sent to the bank with Denny & Carson's deposit as usual—but this time he was instructed to leave the book to be balanced. There was above two thousand dollars in checks, and nearly a thousand in the banknotes which he had taken from the book and quietly transferred to his pocket. At the bank he had made out a new deposit slip. His nerves had been steady enough to permit of his returning to the office, where he had finished his work and asked for a full day's holiday tomorrow, Saturday, giving a perfectly reasonable pretext. The bankbook, he knew, would not be returned before Monday or Tuesday, and his father would be out of town for the next week. From the time he slipped the banknotes into his pocket until he boarded the night train for New York, he had not known a moment's hesitation.

How astonishingly easy it had all been; here he was, the thing done; and this time there would be no awakening, no figure at the top of the stairs. He watched the snowflakes whirling by his window until he fell asleep.

When he awoke, it was four o'clock in the afternoon. He bounded up with a start; one of his precious days gone already! He spent nearly an hour in dressing, watching every stage of his toilet carefully in the mirror. Everything was quite perfect; he was exactly the kind of boy he had always wanted to be.

When he went downstairs, Paul took a carriage and drove up Fifth Avenue toward the Park. The snow had somewhat abated; carriages and tradesmen's wagons were hurrying soundlessly to and fro in the winter twilight; boys in woolen mufflers were shoveling off the doorsteps; the avenue stages made fine spots of color against the white street. Here and there on the corners were stands, with whole flower gardens blooming behind glass windows, against which the snowflakes stuck and melted; violets, roses, carnations, lilies of the valley—somehow vastly more lovely and alluring that they blossomed thus unnaturally in the snow. The Park itself was a wonderful stage winter-piece.

When he returned, the pause of the twilight had ceased, and the tune of the streets had changed. The snow was falling faster, lights streamed from the hotels that reared their many stories fearlessly up into the storm, defying the raging Atlantic winds. A long, black stream of carriages poured down the avenue, intersected here and there by other streams, tending horizontally. There were a score of cabs about the entrance of his hotel, and his driver had to wait. Boys in livery were running in and out of the awning stretched across the sidewalk, up and down the red velvet carpet laid from the door to the street. Above, about, within it all, was the rumble and roar, the hurry and toss of thousands of human beings as hot for pleasure as himself, and on every side of him towered the glaring affirmation of the omnipotence of wealth.

The boy set his teeth and drew his shoulders together in a spasm of realization; the plot of all dramas, the text of all romances, the nerve-stuff of all sensations was whirling about him like the snow-flakes. He burnt like a faggot in a tempest.

When Paul came down to dinner, the music of the orchestra floated up the elevator shaft to greet him. As he stepped into the thronged corridor, he sank back into one of the chairs against the wall to get his breath. The lights, the chatter, the perfumes, the bewildering medley of color—he had, for the moment, the feeling of not being able to stand it. But only for a moment; these were his own people, he told himself. He went slowly about the corridors, through the writing rooms, smoking rooms, reception rooms, as though he were exploring the chambers of an enchanted palace, built and peopled for him alone.

When he reached the dining room he sat down at a table near a window. The flowers, the white linen, the many-colored wine glasses, the gay toilets of the women, the low popping of corks, the undulating repetitions of the *Blue Danube* from the orchestra, all flooded Paul's dream with bewildering radiance. When the roseate tinge of his champagne was added—that cold, precious, bubbling stuff that creamed and foamed in his glass—Paul wondered that there were honest men in the world at all. This was what all the world was fighting for, he reflected; this was what all the struggle was about. He doubted the reality of his past. Had he ever known a place called Cordelia Street, a place where fagged-looking businessmen boarded the early car? Mere rivets in a machine they seemed to Paul—sickening men, with combings of children's hair always hanging to their coats, and the smell of cooking in their clothes. Cordelia Street—ah, that belonged to another time and country! Had he not always been thus, had he not sat here night after night, from as far back as he could remember, looking pensively over just such shimmering textures, and slowly twirling the stem of a glass like this one between his thumb and middle finger? He rather thought he had.

He was not in the least abashed or lonely. He had no especial desire to meet or to know any of these people; all he demanded was the right to look on and conjecture, to watch the pageant. The mere stage properties were all he contended for. Nor was he lonely later in the evening, in his loge at the Opera. He was entirely rid of his nervous misgivings, of his forced aggressiveness, of the imperative desire to show himself different from his surroundings. He felt now that his surroundings explained him. Nobody questioned the purple; he had only to wear it passively. He had only to glance down at his dress coat to reassure himself that here it would be impossible for anyone to humiliate him.

He found it hard to leave his beautiful sitting room to go to bed that night, and sat long watching the raging storm from his turret window. When he went to sleep, it was with the lights turned on in his bedroom; partly because of his old timidity, and partly so that, if he should wake in the night, there would be no wretched moment of doubt, no horrible suspicion of yellow wallpaper, or of Washington and Calvin above his bed.

On Sunday morning the city was practically snowbound. Paul breakfasted late, and in the afternoon he fell in with a wild San Francisco boy, a freshman at Yale, who said he had run down for a "little flyer" over Sunday. The young man offered to show Paul the night side of the town, and the two boys went off together after dinner, not returning to the hotel until seven o'clock the next morning. They had started out in the confiding warmth of a champagne friendship, but their parting in the elevator was singularly cool. The freshman pulled himself together to make his train, and Paul went to bed. He awoke at two o'clock in the afternoon, very thirsty and dizzy, and rang for ice water, coffee, and the Pittsburgh papers.

On the part of the hotel management, Paul excited no suspicion. There was this to be said for him, that he wore his spoils with dignity and in no way made himself conspicuous. His chief greediness lay in his ears and eyes, and his excesses were not offensive ones. His dearest pleasures were the gray winter twilight in his sitting room; his quiet enjoyment of his flowers, his clothes, his wide divan, his cigarette and his sense of power. He could not remember a time when he had felt so at peace with himself. The mere release from the necessity of petty lying, lying every day and every day, restored his self-respect. He had never lied for pleasure, even at school; but to make himself noticed and admired, to assert his difference from other Cordelia Street boys; and he felt a good deal more manly, more honest, even, now that he had no need for boastful pretensions, now that he could, as his actor friends used to say, "dress the part." It was characteristic that remorse did not occur to him. His golden days went by without a shadow, and he made each as perfect as he could.

On the eighth day after his arrival in New York, he found the whole affair exploited in the Pittsburgh papers, exploited with a wealth of detail which indicated that local news of a sensational nature was at a low ebb. The firm of Denny & Carson announced that the boy's father had refunded the full amount of his theft, and that they had no intention of prosecuting. The Cumberland minister had been interviewed, and expressed his hope of yet reclaiming the motherless lad, and Paul's Sabbath-school teacher declared that she would spare no effort to that end. The rumor had reached Pittsburgh that the boy had been seen in a New York hotel, and his father had gone East to find him and bring him home.

Paul had just come in to dress for dinner; he sank into a chair, weak in the knees, and clasped his head in his hands. It was to be worse than jail, even; the tepid waters of Cordelia Street were to close over him finally and forever. The gray monotony stretched before him in hopeless, unrelieved years; Sabbath school, Young People's Meeting, the yellow-papered room, the damp dish towels; it all rushed back upon him with sickening vividness. He had the old feeling that the orchestra had suddenly stopped, the sinking sensation that the play was over. The sweat broke out on his face, and he sprang to his feet, looked about him with his white, conscious smile, and winked at himself in the mirror. With something of the childish belief in miracles with which he had so often gone to class, all his lessons unlearned, Paul dressed and dashed whistling down the corridor to the elevator.

He had no sooner entered the dining room and caught the measure of the music, than his remembrance was lightened by his old elastic power of claiming the moment, mounting with it, and finding it all sufficient. The glare and glitter about him, the mere scenic accessories had again, and for the last time, their old potency. He would show himself that he was game, he would finish the thing splendidly. He doubted, more than ever, the existence of Cordelia Street, and for the first time he drank his wine recklessly. Was he not, after all, one of these fortunate beings? Was he not still himself, and in his own place? He drummed a nervous accompaniment to the music and looked about him, telling himself over and over that it had paid.

He reflected drowsily, to the swell of the violin and the chill sweetness of his wine, that he might have done it more wisely. He might have caught an outbound steamer and been well out of their clutches before now. But the other side of the world had seemed too far away and too uncertain then; he could not have waited for it; his need had been too sharp. If he had to choose over again, he would do the same thing tomorrow. He looked affectionately about the dining room, now gilded with a soft mist. Ah, it had paid indeed!

Paul was awakened next morning by a painful throbbing in his head and feet. He had thrown himself across the bed without undressing, and had slept with his shoes on. His limbs and hands were lead heavy, and his tongue and throat were parched. There came upon him one of those fateful attacks of clear-headedness that never occurred except when he was physically exhausted and his nerves hung loose. He lay still and closed his eyes and let the tide of realities wash over him.

His father was in New York; "stopping at some joint or other," he told himself. The memory of successive summers on the front stoop fell upon him like a weight of black water. He had not a hundred dollars left; and he knew now, more than ever, that money was everything, the wall that stood between all he loathed and all he wanted. The thing was winding itself up; he had thought of that on his first glorious day in New York, and had even provided a way to snap the thread. It lay on his dressing table now; he had got it out last night when he came blindly up from dinner—but the shiny metal hurt his eyes, and he disliked the look of it, anyway.

He rose and moved about with a painful effort, succumbing now and again to attacks of nausea. It was the old depression exaggerated; all the world had become Cordelia Street. Yet somehow he was not afraid of anything, was absolutely calm; perhaps because he had looked into the dark corner at last, and knew. It was bad enough, what he saw there; but somehow not so bad as his long fear of it had been. He saw everything clearly now. He had a feeling that he had made the best of it, that he had lived the sort of life he was meant to live, and for half an hour he sat staring at the revolver. But he told himself that was not the way, so he went downstairs and took a cab to the ferry.

When Paul arrived at Newark, he got off the train and took another cab, directing the driver to follow the Pennsylvania tracks out of the town. The snow lay heavy on the roadways and had drifted deep in the open fields. Only here and there the dead grass or dried weed stalks projected, singularly black, above it. Once well into the country, Paul dismissed the carriage and walked, floundering along the tracks, his mind a medley of irrelevant things. He seemed to hold in his brain an actual picture of everything he had seen that morning. He remembered every feature of both his drivers, the toothless old woman from whom he had bought the red flowers in his coat, the agent from whom he had got his ticket, and all of his fellow passengers on the ferry. His mind, unable to cope with vital matters near at hand, worked feverishly and deftly at sorting and grouping these images. They made for him a part of the ugliness of the world, of the ache in his head, and the bitter burning on his tongue. He stooped and put a handful of snow into his mouth as he walked, but that, too, seemed hot. When he reached a little hillside, where the tracks ran through a cut some twenty feet below him, he stopped and sat down.

The carnations in his coat were drooping with the cold, he noticed; all their red glory over. It occurred to him that all the flowers he had seen in the show windows that first night must have gone the same way, long before this. It was only one splendid breath they had, in spite of their brave mockery at the winter outside the glass. It was a losing game in the end, it seemed, this revolt against the homilies by which the world is run. Paul took one of the blossoms carefully from his coat and scooped a little hole in the snow, where he covered it up. Then he dozed a while, from his weak condition, seeming insensible to the cold.

The sound of an approaching train woke him, and he started to his feet, remembering only his resolution, and afraid lest he should be too late. He stood watching the approaching locomotive, his teeth chattering, his lips drawn away from them in a frightened smile; once or twice he glanced nervously sidewise, as though he were being watched. When the right moment came, he jumped. As he fell, the folly of his haste occurred to him with merciless clearness, the vastness of what he had left undone. There flashed through his brain, clearer than ever before, the blue of Adriatic water, the yellow of Algerian sands.

He felt something strike his chest—his body was being thrown swiftly through the air, on and on, immeasurably far and fast, while his limbs gently relaxed. Then, because the picture-making mechanism was crushed, the disturbing visions flashed into black, and Paul dropped back into the immense design of things.

MOTHER JONES (Mary Harris Jones)   *[1925]*

When Mary Harris Jones (Mother Jones) lost all her belongings in the Chicago Fire of 1871, she joined the Knights of Labor and for the next fifty years she made her home wherever the workingman was in trouble and needed her. Born in Ireland in 1830, she attended high school and normal school in Canada, then left a teaching career in 1861 to marry an ironworker. He and their four children died in a yellow fever epidemic in 1867. Mother Jones herself lived to be a hundred. She published her autobiography at the age of ninety-five.

A Human Judge

In June of 1902 I was holding a meeting of the bituminous miners of Clarksburg, West Virginia. I was talking on the strike question, for what else among miners should one be talking of? Nine organizers sat under a tree nearby. A United States marshal notified them to tell me that I was under arrest. One of them came up to the platform.

"Mother," said he, "you're under arrest. They've got an injunction against your speaking."

I looked over at the United States marshal and I said, "I will be right with you. Wait till I run down." I went on speaking till I had finished. Then I said, "Good-bye, boys; I'm under arrest. I may have to go to jail. I may not see you for a long time. Keep up this fight! Don't surrender! Pay no attention to the injunction machine at Parkersburg. The Federal judge is a scab anyhow. While you starve he plays golf. While you serve humanity, he serves injunctions for the money powers."

That night several of the organizers and myself were taken to Parkersburg, a distance of eighty-four miles. Five deputy marshals went with the men, and a nephew of the United States marshal, a nice lad, took charge of me. On the train I got the lad very sympathetic to the cause of the miners. When we got off the train, the boys and the five marshals started off in one direction and we in the other.

"My boy," I said to my guard, "look, we are going in the wrong direction."

"No, Mother," he said.

"Then they are going in the wrong direction, lad."

"No, Mother. You are going to a hotel. They are going to jail."

"Lad," said I, stopping where we were, "am I under arrest?"

"You are, Mother."

"Then I am going to jail with my boys." I turned square around. "Did you ever hear of Mother Jones going to a hotel while her boys were in jail?"

I quickly followed the boys and went to jail with them. But the jailer and his wife would not put me in a regular cell. "Mother," they said, "you're our guest." And they treated me as a member of the family, getting out the best of everything and "plumping me" as they called feeding me. I got a real good rest while I was with them.

We were taken to the Federal court for trial. We had violated something they called an injunction. Whatever the bosses did not want the miners to do they got out an injunction against doing it. The company put a woman on the stand. She testified that I had told the miners to go into the mines and throw out the scabs. She was a poor skinny woman with scared eyes and she wore her best dress, as if she were in church. I looked at the miserable slave of the coal company and I felt sorry for her: sorry that there was a creature so low who would perjure herself for a handful of coppers.

I was put on the stand and the judge asked me if I gave that advice to the miners, told them to use violence.

"You know, sir," said I, "that it would be suicidal for me to make such a statement in public. I am more careful than that. You've been on the bench forty years, have you not, Judge?"

"Yes, I have that," said he.

"And in forty years you learn to discern between a lie and the truth, Judge?"

The prosecuting attorney jumped to his feet and shaking his finger at me, he said "Your honor, there is the most dangerous woman in the country today. She called your honor a scab. But I will recommend mercy of the court if she will consent to leave the state and never return."

"I didn't come into the court asking mercy," I said, "but I came here looking for justice. And I will not leave this state so long as

there is a single little child that asks me to stay and fight his battle
for bread."

The judge said, "Did you call me a scab?"

"I certainly did, Judge."

He said, "How came you to call me a scab?"

"When you had me arrested I was only talking about the consti-
tution, speaking to a lot of men about life and liberty and a chance
for happiness; to men who had been robbed for years by their masters, who had been made industrial slaves. I was thinking of the
immortal Lincoln. And it occurred to me that I had read in the papers that when Lincoln made the appointment of Federal judge to
this bench, he did not designate senior or junior. You and your father
bore the same initials. Your father was away when the appointment
came. You took the appointment. Wasn't that scabbing on your father, Judge?"

"I never heard that before," said he.

A chap came tiptoeing up to me and whispered, "Madam, don't
say 'judge' or 'sir' to the court. Say 'Your Honor.'"

"Who is the court?" I whispered back.

"His honor, on the bench," he said, looking shocked.

"Are you referring to the old chap behind the justice counter?
Well, I can't call him 'your honor' until I know how honorable he is.
You know I took an oath to tell the truth when I took the witness
stand."

When the court session closed I was told that the judge wished to
see me in his chambers. When I entered the room, the judge reached
out his hand and took hold of mine, and he said, "I wish to give you
proof that I am not a scab; that I didn't scab on my father."

He handed me documents which proved that the reports were
wrong and had been circulated by his enemies.

"Judge," I said, "I apologize. And I am glad to be tried by so human a judge who resents being called a scab. And who would not
want to be one. You probably understand how we working people
feel about it."

He did not sentence me, just let me go, but he gave the men who
were arrested with me sixty and ninety days in jail.

I was going to leave Parkersburg the next night for Clarksburg.
Mr. Murphy, a citizen of Parkersburg, came to express his regrets
that I was going away. He said he was glad the judge did not sentence me. I said to him, "If the injunction was violated I was the
only one who violated it. The boys did not speak at all. I regret that

they had to go to jail for me and that I should go free. But I am not trying to break into jails. It really does not matter much; they are young and strong and have a long time to carry on. I am old and have much yet to do. Only Barney Rice has a bad heart and a frail, nervous wife. When she hears of his imprisonment, she may have a collapse and perhaps leave her little children without a mother's care."

Mr. Murphy said to me, "Mother Jones, I believe that if you went up and explained Rice's condition to the judge he would pardon him."

I went to the judge's house. He invited me to dinner.

"No, Judge," I said, "I just came to see you about Barney Rice."

"What about him?"

"He has heart disease and a nervous wife."

"Heart disease, has he?"

"Yes, he has it bad and he might die in your jail. I know you don't want that."

"No," replied the judge, "I do not."

He called the jailer and asked him to bring Rice to the phone. The judge said, "How is your heart, Barney?"

"Me heart's all right, all right," said Barney. "It's that damn ould judge that put me in jail for sixty days that's got something wrong wid his heart. I was just trailing around with Mother Jones."

"Nothing wrong with your heart, eh?"

"No, there ain't a damn thing wrong wid me heart! Who are you anyhow that's talking?"

"Never mind, I want to know what is the matter with your heart?"

"Hell, me heart's all right, I'm telling you."

The judge turned to me and said, "Do you hear his language?"

I told him I did not hear and he repeated to me Barney's answers. "He swears every other word," said the judge.

"Judge," said I, "that is the way we ignorant working people pray."

"Do you pray that way?"

"Yes, Judge, when I want an answer quick."

"But Barney says there is nothing the matter with his heart."

"Judge, that fellow doesn't know the difference between his heart and his liver. I have been out to meetings with him and walking home down the roads or on the railroad tracks, he has had to sit down to get his breath."

The judge called the jail doctor and told him to go and examine

Barney's heart in the morning. Meantime I asked my friend, Mr. Murphy, to see the jail doctor. Well, the next day Barney was let out of jail.

EMMA GOLDMAN   *[1931]*

Born in 1869 in Lithuania, educated for three and a half years at a Realschule in Prussia, Emma Goldman arrived in this country in 1885. In 1889, she joined the anarchist movement, where she first met Johann Most. Thirty eventful years later she was deported, and after being thoroughly disillusioned by revolutionary Russia, she wandered the globe until her death in 1940. Her views on men were always trenchant and direct. After one unfortunate marriage she determined never to marry again and avoided doing so until late in life, when she needed British citizenship. She decided never to have children because her father had so terrorized her as a child that she feared subjecting any other human being to such torture.

Johann Most

The following week I went to the *Freiheit* office. Several people were already there, busy addressing envelopes and folding the papers. Everybody talked. Johann Most was at his desk. I was assigned a place and given work. I marveled at Most's capacity to go on writing in that hubbub. Several times I wanted to suggest that he was being disturbed, but I checked myself. After all, they must know whether he minded their chatter.

In the evening Most stopped writing and gruffly assailed the talkers as "toothless old women," "cackling geese," and other appellations I had hardly ever before heard in German. He snatched his large felt hat from the rack, called to me to come along, and walked out. I followed him and we went up on the Elevated. "I'll take you to Terrace Garden," he said; "we can go into the theater there if you like. They are giving *Der Zigeunerbaron* tonight. Or we can sit in some corner, get food and drink, and talk." I replied that I did not care for light opera, that what I really wanted was to talk to him, or rather have him talk to me. "But not so violently as in the office," I added.

He selected the food and the wine. Their names were strange to me. The label on the bottle read: *Liebfrauenmilch.* "Milk of woman's love—what a lovely name!" I remarked. "For wine, yes," he retorted, "but not for woman's love. The one is always poetic—the other will never be anything but sordidly prosaic. It leaves a bad taste."

I had a feeling of guilt, as if I had made some bad break or had touched a sore spot. I told him I had never tasted any wine before, except the kind Mother made for Easter. Most shook with laughter, and I was near tears. He noticed my embarrassment and restrained himself. He poured out two glassfuls, saying, "*Prosit,* my young, naïve lady," and drank his down at a gulp. Before I could drink half of mine, he had nearly finished the bottle and ordered another.

He became animated, witty, sparkling. There was no trace of the bitterness, of the hatred and defiance his oratory had breathed on the platform. Instead there sat next to me a transformed human being, no longer the repulsive caricature of the Rochester press or the gruff creature of the office. He was a gracious host, an attentive and sympathetic friend. He made me tell him about myself and he grew thoughtful when he learned the motive that had decided me to break with my old life. He warned me to reflect carefully before taking the plunge. "The path of anarchism is steep and painful," he said; "so many have attempted to climb it and have fallen back. The price is exacting. Few men are ready to pay it, most women not at all. Louise Michel, Sophia Perovskaya—they were the great exceptions." Had I read about the Paris Commune and about that marvelous Russian woman revolutionist? I had to admit ignorance. I had never heard the name of Louise Michel before, though I did know about the great Russian. "You shall read about their lives—they will inspire you," Most said.

I inquired whether the anarchist movement in America had no outstanding woman. "None at all, only stupids," he replied; "most of the girls come to the meetings to snatch up a man; then both vanish, like the silly fishermen at the lure of the Lorelei." There was a roguish twinkle in his eye. He didn't believe much in woman's revolutionary zeal. But I, coming from Russia, might be different and he would help me. If I were really in earnest, I could find much work to do. "There is great need in our ranks of young, willing people—ardent ones, as you seem to be—and I have need of ardent friendship," he added with much feeling.

"You?" I questioned; "you have thousands in New York—all over the world. You are loved, you are idolized." "Yes, little girl, idolized by many, but loved by none. One can be very lonely among thousands—did you know that?" Something gripped my heart. I wanted to take his hand, to tell him that I would be his friend. But I dared not speak out. What could I give this man—I, a factory girl, uneducated; and he, the famous Johann Most, the leader of the masses, the man of magic tongue and powerful pen?

He promised to supply me with a list of books to read—the revolutionary poets, Freiligrath, Herwegh, Schiller, Heine, and Börne, and our own literature, of course. It was almost daybreak when we left Terrace Garden. Most called a cab and we drove to the Minkin flat. At the door he lightly touched my hand. "Where did you get your silky blond hair?" he remarked; "and your blue eyes? You said you were Jewish." "At the pigs' market," I replied; "my father told me so." "You have a ready tongue, *mein Kind.*" He waited for me to unlock the door, then took my hand, looked deeply into my eyes, and said: "This was my first happy evening in a long while." A great gladness filled my being at his words. Slowly I climbed the stairs as the cab rolled away.

The next day, when Berkman called, I related to him my wonderful evening with Most. His face darkened. "Most has no right to squander money, to go to expensive restaurants, drink expensive wines," he said gravely; "he is spending the money contributed for the movement. He should be held to account. I myself will tell him."

"No, no, you mustn't," I cried. "I couldn't bear to be the cause of any affront to Most, who is giving so much. Is he not entitled to a little joy?"

Berkman persisted that I was too young in the movement, that I didn't know anything about revolutionary ethics or the meaning of revolutionary right and wrong. I admitted my ignorance, assured him I was willing to learn, to do anything, only not to have Most hurt. He walked out without bidding me good-bye.

DOROTHY PARKER   [1934]

*Dorothy Parker's poem, "Men," appears on page 13. Here, in a less
exasperated mood, she describes a man whom she has "known for fourteen years and never a cross word . . ."*

A Valentine for Mr. Woollcott

Alexander Woollcott was born in Phalanx, no kidding, New Jersey,
in a gently strange community of which his grandfather was a
founder. The idea was that everybody was to live in one vast establishment, which still stands large as life, and raise their own food
and live happily ever after; and so, apparently, they did. It seems
to have been an enchanted existence, perhaps due in part to the
presence of a beguiling gentleman who got back to Mother Earth
by painting his room in three great stripes of brown, green, and
blue, and taking daily sand-baths. The father of the infant Alexander was a man of introspective nature who kept getting his feelings hurt and moving to another town, and dutifully the family
went where he did, even unto Kansas City. Nor has Kansas City
forgotten that the boy who was to grow up to be co-author of *The
Channel Road* once dwelt there; today a splendid bulldog named
Alexander Woollcott, to the very point of spelling it with all those
double letters, is one of the prides of the place.

We next find our hero in Philadelphia, I forget by what process
of reasoning, where he lived alone through his high school days
and supported himself by his precocious pen. He reviewed books,
and there was some pretty fast work done about taking them around
the corner and selling them as soon as he had damned their con-
tents. Once he entered an essay contest, won in a walk, and was
awarded a gold medal, which he quickly sold, for sentiment was
not yet in him. In Philadelphia he met some enthusiastic alumni of
Hamilton College, so that was where he went next and back there
he still goes whenever he is allowed time. It is to Hamilton, I think,
that he will go when he dies, if he is good.

Then he came to New York—don't we all?—found that he was a
reporter and ripped his nerves to a fringe working on murder cases.
So they made him dramatic critic, possibly to give him a chance to
sit down. Then came That War, which occasionally creeps into his

writings, and then he came back to more dramatic criticism, and then he began shooting out in all directions. But always his love, his sweet, his ladye faire is the stage, and he cannot stay long away from her. With his friend George Kaufman he wrote *The Channel Road,* of which I can only say that I didn't see it, and later he was persuaded—I imagine someone dropped a hat—to tread the boards himself in a play called *Brief Moment,* which, in an engaging manner, he stole right from under its star's pretty little nose. His part required him to lie around on couches a good deal and utter wearied epigrams and experienced advice—a role of which Mr. Donald Ogden Stewart remarked that no matter how thin you sliced it, it was still Polonius.

Still he is faithful to the stage, although his biweekly outings with her wicked stepsister, the radio, might be considered mild cheating. He loves to talk over the radio, he actually loves it; and certainly his civilized gossip along the air has gained him thousands of friends—which in his case was painted lilies to Newcastle. But the play is ever the thing with him, and his and Mr. Kaufman's *The Dark Tower* is, it seems to me, as skilled and entertaining an exhibit as you will find in the town. And I wish to God that were higher praise.

Apart from his work—or perhaps because of it—he has, I think, the most enviable life I know; and it is all his own doing. He plans the pattern of his days, sees its whole fine shape and all its good colors, and then follows it. He is predisposed to like people and things, in the order named, and that is his gift from Heaven and his career, also in the order named. He has, I should think, between seven and eight hundred intimate friends, with all of whom he converses only in terms of atrocious insult. It is not, it is true, a mark of his affection if he insults you once or twice; but if he addresses you outrageously all the time, then you know you're in.

Alexander Woollcott has been told he looks like Chesterton, but he seems to me to resemble less Chesterton than one of his paradoxes. He is a vast man, not tall; mightily built, with tiny hands and feet. Caricatures of himself always delight him, no matter how they were intended. His apartment is hung wih black-and-white libels of Woollcott. That apartment is just what you've always wanted, and so, I am sure, has he. It stands over the East River, so that through a great sheet of plate glass you can look across to Welfare Island or look down and see the corpses drifting lazily by, and there is one whole blessed room given over to shelf above shelf of books about murder. Murder is Mr. Woollcott's other love; it is, to date, unrequited.

It is a shade sad, for one who lives from hand to sheriff, to know that Alexander Woollcott has that apartment, all for his own, and then keeps leaving it. In the first place, he is encumbered with a passion for rather huge dogs, and as soon as he enters delightedly into their possession, he has to take country houses for them. And, besides, he travels like a forest fire. Turn your back, and the man is in Shanghai. He sails invariably with a bleeding heart for those he leaves behind, and three days out he has a complete new outfit of dear ones. It is his boast that, were he lifted from the thousand arms of his friends and dropped in some small, strange town, in two weeks the affairs of that town would be his affairs and if someone mentioned New York to him, he would have to think for several minutes before he could place it. But I think, myself, he ought to smile when he says that.

He is at the same time the busiest man I know and the most leisured. He even has time for the dear lost arts—letter-writing and conversation. It is a good thing to hear real, shaped, shining talk, in these days when halves of sentences are left hanging miserably in the air, with nothing better to sustain them than an "at least, I mean," or an "oh, *you* know." And it is a good thing to know that someone is writing letters and, as a reward, receiving them. It makes you feel that all *that* is being taken care of, and so you can just sit back and take off those heavy shoes. The Lord alone knows where he finds the hours for all he does, though I suppose that those who have always enthusiasm have, also, always time. Alexander Woollcott's enthusiasm is his trade-mark; you know that never has he written a piece strained through boredom. Sometimes, indeed, there are those who feel that he lets himself be carried away, though in a winning way, and gives perhaps overgenerously of his sentiments in his printed words. It was Howard Dietz, God bless him, who, on reading one curiously lace-edged bit of prose, referred to its author as Louisa M. Woollcott.

Alexander Wollcott likes to work; I give you my word, he likes working. He does it rapidly and surely and, you know darn well, expertly. And he likes it. That is the worst thing I know about him; to me, the sight of someone enjoying work is the affront direct. Well. That's the way he is. He is my friend—he can do no wrong. I suppose. Maybe it would be better to slide over that side of him, if the phrase does not conjure up too difficult a picture, and go on

to the best thing I know about him. That is that he does more kindness than anyone I have ever known; and I have learned that not
from him but from the people who have experienced it.

*(Note to Mr. Woollcott: Dear Alex, now will you marry me? Dor-
othy.)*

ZORA NEALE HURSTON   [1935]

*Zora Neale Hurston's researches into Negro folklore led her to many
strange and powerful men, such as Father Watson, who was a mixture
of Paul Robeson and Rasputin. Born in Florida in 1907, she attended
Howard University, graduating from Barnard College in 1928. After she
received her Doctor of Letters from Morgan College in 1939, she spent
her time doing research, teaching, and writing fiction and nonfiction until
her death in 1960.*

The Frizzly Rooster

I heard of Father Watson the "Frizzly Rooster" from afar, from people for whom he had "worked" and their friends, and from people
who attended his meetings held twice a week in Myrtle Wreath Hall
in New Orleans. His name is "Father" Watson, which in itself attests
his Catholic leanings, though he is formally a Protestant.

On a given night I had a front seat in his hall. There were the
usual camp-followers sitting upon the platform and bustling around
performing chores. Two or three songs and a prayer were the pre-
liminaries.

At last Father Watson appeared in a satin garment of royal purple, belted by a gold cord. He had the figure for wearing that sort
of thing and he probably knew it. Between prayers and songs he
talked, setting forth his powers. He could curse anybody he wished
—and make the curse stick. He could remove curses, no matter who
had laid them on whom. Hence his title the Frizzly Rooster. Many
persons keep a frizzled chicken in the yard to locate and scratch up
any hoodoo that may be buried for them. These chickens have, no
doubt, earned this reputation by their ugly appearance—with all of
their feathers set in backwards. He could "read" anybody at sight.

He could "read" anyone who remained out of his sight if they but stuck two fingers inside the door. He could "read" anyone, no matter how far away, if he were given their height and color. He begged to be challenged.

He predicted the hour and the minute, nineteen years hence, when he should die—without even having been ill a moment in his whole life. God had told him.

He sold some small packets of love powders before whose powers all opposition must break down. He announced some new keys that were guaranteed to unlock every door and remove every obstacle in the way of success that the world knew. These keys had been sent to him by God through a small Jew boy. The old keys had been sent through a Jew man. They were powerful as long as they did not touch the floor—but if you ever dropped them, they lost their power. These new keys at five dollars each were not affected by being dropped, and were otherwise much more powerful.

I lingered after the meeting and made an appointment with him for the next day at his home.

Before my first interview with the Frizzly Rooster was fairly begun, I could understand his great following. He had the physique of Paul Robeson with the sex appeal and hypnotic whatever-you-might-call-it of Rasputin. I could see that women would rise to flee from him but in mid-flight would whirl and end shivering at his feet. It was that way in fact.

His wife Mary knew how slight her hold was and continually planned to leave him.

"Only thing that's holding me here is this." She pointed to a large piece of brain coral that was forever in a holy spot on the altar. "That's where his power is. If I could get me a piece, I could go start up a business all by myself. If I could only find a piece."

"It's very plentiful down in South Florida," I told her. "But if that piece is so precious, and you're his wife, I'd take it and let *him* get another piece."

"Oh, my God! Naw! That would be my end. He's too powerful. I'm leaving him," she whispered this stealthily. "You get me a piece of that—you know."

The Frizzly Rooster entered and Mary was a different person at once. But every time that she was alone with me it was "That on the altar, you know. When you back in Florida, get me a piece. I'm leaving this man to his women." Then a quick hush and forced laughter at her husband's approach.

So I became the pupil of Reverend Father Joe Watson, "The Frizzly Rooster," and his wife, Mary, who assisted him in all things. She was "round the altar"; that is while he talked with the clients, and usually decided on whatever "work" was to be done, she "set" the things on the altar and in the jars. There was one jar in the kitchen filled with honey and sugar. All the "sweet" works were set in this jar. That is, the names and the thing desired were written on paper and thrust into this jar to stay. Already four or five hundred slips of paper had accumulated in the jar. There was another jar called the "break up" jar. It held vinegar with some unsweetened coffee added. Papers were left in this one also.

When finally it was agreed that I should come to study with them, I was put to running errands such as "dusting" houses, throwing pecans, rolling apples, as the case might be; but I was not told why the thing was being done. After two weeks of this I was taken off this phase and initiated. This was the first step toward the door of the mysteries.

My initiation consisted of the Pea Vine Candle Drill. I was told to remain five days without sexual intercourse. I must remain indoors all day the day before the initiation and fast. I might wet my throat when necessary, but I was not to swallow water.

When I arrived at the house the next morning a little before nine, as per instructions, six other persons were there, so that there were nine of us—all in white except Father Watson who was in his purple robe. There was no talking. We went at once to the altar room. The altar was blazing. There were three candles around the vessel of holy water, three around the sacred sand pail, and one large cream candle burning in it. A picture of St. George and a large piece of brain coral were in the center. Father Watson dressed eight long blue candles and one black one, while the rest of us sat in the chairs around the wall. Then he lit the eight blue candles one by one from the altar and set them in the pattern of a moving serpent. Then I was called to the altar and both Father Watson and his wife laid hands on me. The black candle was placed in my hand; I was told to light it from all the other candles. I lit it at number one and pinched out the flame, and relit it at number two and so on till it had been lit by the eighth candle. Then I held the candle in my left hand, and by my right was conducted back to the altar by Father Watson. I was led through the maze of candles beginning at number eight. We circled numbers seven, five and three. When we reached the altar he lifted me upon the step. As I stood there, he called aloud, "Spirit!

She's standing here without no home and no friends. She wants you to take her in." Then we began at number one and threaded back to number eight, circling three, five and seven. Then back to the altar again. Again he lifted me and placed me upon the step of the altar. Again the spirit was addressed as before. Then he lifted me down by placing his hands in my armpits. This time I did not walk at all. I was carried through the maze and I was to knock down each candle as I passed it with my foot. If I missed one, I was not to try again, but to knock it down on my way back to the altar. Arrived there the third time, I was lifted up and told to pinch out my black candle. "Now," Father told me, "you are made Boss of Candles. You have the power to light candles and put out candles, and to work with the spirits anywhere on earth."

Then all of the candles on the floor were collected and one of them handed to each of the persons present. Father took the black candle himself and we formed a ring. Everybody was given two matches each. The candles were held in our left hands, matches in the right; at a signal everybody stooped at the same moment, the matches scratched in perfect time and our candles lighted in concert. Then Father Watson walked rhythmically around the person at his right. Exchanged candles with her and went back to his place. Then that person did the same to the next so that the black candle went all around the circle and back to Father. I was then seated on a stool before the altar, sprinkled lightly with holy sand and water and confirmed as a Boss of Candles.

Then conversation broke out. We went into the next room and had a breakfast that was mostly fruit and smothered chicken. Afterwards the nine candles used in the ceremony were wrapped up and given to me to keep. They were to be used for lighting other candles only, not to be just burned in the ordinary sense.

In a few days I was allowed to hold consultations on my own. I felt insecure and said so to Father Watson.

"Of course you do now," he answered me, "but you have to learn and grow. I'm right here behind you. Talk to your people first, then come see me."

Within the hour a woman came to me. A man had shot and seriously wounded her husband and was in jail.

"But, honey," she all but wept, "they say ain't a thing going to be done with him. They say he got good white folks back of him and he's going to be let loose soon as the case is tried. I want him punished. Picking a fuss with my husband just to get a chance to shoot him. We needs help. Somebody that can hit a straight lick with a crooked stick."

So I went in to the Frizzly Rooster to find out what I must do and he told me, "That a low fence." He meant a difficulty that was easily overcome.

"Go back and get five dollars from her and tell her to go home and rest easy. That man will be punished. When we get through with him, white folks or no white folks, he'll find a tough jury sitting on his case." The woman paid me and left in perfect confidence of Father Watson.

So he and I went into the workroom.

"Now," he said, "when you want a person punished who is already indicted, write his name on a slip of paper and put it in a sugar bowl or some other deep something like that. Now get your paper and pencil and write the name; all right now, you got it in the bowl. Now put in some red pepper, some black pepper—don't be skeered to put it in, it needs a lot. Put in one eightpenny nail, fifteen cents' worth of ammonia and two door keys. You drop one key down in the bowl and you leave the other one against the side of the bowl. Now you got your bowl set. Go to your bowl every day at twelve o'clock and turn the key that is standing against the side of the bowl. That is to keep the man locked in jail. And every time you turn the key, add a little vinegar. Now I know this will do the job. All it needs is for you to do it in faith. I'm trusting this job to you entirely. Less see what you going to do. That can wait another minute. Come sit with me in the outside room and hear this woman out here that's waiting."

So we went outside and found a weakish woman in her early thirties that looked like somebody had dropped a sack of something soft on a chair.

The Frizzly Rooster put on his manner, looking like a brown, purple and gold throne-angel in a house.

"Good morning, sister er, er—"

"Murchison," she helped out.

"Tell us how you want to be helped, Sister Murchison."

She looked at me as if I was in the way and he read her eyes.

"She's all right, dear one. She's one of us. I brought her in with me to assist and help."

I thought still I was in her way but she told her business just the same.

"Too many women in my house. My husband's mother is there

and she hates me and always puttin' my husband up to fight me. Look like I can't get her out of my house no ways I try. So I done come to you."

"We can fix that up in no time, dear one. Now go take a flat onion. If it was a man, I'd say a sharp-pointed onion. Core the onion out, and write her name five times on paper and stuff it into the hole in the onion and close it back with the cut-out piece of onion. Now you watch when she leaves the house and then you roll the onion behind her before anybody else crosses the door-sill. And you make a wish at the same time for her to leave your house. She won't be there two weeks more." The woman paid and left.

That night we held a ceremony in the altar room on the case. We took a red candle and burnt it just enough to consume the tip. Then it was cut into three parts and the short lengths of candle were put into a glass of holy water. Then we took the glass and went at midnight to the door of the woman's house and the Frizzly Rooster held the glass in his hands and said, "In the name of the Father, in the name of the Son, in the name of the Holy Ghost." He shook the glass three times violently up and down, and the last time he threw the glass to the ground and broke it, and said, "Dismiss this woman from this place." We scarcely paused as this was said and done and we kept going and went home by another way because that was part of the ceremony.

Somebody came against a very popular preacher. "He's getting too rich and big. I want something done to keep him down. They tell me he's 'bout to get to be a bishop. I sho' would hate for that to happen. I got forty dollars in my pocket right now for the work."

So that night the altar blazed with the blue light. We wrote the preacher's name on a slip of paper with black ink. We took a small doll and ripped open its back and put in the paper with the name along with some bitter aloes and cayenne pepper and sewed the rip up again with the black thread. The hands of the doll were tied behind it and a black veil tied over the face and knotted behind it so that the man it represented would be blind and always do the things to keep himself from progressing. The doll was then placed in a kneeling position in a dark corner where it would not be disturbed. He would be frustrated as long as the doll was not disturbed.

When several of my jobs had turned out satisfactorily to Father Watson, he said to me, "You will do well, but you need the Black Cat Bone. Sometimes you have to be able to walk invisible. Some things must be done in deep secret, so you have to walk out of the sight of man.

First I had to get ready even to try this most terrible of experiences—getting the Black Cat Bone.

First we had to wait on the weather. When a big rain started, a new receptacle was set out in the yard. It could not be put out until the rain actually started for fear the sun might shine in it. The water must be brought inside before the weather faired off for the same reason. If lightning shone on it, it was ruined.

We finally got the water for the bath and I had to fast and "seek," shut in a room that had been purged by smoke. Twenty-four hours without food except a special wine that was fed to me every four hours. It did not make me drunk in the accepted sense of the word. I merely seemed to lose my body, my mind seemed very clear.

When dark came, we went out to catch a black cat. I must catch him with my own hands. Finding and catching black cats is hard work, unless one has been released for you to find. Then we repaired to a prepared place in the woods and a circle drawn and "protected" with nine horseshoes. Then the fire and the pot were made ready. A roomy iron pot with a lid. When the water boiled I was to toss in the terrified, trembling cat.

When he screamed, I was told to curse him. He screamed three times, the last time weak and resigned. The lid was clamped down, the fire kept vigorously alive. At midnight the lid was lifted. Here was the moment! The bones of the cat must be passed through my mouth until one tasted bitter.

Suddenly, the Rooster and Mary rushed in close to the pot and he cried, "Look out! This is liable to kill you. Hold your nerve!" They both looked fearfully around the circle. They communicated some unearthly terror in me. Maybe I went off in a trance. Great beast-like creatures thundered up to the circle from all sides. Indescribable noises, sights, feelings. Death was at hand! Seemed unavoidable! I don't know. Many times I have thought and felt, but I always have to say the same thing. I don't know. I don't know.

Before day I was home, with a small white bone for me to carry.

MARY MCCARTHY [1939]

Mary McCarthy, who was born in 1912 and orphaned in 1918, was rescued from her severe great-aunt by her grandfather and given what she herself calls "a good education," culminating in her graduation from Vassar College. She has written corrosively about various men such as the great-uncle who raised her and the types who stroll in The Groves of Academe. *Pflaumen, "the genial host," is one of those who haunts the loverless divorcee.*

The Genial Host

When he telephoned to ask you to do something he never said baldly, "Can you come to dinner a week from Thursday?" First he let you know who else was going to be there—the Slaters, perhaps, and the Berolzheimers, and John Peterson, the critic. And he could not leave this guest-list to speak for itself, but would annotate it at once with some short character sketches. "Peterson's a queer fellow," he would say. "Of course, he's moody and right now he's too much interested in politics for his own good, but I hope he'll get back soon to his book on Montaigne. That's his real work, and I wish you'd tell him that. You may not like him, of course, but underneath it all John is a marvelous person." He was deferential, ingratiating, concerned for your pleasure, like a waiter with a tray of French pastry in his hand. This one had custard in it and that one was mocha; the chocolate-covered one had whipped cream, and the little one on the side was just a macaroon. With Pflaumen you were always perfectly safe—you never had to order blind.

In a way, it was a kindness he did you, putting it like that. Other acquaintances made the opposite error, calling up to demand, "Are you free Thursday?" before disclosing whether they wanted you to picket a movie house, attend a lecture at the New School, buy tickets for a party for Spain, or go and dance at a new night club. Nevertheless, there was something too explicit about Pflaumen's invitations that made you set down the telephone with a feeling of distaste, made you dress hurriedly, though carefully, for his parties, as if you were going to keep some shameful assignation, made you, stepping out of your door in the new clothes you had bought, look furtively up and down the street before starting for the subway. Pflaumen had taken the risks out of social life, that was the trouble; and you felt that it was wrong to enjoy an evening without having paid for it with some touch of uncertainty, some tiny fear of being bored or out of place. Moreover, behind those bland and humble telephone calls, there was an unpleasant assumption about your character. Plainly Pflaumen must believe that you went out at night not because you liked your friends and wanted to be with them, but because you were anxious to meet new people, celebrities, to enlarge your own rather tacky social circle. No doubt this was at least half true, since with your real friends you seemed to prefer those whose spheres of interest were larger rather than smaller than your own—or at any rate to see more of them, if you could—but in those cases you were able to be sure that you *liked them for themselves.* With Pflaumen, unfortunately, there was never any question of that. Yet every time you accepted one of his invitations you entered into a conspiracy with him to hide the fact that he was a foolish, dull man whom nobody had much use for. And though some of his friends—the rich ones, perhaps—could feel all right about sitting at his table (after all, *they* were doing *him* a favor), you poor ones knew that he had bought your complaisance with his wines and rich food and prominent acquaintances, and you half-hated him before your finger touched his doorbell.

Standing there in the apartment-house corridor, you listened for voices that would mean that other guests had arrived and you would not be alone with him and the unmentionable secret. If you heard nothing, you hesitated, considered hurrying back downstairs and walking round the block till someone else should get there; but perhaps *he* had heard the elevator stop, heard your heels click on the stone floor, and was even now on the other side of the door silently waiting to admit you. You rang, and by the length of time it took him to answer, you knew that he had been in his bedroom after all. He came to the door in a maroon-colored smoking jacket, evening trousers, and black patent-leather shoes; he was newly shaved and scrubbed and powdered, and there was a general odor of Mennen's about him. His whole stocky, carefully exercised body was full of energy—well-directed arrows of delight and welcome shot at you out of his black eyes, and his mouth curved downward in a strenuous, sickle-shaped smile that gave his face an expression of cruelty.

How ill-suited he was, you thought, to his role of *élégant!* What a tireless struggle he must wage against his own physical nature! Looking at him, so black and broad and hairy, you saw that his well-kept person must appear to him like a settler's plot triumphantly defended against the invading wilderness. No wonder he took such pride in the fit of his coat, the shine of his nails, the whiteness of his sharp, jagged teeth. You saw the lines his body ought to have followed; he had the regular merchant's build; though he was not yet thirty-five, you looked for the crease in the waistcoat, but it was always just absent. Whenever you really noticed Pflaumen, you became aware of an additional person, a comfortable, cigar-smoking, sentimental family man, a kind of ancestral type on which the man-about-town had been superimposed, so that his finished personality came out as a sort of double exposure that was very disconcerting. If you were in a sympathetic mood, you might think what a pity it was he had not given in to his real self, had not married some nice girl and had some children, and reproduced in modern terms that atmosphere of bay rum, whisky, spilled ashes, poker chips, potted plants, kindness, and solid comfort that must have been his father's personal climate. How nice he could have been under those circumstances! But if you looked at him hard again, you realized that something else was being held in check, something that did not fit at all with this picture of easygoing German-Jewish family life—something primitive and hungry and excessively endowed with animal vitality. Though it was true that his figure had a mercantile cast to it, in other ways he did not look like a German Jew, but like a member of some early barbarous tribe, a Scythian on a Greek vase. In his habits he was soft and self-indulgent; yet you felt there was a furnace of energy burning in him, and you drew back from the blast. It was this energy that had made it possible for him to discipline his body and his manners into patterns so unnatural to him; and, ironically, it was at the same time this energy that undid him as a society man by making him overdemonstrative, overpolite, overgenial, like a comedian who produces an effect of fatigue in his audience by working too hard at putting his gags across.

He held out his arms to help you with your coat, and what might have been an ordinary service became a tableau of politeness. Your hands shook, missing the buttons, for you felt that the coat was getting too much of the limelight. It would have been kinder to whisk the shabby thing inconspicuously into a closet. If you did not yet know him well, you did not realize that he loved you for that patched fur. It signified that you were the *real thing*, the poet in a garret, and it also opened up for him charming vistas of What He Could Do For You. He led you into his bedroom, where a new novel by one of his friends and a fine edition or two lay open on a table. A lamp with a pale-amber shade (better for the eyes) was burning beside them, and the cushion in the easy chair by the table was slightly mussed. An impression of leisure and the enjoyment of fine things was readily engendered, though you knew that he could not have been back from his office for more than an hour, and that he must have bathed, shaved, dressed, and arranged the final details during that time. Yet he was not a hypocrite, so undoubtedly he had been reading. Five minutes with a book was as good as an hour to him, anyway, for he took literature like wine-tasting—you can get all the flavor in the first sip; further indulgence might only blunt your palate. The room was furnished in a half-monastic style; the bed was narrow, with a monk's-cloth cover. On the walls were pictures by Kunyoshi and Reginald Marsh, some George Grosz water colors and the reproduction of a detail from a mural by Rivera. You sat down behind his desk, a good piece, a little too heavy for the room, in black walnut; it had a great many fancy paperweights on it, and a large marble cigarette lighter, gifts, obviously, from clients in the patent law business. He got out the cocktail shaker, and said, "Let's try it before the others come."

He was disappointed, always, if you pronounced it perfect. He wanted to tinker with it a little, add a dash of Cointreau or curaçao at your suggestion. "You're absolutely right," he would agree at once. "I knew it needed something," and, picking up the shaker, he would hurry out to the bar he had installed in what had once been a linen closet. When he came back the drink would taste exactly the same to you, but Pflaumen's satisfaction in it would be somehow deepened. The process was familiar to you. You had gone through it with other people, at dress rehearsals, at fittings with a tailor or a dressmaker, in a painter's studio, till you had become expert at discovering and pointing out some trifling flaw that in no way invalidated the whole, a prop that was out of place, a coat that wrinkled imperceptibly across the shoulders, sleeves that were a quarter of an inch too short on a dress, a foreground that seemed a little crowded. Once you had made your criticism, everybody would be very happy. It was a form of exorcism—some minor or totally imaginary error is noted and corrected, symbolically, as it were, with the idea that all real and major imperfections have thereby been dealt with—as if by casting out some impudent small devil you had routed Beelzebub himself. Perhaps, also, there was a hope of dispersing responsibility; that cocktail was not Pflaumen's any longer, but yours and his together, as it would never have been if you had merely given it your approval. By arriving early, you had become his hostess, and, all at once, you were sure that Pflaumen had intended this to happen.

Yet this conviction did not disturb you. On the contrary, you felt slightly uplifted, like one of those "good" bums who voluntarily chops half a cord of wood for the lady of the house to square her for the meal she has just put in front of him. Pflaumen rarely gave you a chance to repay his benevolence, so that generally you were uncomfortable with him, dangerously overstored, explosive, a living battery of undischarged obligations. There were, for example, those letters of introduction, a great pile of them now, lying unopened, gathering dust on your desk. If only you had not drunk too much that one night when you had first known Pflaumen! If you had not let him see that you were frightened because you had no job and almost no money left! Above all, if you had not cried about it! The next morning he had sent you a sheaf of letters of introduction, and you had been touched and a little amused by the lack of judgment behind them. But you had presented them all. You had interviewed a brassiere manufacturer in Ozone Park, a crank lawyer downtown who wanted someone to ghostwrite a book on the sunspot theory of economics, an advertising executive who needed some soap slogans, a hotel man, a brilliantine manufacturer. When it was over you were relieved, for somehow you had never felt so out of step, so unwanted, so drably unemployed, as in these offices Pflaumen had sent you to.

But the next week there was a new batch of letters, some of them signed by people you had never heard of, friends of Pflaumen's whom he had got to recommend you for a job; and while you were delivering these, still more letters came in, taking you on errands that grew more and more bizarre. There was a loft in the garment district with *American Research* printed on the door and inside three large rooms that contained nothing but a filing cabinet and a little man with a cigar—you had never found out what his research consisted of. Then there was a bald man on the seventeenth floor of the St. Moritz hotel who wanted a girl to go round the world with him— he, too, was writing a book, on occultism.

After that, you had presented no more letters, but they kept coming in as relentlessly as bills, and there was Pflaumen's voice on the telephone, patient at first, then hurt and puzzled, but always mysteriously complacent. Had you gone to see the man in the Squibb Building? No? Really, it was impossible to understand you. He had been under the impression that you *wanted* a job. You made explanations at first, halting and shamefaced (after all, you supposed, he was trying to help you). Finally, you had quarreled with him; but your rudeness had only added to your debt, and your air of bravado and Bohemian defiance had quickened his admiration. (Such indifference to the question of survival was impractical, of course, but somehow, he knew, in awfully good taste.) You were for him, you discovered, the perfect object of charity, poor but not bedraggled, independent, stubborn, frivolous, thankless, and proud. He could pity you, deplore you, denounce you, display you, be kind to you, be hurt by you, forgive you. He could, in fact, run through his whole stock of feelings with you. A more grateful beneficiary would have given him no exercise for his masochistic emotions; a more willing one would have left his sadism unsatisfied. He was not going to let you go if he could help it. You stood to him in the relation of Man to God, embraced in an eternal neurotic mystery compounded out of His infinite goodness and your guilt.

When the others came, you all went into the living room, which was done in honey beige. There were pieces of sculpture by Archipenko and Harold Cash, and the head of a beautiful Egyptian queen, Nefertiti. Everybody praised the cocktail, and Pflaumen's old friends, of whom there were always a pair, complimented him on a new acquisition—a painting, a vase, a lamp—he had made. All Pflaumen's friends lived on terms of intimacy with his possessions; if someone did not notice a new object, it was as mortifying a slip as a husband's failure to notice his wife's new hat. Indeed, Pflaumen, opening the door of his apartment, often wore that look of owlish mystery that says, "What's new about me?" and the guests, being warned by it, examined the premises sharply till they found the single ornament that was responsible for the host's elation. This acquisitiveness of Pflaumen's was, you thought, just another way of making it easy for his friends to appear to like him. He was giving them something they could honestly admire, and if the objects could be viewed as extensions of Pflaumen's personality, why, then, it followed that his friends admired Pflaumen. It was on such questionable but never questioned syllogisms that his social life was built.

By the time the maid announced dinner and the party moved down to a refectory table set in the foyer, Pflaumen's eyes were damp with happiness. Everything was going well. Voices had risen in lively controversy over the new play, the new strike, the new Moscow trials, the new abstract show at the Modern Museum. Nobody was incoherent; nobody made speeches; nobody lost his temper. Sentences were short, and points in the argument clicked like bright billiard balls. Everyone felt witty. Pflaumen made a great bustle of seating the guests, and finally plumped himself down at the head of the table and beamed at them all as if to say, "Isn't this cozy?" The steak came in, with an orange and sherry sauce, and everyone exclaimed over it. Pflaumen himself kept casting joyous sheep's eyes up at his maid, commending her for the success of "their" dish. (He had put into circulation a dozen anecdotes designed to prove that this Scotchwoman who worked for him, like the maids of all really smart people, was a Character, full of sweet crotchets, bon mots, and rough devotion. Nobody, however, had seen the slightest sign of this, and tonight, as usual, she paid no attention to her employer, but continued to make her rounds with a stony face.) Peas were served, new ones cooked in the French style in their pods, and then the wine was brought in, a Château Latour Rothschild.

This was Pflaumen's apogee. Having tapped on his glass to get the table's attention, he read aloud the Château and the year, and then uncorked the bottle himself, standing up to do it. Somebody at the end of the table, a man with a hearty voice, called, "Look out, there, George Arliss may come out of that bottle!" Pflaumen, pouring a little into his own glass, laughed with the others, but he was not quite pleased—it was the sort of joke he was capable of making himself. "Give us a speech, about the wine," said one of the ladies obligingly. "The way they do at gourmet dinners." "Why," said Pflaumen, still standing at the head of the table with the bottle in his hand, "it's not one of the great Bordeaux—" "I prefer the word 'claret,'" someone else put in, "it's so full of English history." "You mean," retorted Pflaumen, "English history is so full of *it*." He waited for the laugh, which came reluctantly—it was said that Pflaumen had "a pretty wit," but there was something chilling about it; he had never learned how to throw a line away. "Anyway," he went on, with a little laugh, so that no one should think he took all this too seriously, "it's a nice brisk wine, on the astringent side. I thought it would do well with the steak." "Perfect!" exclaimed a lady, though the glasses were still empty. "Of course I think it's silly," continued Pflaumen, starting to go round the table with the bottle, "to be too pedantic about what you drink with what. I'll take a good Burgundy with a broiler and a Rhine wine with a kidney chop any time I can get it." Murmurs of approval greeted this unconventional statement, and Pflaumen passed on down the line, carefully decanting the wine into each glass.

Across the table from you someone refused, and all the rest raised their heads with an identical look of worry. It was the young Russian Jew, the instructor in law at Columbia, who wore a rather quizzical, sardonic expression on a pure Italianate face. His Marxist study of jurisprudence had created a stir. Still, perhaps Fleischer had made a mistake in him. Was it possible that he was not an eccentric but a crank? This act of abstention was a challenge to everyone at the table, an insult to the host. For almost a full minute nobody spoke, but muscles tightened with hostility. In different circumstances the young man might have been lynched.

"You don't *drink?*" said a woman at last in a loud, bewildered voice.

"I drank a cocktail," he admitted. "It went to my head. If I took any more I might make a fool of myself." He twisted his head and looked up at Pflaumen with a disarming boyish grin. "You'll have to give me a course in the art of drinking. That's one subject that was left out of my proletarian education." He pronounced the last words mildly, with a sort of droll self-mockery that deprecated, ever so faintly, his innocence, his poor Russian parents, his studiousness, the Talmudic simplicity of his life. There was a burst of relieved laughter, and after that everyone liked him. Thank God, was the general feeling, he had turned out not to be one of those Marxist prigs!

Once the wine was poured, Pflaumen took very little part in the conversation. He leaned back in his chair with the air of a satisfied impresario, embracing all his guests in a smile of the most intense and proprietary affection. Now and then, this look of commendation would rest particularly on you; whenever this happened, it was as if, in his delight, he had reached over and squeezed you. From time to time, his cup of bliss would appear to run over, and the smile would break into a short high giggle. When the spasm was over, he would take out his handkerchief and carefully wipe his eyes, and the old-fashioned masculinity of this gesture made a strange contrast with the schoolgirlish sound he had just produced. Sitting at his left hand, you looked down at your plate until this display was finished. There was something androgynous about Pflaumen, something not pansy, but psychically hermaphroditic that was always disconcerting you. It was as if the male and female strains in his personality had never blended, but were engaged in some perennial household spat that you were obliged to eavesdrop on. For, when you came to think of it, the Jewish paterfamilias was not the only figure that kept hovering behind your host's well-padded shoulder; there was also a young girl, newly married to a man already coarse and comfortable, a young girl playing house all by herself in a fine establishment full of wedding presents that both astonished and saddened her. Most Jewish men were more feminine than Gentile men of similar social background. You had noticed this and had supposed, vaguely, that it was the mark matriarchy had left on them, but looking at Pflaumen you saw the whole process dramatically. The matriarch had begun by being married off to a husband who was prosperous and settled and older than herself, and her sons she had created in her own image, forlorn little bridegrooms to a middle-aged bride.

In most of the men, the masculine influence had, in the end, overridden or absorbed the feminine, and you saw only vestigial traces of the mother. There might be a tendency to hypochondria, a readiness to take offense, personal vanity, love of comfort, love of being waited on and made much of; and, on the other hand, there would be unusual intuitive powers, sympathy, loyalty, tenderness, domestic graces and kindnesses unknown to the Gentile. But with Pflaumen it was not a question of the survival of a few traits. Two complete personalities had been perserved in him, as in a glacier. Half of him was a successful businessman and half of him was playing house. These dinners of his were like children's tea parties, and in this lay their strength and their weakness. They had the sort of perfection that can only be achieved in miniature. The groaning board was not in Pflaumen's style at all—one exquisite dish, one vegetable, a salad, and some cheese were what you got, rarely a soup, never a dessert. You thought of your little electric stove, your cambric tea or hot chocolate and your *petits fours* from the caterer. But more important than the perfection of the appointments was the illusion of a microcosm Pflaumen was able to create, the sense of a little world that was exactly the same as the big world, though it had none of the pain or care.

Each of Pflaumen's guests had been selected, as it were, for his allegorical possibilities, and every dinner was presented as a morality play in which art and science, wealth and poverty, business and literature, sex and scholarship, vice and virtue, Judaism and Christianity, Stalinism and Trotskyism, all the antipodes of life, were personified and yet abstract. Tonight there was John Peterson, who stood for criticism and also for official Communism. There was Jim

Berolzheimer, a bright young man in one of the great banking houses, who represented capitalism, and his wife who painted pictures and was going to have a baby, and was therefore both art and motherhood. There was Henry Slater, the publisher, very flirtatious, with a shock of prematurely white hair, who was sex, and his wife, an ash-blond woman with a straight bang, who kept a stable full of horses and had no opinions and was sport. There was a woman psychoanalyst who got herself up in a Medici gown and used a cigarette holder. There was a pretty English girl named Leslie who worked on *Time*. There was the young Jew, Martin Erdman, who did not drink. There was Pflaumen himself, who stood for trade-marks and good living, and you, who stood for literature and the Fourth International. After dinner there might be others—a biologist and his wife, a man who was high up in the Newspaper Guild, a matronly young woman who wore her hair in a coronet around her head and was active in the League of Women Shoppers, a Wall Street lawyer, a wine dealer, a statistician.

And here was the striking effect produced by Pflaumen's dinners—you truly felt yourself turning into an abstraction of your beliefs and your circumstances. Contradictions you had known in yourself melted away; challenged by its opposite, your personality hardened into something unequivocal and defiant—your banners were flying. All the guests felt this. If you asserted your Trotskyism, your poverty, your sexual freedom, the expectant mother radiated her pregnancy, the banker basked in his reactionary convictions, and John Peterson forgot about Montaigne and grew pale as an El Greco saint in his defense of Spanish democracy. Everybody, for the moment, knew exactly who he was. Pflaumen had given you all your identity cards, just as a mother will assign personalities to each of her brood of children—Jack is hard-working and steady, Billy is a flash-in-the-pan, never can finish anything he starts. Mary is dreamy, Helen is practical. While it lasted, the feeling was delightful; and at the dinner table everyone was heady with a peculiar, almost lawless excitement, like dancers at a costume ball.

It was only when you caught a glimpse of the author of your happiness, ensconced there, so considerate, so unobtrusive, at the head of his table, that your conviction wavered. To the others, too, he must have been a disturbing factor, for throughout the meal there was a tacit conspiracy to ignore the host, to push him out of the bright circle he had so painstakingly assembled. Once the dinner got under way, nobody accorded him more than a hasty glance. If he dropped a pun or a platitude into the conversation, it was just as if he had dropped a plate—there would be a moment of frozen silence, then the talk would go on as before.

Pflaumen did not appear to mind this; in fact, he seemed to accept it as natural. Here in this apartment, all the rules of ordinary politeness were suspended; and at first you were so caught up in your own gaiety that you hardly noticed this, and it seemed to you, too, perfectly natural that no one should speak to the host. But gradually, as in a dream, you became aware that the laws of the normal world were not operating here, that something was wrong, that nothing was what it seemed to be, that the church bell you were listening to was really the alarm clock. And, just as in a dream, the exhilaration continued for a little, but underneath it ran distrust and terror. You knew that it was not what it pretended to be, this microcosm of your host's, for if it were actually so fine and first-rate, Pflaumen himself would not be in it, even on sufferance. He was the clue in the detective story, the piece of thread, the thumb print, the bullet in the wainscoting, that stares up at the bright detective and tells him that the well-arranged scene before him is the work, not of Nature, but of Man. You had only to look at him to know that the morality play was just a puppet show, that the other guests did not represent the things they were supposed to, that they could be fitted into this simulacrum of the larger world precisely because they were small, unreal figures, and with growing anxiety you asked yourself, "Why am I in it, too?"

The conversation around you began to sound peculiarly flat. "Cultivate your own garden is what I told her," the publisher was saying. "She'll never understand politics." "She'd do better to cultivate her gardener—like Lady Chatterley," put in the English girl. Next to her, John Peterson went on talking through her joke. He was a little tight. "This back-stabbing that goes on here makes me want to vomit," he said. "I can't listen to it after what I've seen in Madrid. I've heard La Pasionara sing. What do these petty political squabbles mean to her? She's got a heart as big as the Spanish earth."

Suddenly you knew that you must cut yourself off from these people, must demonstrate conclusively that you did not belong here. You took a deep breath and leaned across the table toward John Peterson. "God damn you," you said in a very loud voice, such as you had once heard a priest use to denounce sinners from the pulpit, "God damn you, what about Andres Nin?" You felt your body begin to shake with stage fright and the blood rush up into your face and you heard the gasp go around the table, and you were gloriously happy because you had been rude and politically unfashionable, and really carried beyond yourself, an angel warrior with a flaming sword. Surely there could be no doubt that you had put yourself beyond the pale. But when you looked up you saw that Pflaumen was beaming at you again, his eyes wetter than ever, as proud as if you had just spoken your first word to an audience of aunts.

"Meg is a violent Trotskyist," he said tenderly. "She thinks the rest of us are all GPU agents." The publisher, who had been concentrating on the English girl, looked across the table at you, sizing you up for the first time. "My God," he said, "you're certainly spirited about it." Martin Erdman was watching you, too. He clapped his hands twice in pantomime and gave you a long, ironic smile. You bent your head and blushed, and, though you were excited, your heart sank. You knew that you were not a violent Trotskyist, and Erdman must know it, too. It was just that you were temperamentally attracted to unpopular causes—when you were young, it had been the South, the Dauphin, Bonnie Prince Charlie; later it was Debs and now Trotsky that you loved. You admired this romantic trait in yourself and you would confess humorously, "All I have to do is be *for* somebody and he loses." Now it came to you that perhaps this was just another way of showing off, of setting yourself apart from the run of people. Your eyes began to fill with tears of shame; you felt like Peter in the Garden, but yours was, you knew, the greater blasphemy —social pressure had made Peter deny the Master; it had made you affirm him—it was the difference between plain and fancy cowardice.

You held your eyes wide open to keep the tears from falling. The others, staring at you, must certainly think that your brimming eyes testified to the depth of your feeling for the murdered Nin. You tossed your head slightly and the tears began to settle.

"You *are*," you said, "a lot of you, GPU agents. The trouble is you're such idiots you don't even get paid for it."

It was a harsh joke, but it was a joke, and it was your peace offering. There was a cackle of laughter, and then everyone but John Peterson and Erdman was looking at you fondly, as if they were all much older than you were. Peterson cast you a malignant glance from his pale eyes, but he did not say anything. He was not too drunk to know that though the others actually agreed with him about Nin (or else did not care), temporarily, in some way, you had got them on your side. Erdman did not speak either; he nodded his head twice in the same tempo he had clapped his hands in, and kept smiling at you with that strange, mocking, affectionate expression.

You saw how profitable that exchange had been for you—it had earned you an enemy and, you thought, a lover. The first thing made you feel good, and the second saddened you. The next morning the phone would wake you and you would reach out and take it dreamily and it would be Erdman speaking very softly, asking you to have tea with him. You could see how it would all be. You would go to bed with him finally, but it would not last long, because you had both been compromised at this dinner party, and you had both understood this and understood each other. "Have you seen Pflaumen lately?" he would ask from time to time, and you would not be able to meet his eyes when you answered yes or no. He would not pursue the subject (you would never dare discuss Pflaumen together), but both of you would be silently asking the same question—what weakness, what flimsiness of character, what opportunism or cynicism had put the other into Pflaumen's hands?

On the other hand, you would treat each other gently, with a special tenderness, as though you were both wounded. For if, in one way, your love would be full of doubt, in another, it would be overfull of comprehension, lacking in mystery, like the grave, dreary love between brother and sister. You had recognized him in the scene about the wine; he had recognized you in the scene about Nin. You would have liked, both of you, to play a lone hand; but you had not been strong enough for it. In each case, your war of independence had been an inglorious *Putsch* (*"Excuse me, Officer, I was only fooling"*).

While the coffee and liqueurs were being served, new people came in, and the party broke up into smaller units. The publisher whispered in the English girl's ear; the banker talked Bermuda with the publisher's wife. John Peterson, glassy-eyed, exhorted the woman psychoanalyst—"But surely in his later years Freud played into Hitler's hands." You stood beside Martin Erdman, not talking, listening to the others, sharing an ironic smile between you. Pflaumen sat on a sofa beside the expectant mother; he was telling her about a new product he had just had trade-marked, while she went through a pantomime of congratulation. Only she could afford to be polite, for she had nothing to gain now from social intercourse, and, being easily fatigued, nothing much to give. She was comfortable with Pflaumen; he took her hand and she let him hold it; he was one of her oldest friends.

What had happened to you with Erdman was happening with others all over the room. Men were taking out address books or repeating phone numbers in low voices. There was a slight shuffle of impatience; nothing could be done here; it was time to go and yet it was much too early.

People got up and shifted around, like people in a railroad station when the stationmaster has come in to announce that the train will be forty minutes late. New combinations were formed. The publisher was sitting on the arm of your chair now, asking if you would like to write an opinion on a manuscript. You agreed, and for you, too, now the party was over. You had got everything you came for— a new lover and some work to do. Pflaumen came and sat at your feet on the floor. "You were wonderful," he said, looking up at you with that overenergetic expression of delight. You had an unaccountable impulse to kick him exactly where the paunch should have been. "The Berolzheimers are crazy about you," he went on, ignoring your angry look, putting it down to "temperament," an inestimable commodity. "They want me to bring you to dinner next Wednesday." You raised your eyebrows into circles of surprise; yet you had known, ever since that scene at the table, that the Berolzheimers would invite you. They were pleasant and they would have a nice house with good food, and there would be new people there; it would be interesting to see the world through a banker's eyes.

"Are you having fun?" asked Pflaumen, drawing his knees up and hugging them with his arms in a real ecstasy of coziness.

"Yes," you said. "It's a very gay party."

"Erdman is interesting—" he began tentatively.

You don't miss a trick, you thought, but you answered him impassively. "Is he?" you said. "I can't really tell. I haven't talked much to him."

Pflaumen looked hurt.

"Of course," he said, "it's none of my business—"

"I don't know what you mean," you said, in a stubborn childish voice.

The warm, twosey smile had died on his lips, but he revived it with an effort.

"Personally," he went on, "I should have thought Peterson was more in your line. I asked him specially because I thought he could do you some good—"

He paused. The unresolved sentence hung coaxingly in the air, begging your denial, your explanation, your attention. But cruelly you ignored it, and leaned back in your chair, as if to catch the words of the neighboring conversation. "Did you hear that?" you said finally. "They are picketing *The Tsar to Lenin*."

Pflaumen glanced up at you, refusing the diversion. "Oh, Meg," he murmured reproachfully, "I thought we were such friends."

"Don't be tiresome!" you exclaimed. "Why don't you get me another highball?" You put your glass in his hand with a decisive gesture.

"All right," he acceded, scrambling to his feet. You thought you had won. At a single sharp word that hungry ego had scuttled back into the shell of function, where friendship and hospitality were identical and every highball was a loving cup. But he had taken only a few steps toward the bar, when he stopped, as if he had forgotten something, and turned back to you with an anxious face. "You're not drinking too much, are you?" he asked, in a true stage whisper. Several people, including Erdman, turned their heads.

At last, you thought, the bill had come in. The dinners, the letters of introduction, the bottle of perfume, the gardenias, the new Soviet film, the play, the ballet, the iceskating at Rockefeller Plaza had all been invoiced, and a line drawn underneath, and the total computed. How recklessly you had accepted, like a young matron with a charge account ("Take two, madam; the bill will not go out till after the first of the year"). Now, when you looked at it, the total was staggering; it was more than you could pay.

You remembered suddenly all the warning signs. How deep Pflaumen always was in the confidence of his friends, how offended if two of them should meet in his absence! How careful people were to serve the whisky Pflaumen's client made—you recalled how a young husband had hurried out, unshaved, to the liquor store, so that the label on the bottle should be right when Pflaumen arrived for highballs; you remembered another husband pouring wine into a decanter so that Pflaumen should not know that it came from his client's competitor. And how fond Pflaumen was of talking about loyalty! "It's the only thing I expect of my friends," he would say, sententiously. Loyalty, you now perceived, meant that Pflaumen should never be left out of anything. He was like an x that you can never drop out of an equation no matter how many times you multiply it or add to it this side of infinity. All at once, you saw how he could be generous and humble and look predatory at the same time; the hawklike mouth was not deceptive, for he was a true bird of prey—he did not demand any of the trifles that serve as coin in the ordinary give-and-take of social intercourse; he wanted something bigger, he wanted part of your life.

For the first time, you understood why it was that this apartment of Pflaumen's affected you so unpleasantly, why you went there almost surreptitiously, not telling anyone, so that your closest friends were hardly aware that you knew Pflaumen. You saw that it was indeed a house of assignation, where business deals, friendships, love affairs were arranged, with Pflaumen, the promoter, taking his inevitable cut. When you had refused to tell Pflaumen about Erdman —though, so far, there was nothing really to tell—you had violated the code. You had tried to cheat him of his rightful share; you had been guilty of disolyalty. And he was going to crack down on you; he had, in fact, already begun.

When he came back from the bar with your glass in his hand, he was smiling, but the downcurved lips were strained and angry. You took the glass and set it down; Erdman in a cheap tweed coat was making his way toward you, ready to say good-bye. You smiled at him faintly, knowing that Pflaumen was watching you, and knowing, too, with a certain vindictive happiness, that of all the things about Erdman, Pflaumen was most envious of that baggy Kollege Kut coat with its raglan collar. You thought of your own poor coat, and you could see the two of them hanging side by side in Pflaumen's closet, like two pairs of shoes outside a hotel room in a naughty French movie, sentinels to a private, serious world that Pflaumen could never—even vicariously—invade.

The two men were shaking hands. "Come again," said Pflaumen, "and I'll get Farwell from the Yale Law School to meet you. And bring your wife," he added, in an emphatic voice. "You ought to meet her, Meg."

"Yes," you said thinly. "I didn't know Mr. Erdman was married."

"He tries to keep it dark," said Pflaumen, suddenly very jovial. He slapped Erdman on the back and began to propel him toward the door.

You went quietly into the bedroom and took your coat out of the closet. By the time Pflaumen returned from the elevator, you were ready to go.

"You're not leaving?" he said, looking alarmed. "If you wait till the others go, I'll drive you."

"Don't bother," you said. "I'm used to the subway."

"But what about the Berolzheimers?" he asked breathlessly, in a sort of panic. Clearly he had not intended that things should go quite so far. "Next Wednesday?"

You had forgotten about the Berolzheimers. Now you hesitated, weighing the invitation. Sooner or later you would break with him, you knew. But not yet, not while you were still so poor, so loverless, so lonely. "All right," you said, "you can pick me up at my place."

The time after the next, you promised yourself, you would surely refuse.

MARGARET CASE HARRIMAN   [1943]

Margaret Case Harriman was born in New York in her father's hotel, the Algonquin, and attended the Gardner School and Madame Morel de Fos's at Autel, near Paris. Soon after she returned from abroad, she began to work for Vanity Fair. *In recent years she has been a free-lance writer, publishing in such magazines as* The New Yorker *and* Harper's.

Mr. Miller and Mr. Hyde: Gilbert Miller

Gilbert Miller, the theatrical producer, is a man whom people love to explain. When Miller's friends run out of listeners, they can be happy just explaining him to one another in earnest little chats like one that took place on a certain evening between a fashionable young woman and a successful playwright in the lobby of the Henry Miller Theatre after the first act of *Harriet,* a Gilbert Miller production.

"Gilbert sometimes seems abrupt and even rude, but I feel that it's simply because he's terribly *shy,*" said the lady, uttering this familiar defense of bad manners in the illustrious as earnestly as though she had invented it.

"He has none of the defenses of artificiality," the playwright said. "He is Nature's child, fundamentally kind, generous, intensely loyal to his friends, inevitably misunderstood."

"Yes, isn't he!" the lady agreed enthusiastically. "I think of Gilbert as terribly naïve in a sort of *Irish* way—you know, *fey.* And, of course a complete artist in the theater, don't you think?"

"Absolutely," said the playwright. "His taste is exquisite and his attention to detail is staggering—"

"And he is definitely not a snob, as some people accuse him of being," the lady interrupted. "He loathes the social game, and I always feel he would be much happier staying home and playing his Viennese records. He's a *simple* person, really, just a simple, sensitive, charming person."

"Oh, come," said the playwright, seeming to tire of dialogue over which he had only partial control, "Gilbert's a son of a bitch, and we both know it."

The interesting thing about this conversation, to other students of Miller, is that all of it is true. He is a variable man, and his transitions from one mood to another are so swift and often so apparently causeless that, as one lacerated pal put it, "You can't depend on his friendship, but you can't depend on his enmity either." A Hollywood acquaintance, watching Miller in action, expressed an opinion that mystified several people for a while. "That Miller, he's a regelar Freddie March," he said, leaving his interpreter to explain that Miller's behavior suggested Frederic March's in the title roles of the picture *Dr. Jekyll and Mr. Hyde.* The comparison is irresistible to anyone who knows Miller. Normally (or as Dr. Jekyll), he is jovial, entertaining, chatty, and unruffled by any cracks about himself that he may hear popping around him. When Arthur Richman, who wrote *The Awful Truth,* one of Miller's successful productions, remarked to a friend, "You have to know Gilbert to dislike him," Miller heard about it and called up Richman to compliment him on a good line, laughing good-naturedly. His laugh is rich and throaty, a plump man's laugh, and his voice is high—two characteristics that contrast strangely with the swarthiness of his appearance and the glitter of his small, exceptionally bright eyes. He looks a little like one of the larger and later Roman emperors, and he moves purposefully but with a disillusioned air, like an overburdened sheep dog.

When he is overtaken by his personal Mr. Hyde, his wrath descends impartially upon the great and upon the humble who cannot answer back. In 1927, Miller brought Leslie Howard from England to play opposite Jeanne Eagels in *Her Cardboard Lover.* After the opening night at the Empire Theatre Howard was the town's pet, and John Donnelly, house manager of the Empire, hung a portrait of him in the theater lobby. A picture in the Empire lobby, along with those of Sarah Bernhardt, Maude Adams, John Drew, and other great players who have acted there in the fifty years since the theater was built, means almost as much to a young actor as a niche in Westminster Abbey might mean to a Bloomsbury scribbler. Donnelly's tribute to Howard was justified, but Miller, coming into the theater later that day, saw the picture and was annoyed because he hadn't been consulted about it. With a bull-like lunge, he climbed onto a cushioned seat under Howard's portrait, tore the picture from the wall, and threw it to the floor, smashing the glass and the frame. "Who did this?" he yelled, scrambling down from the seat. Donnelly, attracted by the noise, admitted that he had hung the picture. What Miller said to him is obscured by time and by the fact that people who have witnessed Miller's rages wince, close their eyes, and shake their heads when they are asked to repeat his actual words. Such words, they think, are better forgotten. When the storm was over, the Howard picture was repaired and rehung, with Miller's approval and even, as he was then able to point out, at his suggestion.

A refinement of the Miller temper came to light one Christmas not long ago when he was angry with a member of his office staff about something or other and gave him the task of counting out gifts of money for the office personnel and sealing each amount into an envelope bearing the recipient's name. The employee sorted and enclosed money for the whole office force before he discovered that there was no Christmas present for him at all. Miller's methods of getting rid of erring employees range from sudden dismissal to a kind and patient campaign warranted to make the hireling sick of his job. It was probably such tactics of Miller's that led Robert E. Sherwood, the playwright, who is a gentle and slow-speaking man, to make a famous remark one time when he was faced by the distasteful chore of firing the director of one of his own plays. "I haven't the temperament or the experience to handle a situation like this," Sherwood told the director forlornly, "and when it arises I do not ask what would Jesus do, or what would Abe Lincoln do, but I ask what would Gilbert Miller do—and then I cannot do it."

Miller's two most intimate friends are E. Ray Goetz, the retired producer, and Alexander Ince, the Hungarian publisher, for whom Miller backed the late *Stage* magazine. Both men deny that their chum's unpredictable temper is the reason he is not universally adored. Goetz says it is because Miller has a preoccupied air that makes people think he isn't listening when they try to talk to him. "Don't fool yourself," Goetz adds. "He can quote every word two years later." Ince, a slight, lively man, is more eloquent. "People in the theater are full of emotions they got to use," he says, "and they can't love anybody they can't feel sorry for once in a while. Take Charlie Dillingham. He was constantly broke, so everybody loved Charlie Dillingham. Take Max Gordon. He went broke, got sick, and was quivering in a hospital for months, so everybody loves Max Gordon. Al Woods—one million people will tell you about the time they dashed into Al's hotel room just in time to grab him as he was throwing himself out of the window. So everybody loves Al Woods. But Gilbert Miller? Listen. When Gilbert lost his money in the stock market in 1929 and 1930, he had four hits running in New York— *Journey's End, Berkeley Square, Dishonored Lady,* and *Candlelight* —and six shows doing from fair to terrific in London. When he had one of his worst years in the theater, in 1933, he made a fortune in foreign exchange, selling the dollar short all over Europe. Also, he was born to an advantageous position in the theater as the son of a famous actor, and he is married to Kitty Bache, the daughter of the late Jules Bache, the financier. Can anybody feel sorry for such a man? No. Therefore—" Ince smiles and spreads his hands—"very few people love Gilbert Miller."

The society of Europeans, relaxed and worldly, soothes and becomes Miller, who knows Europe better than he knows Shubert Alley. His familiarity with the French, German, Hungarian, and Viennese theater and his gift for languages distinguish him from theatrical producers like Al Woods, for instance, who is said to have moved fretfully from the Crillon to Claridge's, the first time he visited Paris, because he couldn't pronounce "Crillon." Miller speaks French, German, Italian, and Spanish well, and can get along in Hungarian. A great raconteur in congenial company, he likes to tell stories involving the use of two or three languages, and this has always made a hit with the cosmopolitan people he came to know in his travels before the war. When one of his preoccupied moments overtakes him, he can also interrupt, outshout, or brush off the same people in any one of five languages, and there are some admirers who find his ruthlessness refreshing. "You see," Miss Margaret Case of *Vogue* recently explained to an acquaintance who had received the full Miller treatment and was vibrating under it, "Gilbert is not quite a *civilized* person." Miss Case's tone was fond and implied that "civilized" was, in her opinion, just another word for "hackneyed."

Some of the friends who like to interpret Miller have reasoned it out that his unhackneyed behavior is a luxury he allows himself as a solace for a lonely and neglected childhood, but people who grew up with him say that he was never any more frustrated than any other celebrity's child. Miller's own account of his early days is voluble but hampered by his conversational style, which is lively but cluttered. Ask him where he was born, and you are likely to get three unrelated anecdotes, two in French and the other about Charles Dillingham's reply to the difficult actress who complained to him that she was playing to an empty theater. "Dillingham asked her why she didn't call up her first husband and get him to paper the house," Miller chuckles. "Her first husband was a paperhanger, you know, and she was trying to forget it."

For the record, Miller was born in New York sixty years ago this July, the second son of Henry Miller, the actor-manager, and the former Bijou Heron, who had been an actress until she married Miller and retired from the stage. Gilbert had an older brother, Henry, Junior, who was called Jack and who died years ago at the age of twenty-eight, and a younger sister, Agnes. Agnes married Tim McCoy, the movie cowboy hero, who later became a lieutenant colonel in the Army, and had two sons by him, D'Arcy and Gerald McCoy. When the McCoy marriage ended in divorce some years ago and Agnes remarried, Gilbert Miller persuaded her to let him send Gerald to Yale and to change his name legally to Miller. Gerald Miller is now in the Army and his brother, D'Arcy McCoy, is serving in a Canadian tank corps. Agnes Miller's second marriage was also unsuccessful, and, resuming her maiden name, she joined the WAC last year and became an officer candidate at the First WAC Training Center in Des Moines. The maternal grandmother of Gilbert, Agnes, and Jack Miller was Matilda Heron, one of the first actresses to play Camille in America, and the first translator of *La Dame aux Camélias* into English. Miss Heron's version, in which she coolly changed the name of Dumas's heroine from Marguerite Gautier to Camille, has become the standard English translation, and Gilbert Miller still enjoys meeting baffled Frenchmen who ask him what this Camille is doing in the place of Dumas's Marguerite. "My grandmother fixed that," he tells them.

Henry Miller was not wholeheartedly a family man and he seems to have regarded his children, especially Gilbert, with a quizzical detachment that occasionlly flowered into insult. Once, when the elder Miller was starring in *Cyrano de Bergerac*, an admirer called on him in his dressing room at the theater and noticed a wig block, the featureless dummy actors keep their wigs on when they are not in use. "What's that?" the visitor asked. "It's a bust of Gilbert," Miller replied at once. Bee Drew Devereaux, who is John Drew's daughter, and was a childhood friend of Gilbert, insists that Henry Miller was sacrificing truth for the sake of a laugh, for Gilbert, she says, was a handsome boy, closely resembling her cousin, John Barrymore. Miller admits his former beauty and calmly accepts the start of surprise with which strangers receive news of it. "Would you believe it?" he says amiably. The Henry Millers and the John Drews were friends, and Mrs. Miller and her three children spent several summers in the 1890's at Mrs. Raynor's boarding house in Westhampton, where the Drews also boarded with their daughter and their nephews and niece, Lionel, John, and Ethel Barrymore. Mrs. Miller and Mrs. Drew were Auntie Bijou and Aunt Dodo to all the children, but for Mr. Drew, who was always known as Uncle Jack to his family and close friends, Gilbert invented a special nickname; he called him Uncle Turveydrop, after the Dickens character who was "a model of deportment." Lionel Barrymore, who, it was generally conceded among the Westhampton group, would never amount to much, was known as Sloppy Joe. The Drews and the Barrymores called Gilbert Gillypod, and Ethel Barrymore, who has since starred in Gilbert Miller productions of *The Constant Wife* and other plays, could always brighten the darkest moment of a rehearsal by calling Miller Gillypod again. At the sound of that name, spoken in Miss Barrymore's thrilling voice, he would relax into a sigh and a reminiscent beam. Miller's chief recollection of Jack Barrymore during the Westhampton days is that he and Jack built a boat in which they sailed away forever, across Moriches Bay, leaving a note that said, "Pursuit is useless. Do not attempt it." They didn't come home until suppertime, as Miller recalls it.

When Gilbert was twelve his mother took him to Europe, where he spent the next seven years going to Catholic schools in Germany, France, and Spain. In Dresden he made himself unpopular with his teachers by rolling derisively in a classroom aisle, one time, when a German pupil rose and delivered in a Teutonic roar a poem beginning, *"Muttersprache wunderbar, ach! Wie klingt es schön und klar."* This guttural shout, describing the beauty of the mother tongue and how softly it falls on the ear, was too much for Miller. He still speaks German the way Beethoven might put a nickel in a juke box, tentatively and full of hate. He was happier at a French school in Passy, where a sympathetic *frère* announced, on Gilbert's arrival, that he was putting him at table in the refectory with "seven other little Americans" to ward off homesickness. Gilbert rapidly learned French and Spanish, both with a strong Argentine accent, from the seven other little Americans, all of whom turned out to be from Buenos Aires. He lost the accent later and his French is now Parisian. The Henry Millers separated while Gilbert was abroad, and when he returned to America, at the age of nineteen, he went to live in a bachelor flat on Murray Hill. He carried a cane, was addicted to overcoats with fur collars, and had such a natty, international air that his father took to referring to him as Count the House.

To the impartial biographer, Gilbert Miller's career, from the time he was nineteen until his thirty-second year, resembles the progress of a man walking under water. In 1904, he joined the Marines and served two years in Haiti. Back in civilian life in New York, he worked in a bank for a while and then underwent a brief spell of acting. His Continental aura had impressed Amelia Bingham, a popular actress of that day who was planning to produce and star in a play with a French name, *Olympe,* and Gilbert found himself playing a footman in the show. Later, in stock companies, road companies, and a production called *Julie Bon-Bon,* he quickly became known as one of the worst actors anybody connected with these enterprises had ever seen, and his performances were not improved by the occasional appearance of his father, who would turn up in a front row and just sit staring at him. "Your carriage has improved, and so has your diction," he told Gilbert after beholding him as the juvenile lead in *Zira,* a romantic comedy. "You have gained poise. There are unquestionably many parts you can play. What I have just witnessed is not one of them." When Gilbert was twenty-three, Henry Miller removed him from the stage, as a gardener might pick a bug off a rose, and put him to work as company manager of the Henry Miller outfit. Nine years later, in 1916, Gilbert made his first independent attempt to better his condition when his father, in collaboration with Al Woods, arranged for a London production, with an English cast, of *Daddy Long-Legs,* the sentimental comedy which the elder Miller and Ruth Chatterton had played in New York and on tour. Choosing a weekend when his father happened to be out of town, Gilbert went to Al Woods and got him to agree to send him to England as company manager for the show. When Miller *père* returned to town and heard about it, he rang up Woods violently. "Don't *do* this horrible thing!" he shouted. "Don't you know my son will ruin the whole production? Stop everything until I get there— I'm coming right down to your office in a taxi." In spite of the scenes that followed, Woods stood by his agreement with Gilbert, and soon the young company manager gratefully sailed for England.

He regards this assignment as the beginning of his career as a producer, but circumstances and the passing of time have slightly obscured his gratitude to Woods. In 1929, in New York, Gilbert Miller produced *Candlelight,* a play to which Woods owned the moving-picture rights. Soon afterwards Woods sold the picture rights to Metro-Goldwyn-Mayer for $20,000, agreeing to pay his partner half. Woods had by that time fallen upon a run of hard luck, and his long-simmering debtors attached the Hollywood money before he could pay Miller his share. Woods now admits his fault in not paying up promptly and agrees that Miller had a just complaint, but it was Gilbert's method of complaining, he says, that broke his heart. Miller sued him. Woods went into bankruptcy, and some theater people, including Woods, believe that he might have avoided financial ruin if Miller's lawsuit had not given him the final shove.

The London job with *Daddy Long-Legs* is a milestone to Miller chiefly because it brought about his first business contact with Charles Frohman, Inc. Frohman was an old friend and associate of Henry Miller, and Gilbert had once had a rocking horse named Charlie Frohman, after the producer, but the relationship never got out of the nursery until *Daddy Long-Legs* proved to be such a hit at the Duke of York's in London that Gilbert extended his lease on the theater, which was owned by the Frohman company. After the death of Charles Frohman on the *Lusitania,* in 1915, control of the company had passed to Alf Hayman, its cigar-chewing, tough-talking general manager, to whom Henry Miller once frostily referred to as "the imitation rough diamond." Shortly before his own death, six years later, Hayman sold the company to Adolph Zukor and Jesse Lasky of Famous Players-Lasky, a corporation which had absorbed Paramount, at that time a film-distribution and sales company. The Paramount-Famous Players-Lasky combination became Paramount Pictures in 1935. In 1920, Zukor and Lasky, traveling abroad, looked up Gilbert Miller, the lessee of one of the London theaters they had acquired along with Charles Frohman, Inc. Miller had by then managed for his father the English productions of such plays as *Nothing But the Truth, Monseur Beaucaire,* and *Too Many Cooks,* and he had developed business and social relations with Englishmen important in the theater, including Charles Hawtrey, Charles B. Cochran, and Henry Ainley. He had also served in the war, in Paris, as a first lieutenant in the Intelligence Division of the American Army. In 1921 he returned to the United States as general manager of Charles Frohman, Inc., a position he occupied until 1932, at a salary of $1,000 a week plus fifty percent of the Frohman profits. His contract allowed him to spend six months of each year in Europe, and he celebrated its signing by leaving almost immediately for Budapest, where he bought Ferenc Molnar's play *The Swan,* which Victor Jacobi, the Hungarian composer, had told him about in New York.

The Hollywood bosses objected to paying good money for *The Swan* until Zukor said, in one of those canny, elliptical statements peculiar to Hollywood, "Give Miller his head, and if he's wrong maybe we're paying him too much money anyway." Miller's production of *The Swan,* with Eva Le Gallienne, Basil Rathbone, and Philip Merivale, ran seven months in New York, and it was followed by other equally successful Hungarian, Viennese and French adaptations, which included *The Grand Duchess and the Waiter, The Play's the Thing, The Captive, The Late Christopher Bean,* and *Her Cardboard Lover.* Miller did well, too, with English plays—*The Constant Wife, Our Betters, Journey's End, Berkeley Square,* and, more recently, *Oscar Wilde* and *Victoria Regina.* Since 1921—eleven years with the Frohman company and twelve as an independent producer —Miller has presented over ninety plays in New York, of which only about twenty were written by Americans. He commissioned young American playwrights, notably Philip Barry, Sidney Howard, and Robert E. Sherwood, to adapt several of his early imported Continental successes, but he was cool toward their efforts to write original plays. A number of people who know the theater believe that it was partly Miller's discouraging attitude that inspired some of these writers and their colleagues to form the Playwrights Company, their own highly successful producing organization.

The formation of the Playwrights Company in 1938 almost exactly coincided, in fact, with a battle between Miller and the Dramatists' Guild which had been simmering for a couple of years. In 1936 Miller had refused to sign the Guild's basic agrement, which stipulated, among various things, that producers deal with British and other foreign playwrights according to the same (Guild) rules that protect American authors. This clause was designed to safeguard British playwrights, who sometimes dreamily sold their works to American managers for less money than native boys and girls demanded. Miller and the Guild officers bickered along for two years, and during this time Miller arranged for the New York production of two British plays, one by Frederick Lonsdale, the other by J. B. Priestley.

Neither Lonsdale nor Priestley found fault with his contract, but the
Guild objected and its president, Robert E. Sherwood, brought matters to a head in an interview published in the *Times* and in other
New York papers in September, 1938. Sherwood declared that Miller
should have pointed out to the British playwrights that the contracts
had been drawn up according to his own rules rather than the
Guild's, and added that he, and possibly quite a number of fellow
playwrights, would just as soon have no further dealings with such
a producer. After a few more parleys, Miller signed the basic agreement that month. The two plays which had hastened the crisis
turned out to be scarcely worth it all. *Once Is Enough,* by Lonsdale,
ran for three months, and the Priestley drama, *I Have Been Here
Before,* lasted two weeks.

The war has closed most European dramatic sources, and their loss
is a blow to Miller, who has always been better at putting on plays
he has seen acted on some other stage than at putting on those he is
obliged to read from scripts. He is a great reproducer, but theater
people say that as a director he finds it almost impossible to visualize
a play he has never seen. As he likes to direct, this has led to embar-
rassments. *Harriet,* which he directed during its early weeks of rehearsal, was the first play in a long time he had to put on cold, with
no performances in London, Budapest, or Vienna to remember.
Three weeks before the play opened in New York last year, Helen
Hayes, who played Harriet, was seen to sit down tensely in a corner
of the rehearsal stage and fold her lips. This amounts to antics for
Miss Hayes, who is revered by everybody in the theater as one of its
gentlest and most tactful actresses. Presently she pounded the arm
of her chair with her fist and said, "It's no use, Gilbert, we've got to
get a *director!*" She is said to be the only player living who can make
Gilbert Miller meek, and next day Miller called in Elia Kazan, the
young Group Theatre director who, the same season, successfully
staged *The Skin of Our Teeth.* Kazan gathered the cast around him
and started over from the beginning. Miss Hayes and Miller are
good friends and share many pleasing memories of the four-year run
(in New York and on tour) of *Victoria Regina.* Once, when a party
was given at the Waldorf-Astoria to celebrate some anniversary of
Victoria, Miss Hayes left at about two in the morning and charged
Miller to see that her husband, Charles MacArthur, got home all
right. By five o'clock, when MacArthur was ready to go home, it
seemed wise to convoy him there, and Miller nobly drove him all
the way to the Hayes-MacArthur residence in Nyack, returning to

fall groggily into his own bed in New York. Almost at once the telephone woke him, and Miss Hayes demanded to know where Charlie was. Miller said he had driven him home to Nyack. "To Nyack!" Miss Hayes wailed. "Good heavens, Gilbert, I *told* you we were staying at the Waldorf-Astoria!"

Miller has been married three times. His first wife was Jessie Glendinning, a young actress in his father's company. By that marriage, which ended in divorce, he has a daughter, Dorothy, and a grandson who live in Toronto. Miller's second wife, from whom he was also divorced, was Margaret Allen, whom he met during his first trip to England. In 1927, Kathryn Bache married him in spite of the worried protests of her father, who warned her, among other things, that the theatrical business was a flimsy and undependable source of income. Miller cozily remembers that after the stock market crash, two years later, his father-in-law said to him, apropos of some investments Miller had made through the Bache brokerage office, "*You* don't have to worry—you've got a good business!" Until Mr. Bache's death this year he and the Millers were an amiable trio, and they all lived together in Bache's house on Fifth Avenue, of which the Millers occupied the two top floors. The house also contained Bache's art collection, which he had presented to the State of New York with the understanding that the house was to become a museum after his death. This gesture was not without its practical side, since it enabled Bache to live in the house on museum terms, or tax-free. On certain days specified by the Bache office in Wall Street, the public was admitted to the first three floors to view the collection, and some thirty or forty students, painters, and possibly a few housewives curious to see the inside of a Fifth Avenue mansion would wander through the rooms in the wake of a guide or a teacher from an art school. Sometimes sensitive newcomers were brought to a sudden, astonished halt in a small study on the second floor, where they were faced by two life-sized, tinted, terra-cotta heads of Bache and Mrs. Miller, standing importantly between a Frans Hals portrait and a Rembrandt Christ.

The Millers now have a dwelling on Park Avenue, and except for their recent period of mourning, live a full life socially, entertaining, dining out, and going to the theater, where Miller, for whom all theater seats are too small, is often possessed by a creeping form of his Hyde alter ego and is saved from an outburst only by his talent for going to sleep quickly and sleeping throughout a performance. One night the Millers went to see *The Skin of Our Teeth*, which Gilbert, who had turned it down when Thornton Wilder offered it to him, so volubly disliked that Mrs. Miller wanted to leave after the first act. Her husband said no, their seats were in the first row and they would be missed, and he couldn't risk offending his old friends Tallulah Bankhead and Fredric March. As the curtain rose again he dozed off, unaware that the play was proceeding toward the scene in which Miss Bankhead lures Mr. March off the stage into the orchestra pit, which happened to be directly at Miller's feet. He woke up with a start, under the impression that the actors had suddenly chosen to continue the play sitting on his knees, and found March and Miss Bankhead icily regarding him from about a yard away. The Millers left quietly at the next intermission.

Generally Mrs. Miller is philosophical about her husband's drowsiness in the presence of entertainment. One evening, a guest in the Miller apartment pointed to the host, who was sleeping quietly beside a blaring radio. "Gilbert has perfected the knack of sleeping through dramas," his wife explained. "Now he's practicing to be able to sleep through musical comedies too."

Although Gilbert Miller is physically built along lethargic lines, his wildly fluctuating moods change as swiftly as the reflections of a man passing a series of Coney Island mirrors. Within the space of a half hour, Miller can be cushiony and smiling, black-browed and stubborn, and contorted into fury. Sometimes he manages to combine all three aspects in a single antic. Frederick McKay, a friend and associate, once happened to be in Miller's office in Rockefeller Center when a secretary brought in the wrong papers, or made some such mistake. Miller raged at her so mercilessly that McKay, embarrassed, turned to leave. Miller grabbed his wrist. "Don't go," he commanded, and at that moment the telephone rang. Still holding McKay's wrist and hastily telling the secretary to wait where she was, Miller picked up the receiver and carried on a cooing and sociable conversation with the Palm Beach acquaintance who had rung him up. Then he replaced the receiver and, without loosening his grip on McKay, resumed his tirade against the secretary where it had been interrupted.

Middle age, occasional ill-health, and seventeen years of quiet matrimony have mellowed his temper, so that now he almost visibly counts ten before he yells, but his awareness of this improvement sometimes irritates him to a frazzle. "Goddamit, I can't even get *mad* any more!" he shouted at his wife one day not long ago when things were annoying him. He has always had a disarming way of admitting that his disposition is far from angelic. Several years ago he asked a friend in Washington to sound out one Frank P. Morse, a Washington broker whom both men knew, as to whether Morse would like to come to New York to be Miller's general manager. The friend reported that Morse had declined, saying frankly that Gilbert's fits of temper were more than he would care to stand. "But doesn't he realize," Miller gravely inquired, "that I would be away in Europe six months of every year?"

Miller's lightning changes of character remind some people of Dr. Jekyll and Mr. Hyde, but European pals who have seen him glow with pleasure and burn with rage think of him indulgently as being more like the kind of waltzing mouse that circulates dreamily for a while and then suddenly, in another mood, dashes itself to pieces. Toward Europeans, whom he loves, Miller comes nearest to being consistently gentle. In 1938, when the news got around that Hitler intended to occupy Austria, Miller heard the tidings in Vienna. For all anyone knew then, the Germans planned to march on into Hungary as well, and Miller worriedly sent word to his friend and Hungarian representative, Alexander Ince, who was in Budapest, saying that Hitler was coming to Vienna and that Ince had better join Miller there immediately and fly to Paris. Ince wired back, "Sorry I cannot join you in Vienna. Wally Beery is coming to Budapest." This lightheartedness was typical of the times and of the world that Miller, as a producer active and well known on both sides of the Atlantic, had come to inhabit and enjoy. In 1938, his production of *Victoria Regina* was in its third season in New York, with Helen Hayes, and its tenth month in London, with Pamela Stanley. His newer play, *Oscar Wilde*, was a success on Broadway and he had two companies of *Tovarich* touring American cities. He was also planning a London production of that box-office boon, *The Women*, through an arrangement with Max Gordon, who had presented it in New York. "I don't produce plays in England, and Gilbert had the high hat on there" is the way Gordon, a picturesque talker, explains the deal. Miller's high hat had gleamed in most of the European capitals by 1938. *The Women* would be his seventy-third London production, and his success, in London and in New York, with English adaptations of plays by Middle-European playwrights such as Molnar, Lajos Biro, and Melchior Lengyel had made him equally prominent in Vienna, Budapest, and Prague. He had been having a fine time in Vienna until the *Führer* flounced in, and the rumble of war was less strong in his ears than the strains of the *Wienerwalzer*, which he likes to hum along with an orchestra, swaying his big body and keeping time with a plump hand. He left Vienna reluctantly, flying to Paris in one of his own planes. He generally traveled in a Stinson, sometimes flying it himself, occasionally taking along Frank Steinman, his pilot. Miller was a great one at trading in old planes for new, and at one time he owned five. Most of them were upholstered in red leather and had windows you could turn up and down, like the windows in a limousine.

The war burst upon Miller and his wife the following year in a way that was almost personally insulting, though accidental. Flying from Zurich to Paris, with Miller piloting, they were fired on by French antiaircraft guns as they crossed the French frontier. Mrs. Miller describes the incident coolly today, apparently unaware that the implied picture of the Millers' prewar social schedule is more staggering to the average listener than the fracas at the frontier. "We had flown from London to Geneva to see the Goya collection that had been evacuated from Spain," she relates. "Then we went on to Lausanne for dinner and ran into Grace Moore, and she gave us two tickets she couldn't use for the Toscanini concert in Lucerne the next night, so we flew to Lucerne in the morning. Somebody in Lucerne told us about a wonderful fair they were having in Zurich, so next day we went to the fair." She pauses reflectively here and murmurs, "It was really too beguiling." Then she continues, "That night we were dining at the British Embassy when a naval attaché, Captain Holland, told us we'd better get out of Zurich because the war situation looked bad, so we took off in the morning for Elsie Mendl's at Versailles. Of course we knew there was a rule that private planes mustn't fly over the militarized zone at the frontier, and we made the detour, according to Gilbert's map. But they had changed the detour in case of war, and it seems we were flying right smack across the military zone. A lot of guns roared at us and bullets began whizzing past the plane. Luckily we weren't hit, but I was never so glad to get anywhere in my life as I was when we arrived at Elsie's and found them all sitting around having champagne, and everything back to normal."

Miller learned to fly at the age of fifty, and says that he was inspired by the example of Leland Hayward, the Hollywood agent and amateur pilot, a younger and more erratic man. "If that nut could fly a plane, I figured I could too," is the way Miller puts it. The two men have a comon commercial interest in aviation. Hayward is chairman of the board of Southwest Airways, which operates, for the United States and British governments, four training fields near Phoenix, Arizona, and Miller is a large stockholder in the company. Flying instructors say that Miller is a good pilot, but some erstwhile passengers feel that he has a tendency to dream at the controls, and at least one claims to have seen him set the instruments and relax cozily, at six thousand feet, to read the manuscript of a new play. One time, flying alone through fog from London to visit Lord Brownlow, a friend who lived in the country, he got lost when his map blew out of a window and, coming down to ask directions, he landed in a hedge surrounding a cottage. The lady of the house came out and regarded him coldly, her hands on her hips. "Why don't you look where you're going?" she demanded. Miller arrived at Brownlow's six hours late, in such a temper that he made another bad landing, this time on his host's private field. According to E. Ray Goetz, who was present, the plane bounced in the air three times while Brownlow and Goetz looked on in horror, expecting it to turn over and burst into flames. It came to rest at last, upright, and Miller piled out, cursing, and strode savagely toward his host. "What's the idea of letting your field get in that condition?" he roared.

Miller has a curious indifference to maps, and once, undertaking to fly a friend from Paris to Nuremberg to lunch at a restaurant he had heard about, came down by mistake in Düsseldorf, a couple of hundred miles away, thinking it was Nuremberg. It was lunchtime, so they lunched cheerfully in Düsseldorf. Miller has turned over to the American and British governments the planes he owned at the outbreak of the war. A man who felt relieved by this news was a Hungarian friend whom Miller had taken for a flight over Manhattan some years ago, swooping around thrillingly to point out all the sights. When they came down, Miller, eager to keep his guest amused, suggested, "What do you say we go and have a Turkish bath?" The Hungarian wiped his brow. "No thanks, I've had mine," he said.

FRANCES PERKINS   *[1946]*

Frances Perkins, who was born in Boston in 1882, is perhaps best known for her activities as Secretary of Labor, a position which she held throughout Franklin D. Roosevelt's three terms of office. After receiving her B.A.

from Mount Holyoke College in 1902 and her M.A. from Columbia in 1910, she wrote her first book—on Hazards from Fire in New York Factories. Her latest book is the clear-eyed, admiring portrait of the President she knew so well, a chapter of which appears below.

He Liked People

Roosevelt's ways of associating himself with many and different kinds of people, which began to show themselves even before he was Governor, endeared him to the common people as they came to know him, and made the common people entirely comprehensible to him. There was a bond between Roosevelt and the ordinary men and women of this country—and beyond that, between him and the ordinary men and women of the world. He was profoundly loyal to them. Even when good reasons were presented for not carrying out a program that would be beneficial to them, he would examine, appreciate, and even understand the arguments against a project, but persist. Too much of an investment; too much government interference; too much control over people's affairs. He could see the logic but he would say, "Yes, but the people need it. They expect it," and he could not let them down.

His power to associate himself with others came to him rather gradually. One could see it develop from his start as Governor and later as President. His early life did not show much of this ability, but as he grew older, as he went through the horror of his illness and crippling, as he met many persons on many levels, he developed the capacity to associate himself with great numbers of people. He did not and could not know them all individually, but he thought of them individually. He thought of them in family groups. He thought of them sitting around on a suburban porch after supper of a summer evening. He thought of them gathered around a dinner table at a family meal. He never thought of them as "the masses."

When he talked on the radio, he saw them gathered in the little parlor, listening with their neighbors. He was conscious of their faces and hands, their clothes and homes.

His voice and his facial expression as he spoke were those of an intimate friend. After he became President, I often was at the White House when he broadcast, and I realized how unconscious he was of the twenty or thirty of us in that room and how clearly his mind was focused on the people listening at the other end. As he talked his head would nod and his hands would move in simple, natural, comfortable gestures. His face would smile and light up as though he were actually sitting on the front porch or in the parlor with them. People felt this, and it bound them to him in affection.

I have sat in those little parlors and on those porches myself during some of the speeches, and I have seen men and women gathered around the radio, even those who didn't like him or were opposed to him politically, listening with a pleasant, happy feeling of association and friendship. The exchange between them and him through the medium of the radio was very real. I have seen tears come to their eyes as he told them of some tragic episode, of the sufferings of the persecuted people in Europe, of the poverty during unemployment, of the sufferings of the homeless, of the sufferings of people whose sons had been killed in the war, and they were tears of sincerity and recognition and sympathy.

I have also seen them laugh. When he told how Fala, his little dog, had been kicked around, he spoke with naturalness and simplicity. He was so himself in his relation to the dog, based on the average man's experience of the place of a pet in the home, that the laughter of those gathered around radios of the country was a natural, sincere, and affectionate reaching out to this man.

The quality of his being one with the people, of having no artificial or natural barriers between him and them, made it possible for him to be a leader without ever being or thinking of being a dictator. I don't think he fully appreciated this aspect of his nature as a part of his leadership, but he intuitively used it. It was this quality that made the people trust him and do gladly what he explained was necessary for them to do. While some of his political enemies said that these were merely the signs and marks of a slick politician, the more one associated with him the more one knew that however political he might be, and he certainly did have great political skill, this quality was not a political device at all.

The truth is that he liked to broadcast to "my friends." He would rather talk to people than sit at his desk and be President. He wanted to talk to them about the things he thought they cared about. In particular, he wanted to talk everywhere about what could be done to make this a better, more beautiful, and more sustaining country. Among his deepest satisfactions was the evidence that when he did explain matters to the people, they understood and supported him and took the necessary action to solve a problem.

Details for improvement of the state and later of the country interested him enormously. He never ceased to want to look after the tree belt which had been planted experimentally at his suggestion in an effort to counteract the effect of drought, dust storms, and soil erosion in some parts of the country. He was always deeply interested in the development not only of the Tennessee Valley Authority but of a Missouri Valley Authority, and other river developments, believing that it would make the desert blossom and that more people could find happy, comfortable homes in those areas.

Although he had been around a good deal and seen a lot of life, including its seamy side, he remained essentially a trusting person. This was true when he became Governor, and remained true later. He never believed that anyone would willingly wrong or damage him. His tendency to think that everybody was all right exposed him to a considerable amount of intellectual danger. The only people who repelled him were pompous bores who bragged about themselves.

He would not have liked to be thought of as an unsophisticated person. He often told the story of certain comments of Madame Chiang Kai-shek, when the wife of the Chinese leader was visiting in Washington. He told it with such relish that one realized that it revealed a quality of his own nature he was not aware of. He once asked Madame Chiang about Wendell Willkie's visit to China. She replied courteously that China had enjoyed having him.

Roosevelt said, "What do you really think of Wendell Willkie?"

"Oh, he is very charming," Madame Chiang answered.

"Ah, yes, but what did you *really* think?"

"Well, Mr. President, he is an adolescent, after all."

Roosevelt pursued the subject and tempted fate by saying, "Well, Madame Chiang, so you think Wendell Willkie is an adolescent—what do you think I am?"

"Ah, Mr. President," said Madame Chiang, a very experienced woman, "you are sophisticated."

As Roosevelt told this story there was a gleam of pleasure and, shall I say, simple human vanity in his eyes. His obvious pleasure belied its point.

Most men who have been long in politics have only political friends with the exception of a handful of relatives and the boys they went to school with. But Roosevelt had a great many friends who had no relation whatever to his political life, and the politicians with whom he had real political friendship did not always join the circle in which he took his ease.

He was attracted to so many different people and varying minds that he could not have built all his friendships exclusively among his political adherents and associates. He had a liking for people who had no political contacts at all. He responded to them and to the ideas of their special fields.

This capacity for friendship with a great variety of people who shared no political responsibility or interest with him was partly the result of his complex nature. He was easy of access to many types of minds. Moreover, these various minds stimulated him, and the refreshment he gained from his nonpolitical friends was a considerable factor in his health and happiness.

A daily diet of politicians and government officers gets quite dreary. Mrs. Roosevelt, well aware of the extent to which he was imprisoned by high office, made a point of bringing in, in an informal way, a great many people from all walks of life. Politicians, scholars, writers, churchmen, as well as personal friends, would drop in.

Mrs. Roosevelt also invited many theater people, musicians, artists, scientists, and explorers. Thus the President's natural, varied interests were satisfied, and he was able to endure the relative confinement of his life with more ease and grace. At the same time he could share in intellectual and artistic developments.

I recall that I met Carl Sandburg in Indianapolis early in 1933 and heard him sing from his collection of American folk songs. When I told him how much I had enjoyed the songs, he said, "I think so much of President Roosevelt I would like to do something for him. I don't know what I can do, but perhaps I can bring my guitar and sing some of these songs for him. Do you think he would like it?"

I told Mrs. Roosevelt and she invited Sandburg. He came with his guitar. After a family dinner he played and sang. The President was delighted with the songs and the singer. It was an evening that left him refreshed.

Roosevelt had a great many friends among artists. There was something natural and simple about most of them which made it easy for him to make quick contact with them. When the Civil Works project for work relief was getting under way, the decision to include artists in it was Roosevelt's own. A number of good, successful artists were greatly disturbed by the poverty and total loss of income which came with the depression to very competent painters. Alfred Barr, Director of the Museum of Modern Art, conceived the idea that artists should have the relief that other people were getting. He promoted it at every hand, mentioning it to a young girl who was a member of the family of a cabinet officer. Having no particular judgment about public affairs but being ardent about painting, she persuaded her reluctant parent to take it up with the President.

The President's immediate reaction was, "Why not? They are human beings. They have to live. I guess the only thing they can do is paint and surely there must be some public place where paintings are wanted."

He said paintings would look better than the old photographs and calendars which hung in public offices. So work was given to a great many artists at the standard wage of fifteen dollars a week that everyone else got. Post offices, town halls, schools, and other public buildings were covered with murals paid for at that wage and a great number of "easel pictures" were turned out in every section of the country. This, of course, led to other projects in the fine arts—music, theater, and historical research.

Roosevelt responded to the idea, not because he had any particular knowledge of the arts but because the people that practiced them were human beings and, like others, must earn a living.

George Biddle, the painter, once said of him, "You know, it is strange. Roosevelt has almost no taste or judgment about painting, and I don't think he gets much enjoyment out of it; yet he has done more for painters in this country than anybody ever did—not only by feeding them when they were down and out but by establishing the idea that paintings are a good thing to have around and that artists are important."

Roosevelt, in fact, did not appreciate paintings. The only pictures he really cared about were pictures of ships, and he judged those by the correctness with which the rigging was arranged and painted and by the details of construction. The pictures he selected from the art project for his office, while not the worst in the collection, were certainly not good.

He was amiable about letting artists paint his portrait, and someone was always wanting to. Again he had little judgment about what constituted a good portrait. I protested once, when we were talking in the Oval Study, about a half-finished portrait of him and said I wished he would have a serious portrait painted by one of our best painters, to leave as his official portrait. "I am going to have Bay Emmett paint that," he replied gaily. "I like her things. They are always nice."

He looked reflectively at a portrait hanging over the door—a portrait by Lydia Emmett of Mrs. Roosevelt when she was very young. He said, "I always liked that portrait of Eleanor."

"Well, it is very sweet," I replied. So it was. It showed a young woman with light, shining, wavy hair, blue eyes, and a sweet smile; it looked like many other charming portraits by Lydia Emmett, who specialized in painting children.

"Yes," I repeated, "sweet."

The president looked at it again. "I always liked it. That's just the way Eleanor looks, you know—lovely hair, pretty eyes." He nodded with reminiscent pleasure, and I made a mental note, "That's hardly art criticism but it is a record of affection any woman would be glad to receive. A woman whose husband still thinks that a flattering portrait made in the freshness of youth is a perfect likeness of her in middle age has a certain satisfaction."

He paused, I remember, to tell me what beautiful hair Eleanor had, and since this was an enthusiasm I shared with him, we discussed it for a moment. I told him I had always admired the way she dressed her hair for the evening. How magnificent she looked with her light brown hair piled on top of her head! He agreed and added, "And she always looks magnificent in evening clothes, doesn't she?" It was true, she does.

These friendships with people in the arts were not only restful and refreshing to Roosevelt but turned out to have political significance. Though that was not the intention, these men and women added their influential voice to the thousands of Americans who believed in Roosevelt and supported him in his political and economic programs.

Jo Davidson, the sculptor, who did a fine, serious head of him in 1934, became a great friend. Being a man of broad interests, he conceived the idea that artists would like to be politically effective. In 1944 he and others organized a strong and lively campaign group— the Independent Voters' Committee of the Arts and Sciences for Roosevelt, now called the Independent Citizens' Committee of the Arts, Sciences, and Professions.

All kinds of people from all parts of the world came to visit at the White House, and Roosevelt rejoiced to have them staying in the President's house, the property of the people of the United States. Favorite guests were put in the Lincoln bedroom and they usually had great satisfaction out of that experience. Lillian Wald, distinguished founder of the Henry Street Settlement and the District

Nursing Association, told me that her visit in the last year in which she was able to carry on any active life at all was perhaps the greatest satisfaction she had ever known.

But whoever came was received comfortably and warmly, was made to feel welcome, and for the time that he was under the roof became a part of this large, inclusive family.

When Their Britannic Majesties were coming for their state visit, someone suggested to the President that it would be nice to assemble for the occasion some of the finest examples of early American furniture, rugs, and hangings from museums and private homes, and to furnish Their Majesties' rooms on the second floor of the White House with them. The person making the suggestion pointed out that when Their Majesties had visited Paris the year before, furniture had been brought in from the Louvre and Versailles, and two beautiful suites had been furnished for them with museum pieces which they had greatly admired. Wouldn't it be nice to give Their Majesties a taste of our life of days gone by?

"No," said the President immediately. "I don't think they would like living in a museum. I think it would bore them. You know, I think they will be tired when they get here. They would rather rest than sleep in a museum."

He preferred comfort rather than show and thought they would. He wanted their entertainment to be not only interesting but pleasurable, and he managed to make it so. Their Majesties stayed two days under his roof as house guests, occupying the best guest rooms on the second floor of the White House just as any other visitors do. There were two state dinners, a garden party, a reception by Congress, a formal visit to Mount Vernon. Here the President had managed to make it agreeable and comfortable by going down on the river and driving back by way of the CCC camp, which the President felt sure the King would be curious to see.

The President had asked the ladies of the Mount Vernon Association to make the occasion especially agreeable, and they had indeed. All the restraining ropes were down, with the guests going into Washington's room and sitting down on the chairs and sofas. I shall never forget the Queen sitting at the little spinet in Martha Washington's morning room and playing a tinkling little tune; nor shall I forget the picture of the King of England opening the bookcases in George Washington's library and browsing among his books. All these little things to make the visit human the President himself had suggested.

Although they went through state ceremonial performances, the guests enjoyed themselves. At a dinner given for them by the President, I sat beside their personal physician, who said, "I've been delighted with this visit. Their Majesties have relaxed and rested and there has been no nervous strain at all. Just wonderful. It's that President of yours, Mr. Roosevelt. He just makes them feel so at ease."

When Their Majesties went to Hyde Park to visit, even greater simplicity prevailed, because here they were truly house guests in a private house and there were no state occasions and formal dinners. There was only the pleasure of visiting a large, pleasant, informal family in the country and being included within it. Even the picnic which has been so publicized because of the "hot dogs" was successful. Hot dogs are a nice food for al fresco meals, and it was charmingly, becomingly, and comfortably done, in exactly the way the Roosevelts had been giving picnics for friends and neighbors for years.

This capacity to entertain the great and the simple, the important and the unimportant, of the earth with the same comfortable hospitality made a contribution not only to international relations, but to the warm friendliness of American life. Franklin Roosevelt's way of life seemed so American to ninety-five percent of the Americans that they felt they too could have visited in his home and been as comfortable, and they were right.

The good will which the visit of Their Majesties created in this country was due to their own charm, good sense, and intelligence, as well as to the easy, affable way in which Roosevelt introduced them to American life and American people.

The Queen gave Roosevelt pleasure when she sent for Harry Hopkins's little daughter, Diana, who was staying in the White House at the time, as her mother had just died. The child, of course, wanted to see the Queen, and Her Majesty, learning of this, arranged to receive Diana in the upper hall when she was dressed for the state dinner in rose tulle with spangles, wearing the diamond tiara and jewels of state.

"It will mean more to the little girl," she said, "to see me dressed like this than in my traveling frock." It did, and the President told me the story later, adding, "She's a very nice woman—considerate and human."

Not all important visitors were so agreeable. Some were demanding and placed a burden on the staff of the White House and on their host and hostess. But Roosevelt never lost his poise or affability.

Winston Churchill, of course, became a real friend of Roosevelt's though originally Roosevelt was so uncertain about him that when Churchill was asked to form a government in 1940 the President asked several associates what kind of a man he really was. Their friendship grew out of mutual need and a common ability to appreciate the drama of history, as well as out of the burdens of those who must make the history.

He teased Churchill unmercifully, but that was a sign of his being "in the family." It was Roosevelt's habit to indulge in friendly teasing bouts, and he expected to get back as good as he gave.

It never pained him to stretch his family circle and include visitors, friends, cousins, in family festivals. His Christmas habits were traditional and large. He horrified all the safety-first people by insisting on wax tapers lighted on his Christmas tree even in the sacred White House, and he really liked to read Dickens aloud to a large group of family and friends on Christmas Eve.

His zest for people would have kept him from becoming a "stuffed shirt," if there ever had been any such danger. His naturally democratic good manners grew even better after use at the White House. The Roosevelts did all the formal entertaining that is ever done and a lot besides, just to give pleasure to people ordinarily overlooked. I remember once that after a wartime dinner for the cabinet he went and sat down in the Red Room with the wives, remarking, "I want to see all the girls. I haven't seen you in months and I see your husbands too much." It gave them great pleasure.

His manner of greeting people at formal receptions as they came down the receiving line was remarkably warm and gave each person the feeling that the President had just been waiting for him to come along. Those of us who stood in the next room used to notice that people came through the narrow doorway, after shaking the President's hand, smiling and happy. Roosevelt made them feel that way —from dyspeptic ambassadors and gold-braided admirals to timid old-maid government librarians. The only person I remember coming out of F.D.R.'s warming presence with an austere, indifferent, even sneering look on his face was Mr. Justice McReynolds. With few exceptions, even people who regarded themselves as Roosevelt haters felt agreeable toward him in his presence. They could not resist his contagious fondness for people—all kinds of people.

As he grappled with world affairs in the later years of his administration, Roosevelt's mind became preoccupied with the life and welfare of people everywhere. This was shown strikingly by his curiosity about the way of life of ordinary folk in all the countries he visited after the war began.

When he visited Brazil, although it was a state visit, with public officials as his principal point of contact, he noticed how men unloaded ships. He saw what kind of men the longshoremen were. He saw what the houses of poor people down by the waterfront were like. He had an impression that there was overcrowding in the tenements. The faces of the people in the poorer quarters of the city were fresh in his mind weeks later as he described the trip.

His secret trip to Casablanca to meet Churchill, De Gaulle, Giraud, and others was full of sufficient official and military necessity to occupy him, but he found time to note and tell me later about the poverty of the Arab people. He spoke of the frightful shortage of clothing. A man's half-worn shirt, he noted, cost enough to feed a family for days. Coffee and tea were so badly wanted that one clever piece of Allied propaganda was to drop small bags of coffee or tea from airplanes with U.S.A. or U.K. printed on the cloth. The evidences of untreated disease registered with him. He thought both Casablanca and Marrakech very beautiful and loved the sunshine and the climate. He thought it ought to be possible to make North Africa a great resort after the war; then the "people would have work to do and could earn a decent income."

His journey to Teheran was managed so that he had little opportunity to see the life of the Persian people, and his whole mind and feeling were concentrated on becoming acquainted with and understanding Marshal Stalin and the Russians. He was extremely curious about the Persians and was sorry that he got no opportunity to observe them.

He told me later that he didn't understand why he was not allowed to see the city. He went directly to the American Embassy upon arrival. He knew that the route from the airport to the Embassy had been over back streets, while crowds waited along the principal streets to see him. But that was merely a Secret Service security procedure which he understood. Almost immediately representations were made that it was unsafe for him to stay in the American Embassy, that some kind of plot was afoot. The Russians insisted that he come to their Embassy, which was inside a compound, where he could be guarded more adequately.

He told me he didn't believe there had been any plot and didn't think so at the time, but it was clear that Stalin wanted him to come to the Russian Embassy. Roosevelt was distressed, because to make it possible for him and his large company to move in, Stalin had to move to a small cottage on the Embassy grounds. Being in the Russian Embassy, he saw a lot of Russians, but he didn't see any Persians.

The Russians interested and intrigued him. He couldn't get the servants around the house to talk to him. They rendered efficient service, smiled broadly and charmingly, but said nothing. And although he was accustomed to a gay exchange of personal greetings and ideas with people in other countries, he liked them.

He had gone prepared to like Stalin and determined to make himself liked. He told me the story of his encounter with Stalin while I was trying to talk with him about a particular piece of legislation then in the Congress. He had the look in his eyes I often recognized as being way off somewhere. As I tried to talk about the legislation, he replied, "Um-um."

Then suddenly he turned, as he often did, breaking in with what was on his mind. "You know, the Russians are interesting people. For the first three days I made absolutely no progress. I couldn't get any personal connection with Stalin, although I had done everything he asked me to do. I had stayed at his embassy, gone to his dinners, been introduced to his ministers and generals. He was correct, stiff, solemn, not smiling, nothing human to get hold of. I felt pretty discouraged. If it was all going to be official paper work, there was no sense in my having made this long journey which the Russians had wanted. They couldn't come to America or any place in Europe for it. I had come there to accommodate Stalin. I felt pretty discouraged because I thought I was making no personal headway. What we were doing could have been done by the foreign ministers.

"I thought it over all night and made up my mind I had to do something desperate. I couldn't stay in Teheran forever. I had to cut through this icy surface so that later I could talk by telephone or letter in a personal way. I had scarcely seen Churchill alone during the conference. I had a feeling that the Russians did not feel right about seeing us conferring together in a language which we understood and they didn't.

"On my way to the conference room that morning we caught up with Winston and I had just a moment to say to him, 'Winston, I hope you won't be sore at me for what I am going to do.'

"Winston just shifted his cigar and grunted. I must say he behaved very decently afterward.

"I began almost as soon as we got into the conference room. I talked privately with Stalin. I didn't say anything that I hadn't said before, but it appeared quite chummy and confidential, enough so that the other Russians joined us to listen. Still no smile.

"Then I said, lifting my hand up to cover a whisper (which of course had to be interpreted), 'Winston is cranky this morning, he got up on the wrong side of the bed.'

"A vague smile passed over Stalin's eyes, and I decided I was on the right track. As soon as I sat down at the conference table, I began to tease Churchill about his Britishness, about John Bull, about his cigars, about his habits. It began to register with Stalin. Winston got red and scowled, and the more he did so, the more Stalin smiled. Finally Stalin broke out into a deep, hearty guffaw, and for the first time in three days I saw light. I kept it up until Stalin was laughing with me, and it was then that I called him 'Uncle Joe.' He would have thought me fresh the day before, but that day he laughed and came over and shook my hand.

"From that time on our relations were personal, and Stalin himself indulged in an occasional witticism. The ice was broken and we talked like men and brothers.

"You know," continued the President, "he was deeply touched by the presentation of the sword which Churchill brought him from the British people. It was a magnificent ceremonial sword on a crimson velvet cushion, and Churchill made one of his best brief speeches. Churchill himself was pretty well worked up with emotion as he expressed the admiration of the British people for the Russians' gallant battle and for Stalin's magnificent leadership.

"As Stalin rose to accept the sword he flushed with a kind of emotional quality which I knew was very real. He put out his hands and took the sword from the crimson cushion. There were tears in his eyes. I saw them myself. He bowed from the hips swiftly and kissed the sword, a ceremonial gesture of great style which I know was unrehearsed. It was really very magnificent, moving, and sincere.

"He is a very interesting man. They say he is a peasant from one of the least progressive parts of Russia, but let me tell you he had an elegance of manner that none of the rest of us had.

"Churchill brought along his daughter Sarah to act as a secretary and assistant. Naturally, she wasn't at the conferences, but one day we were being photographed for the press and Sarah came out on the porch where we were sitting to bring her father something. Marshal Stalin rose at once on the entrance of a lady and looked slightly embarrassed because he wasn't sure who she was.

"Churchill took her by the arm and said, 'Marshal Stalin, may I have the honor to present to you my daughter, Sarah?'

"Stalin bowed from the hips, took her hand and kissed it in the old-fashioned, elegant European manner. The rest of us said, 'Hello, Sarah,' or 'Howdy.' The contrast was marked, and we all somehow felt that the Marshal had the best of that moment."

The President went on reflectively, "I wish I understood the Russians better. Frances, you know the Russians, don't you?"

I replied, "No, I'm sorry to say I only know the ones who have been here at the Embassy and the Russian refugee taxicab drivers in Paris."

"I thought you knew them. I seem to remember you brought some of them to me."

I reminded him that I had brought Colonel Hugh Cooper to see him in 1933. I had met Cooper and had been fascinated by his experiences in building the Dnieprostroy Dam and by his estimate of the Russians, and had introduced him to the President knowing that he wanted to recommend that the U.S.A. recognize Russia officially.

"Well," said the President, "I wish someone would tell me about the Russians. I don't know a good Russian from a bad Russian. I can tell a good Frenchman from a bad Frenchman. I can tell a good Italian from a bad Italian. I know a good Greek when I see one. But I don't understand the Russians. I just don't know what makes them tick. I wish I could study them. Frances, see if you can find what makes them tick."

"Do you mean that seriously?" I replied.

"Yes, find out all you can and tell me from time to time. I like them and I want to understand them."

Unfortunately, I had no time to make a profound study of the Russians, but I read a few books. I read B.H. Sumners and William Henry Chamberlin and one or two others. I talked with a few people who had lived in Russia, and from time to time I made a little digest about what they said and what the books said.

I did not know the geography of the land until I read it in Sumners. Nor did I realize the relatively recent expansion of the whole Russian population into the grass steppe of the Ukraine and beyond to the East.

The President became interested in these little digests I made for him and often said, "You know, I want to go to Russia myself."

I think he encouraged people to go to Russia from that time on. He was fascinated with the stories they brought back. He was delighted with the description of going to the opera in Uzbek related by Donald Nelson, war production chief, who went on a mission overseas for the President. He asked questions based on his recently acquired knowledge of the tribes and races in Russia, about the differences in the people in the different parts of the country, and the way the more primitive groups had responded to the new economic system and the educational program of the revolutionary period.

It was the people and what made them develop that interested him. I think he would have gone on studying the Russians for many years. He had gained some insight into the devotion the men he met had for their economic, social, and political system of Communism.

I told him how one American who had lived in Russia a great deal had responded to my question, "What makes the Russians tick?" with these words, "The desire to do the Holy Will."

I had reproached my informant with confusing the prerevolutionary and deeply religious Russian with the modern Russian, but he had insisted that the same quality persisted.

When I told this to the President, he said, "You know, there may be something in that. It would explain their almost mystical devotion to this idea which they have developed of the Communist society. They all seem really to want to do what is good for their society instead of wanting to do for themselves. We take care of ourselves and think about the welfare of society afterward."

Perhaps the most striking illustration of his sense of responsibility, his vocation of service to the people, came out in one of the last conversations I had with him. He had just come back from Yalta. He had been flown rather low, at his request, over Saudi Arabia, a desert country. He could observe from the air the meager vegetation and the limited cultivation of the land. A cheerless, dreary place, it seemed, with little local food supply and no more possible because of the aridity.

He turned to one of the Army engineers traveling with him. "Why don't they raise something here? Is the soil absolutely infertile?"

"No," answered the engineer, "it is good soil and could be used if there were any water at all."

"Can't they irrigate?" asked the President.

"They can't irrigate because there isn't any water here to irrigate with," replied the engineer.

"But," said the President, "there must be some water here. The people must drink and the animals must be watered."

"Yes, there are wells here and there in an oasis, but water, as you know, is sold at a high price."

"How do they get the wells? Dig them?"

"That is the answer."

"How far below the surface is the water table?"

"About fifty feet."

"Is there real water there?"

"Yes, I think so. I think there is a lot of water fifty feet below the surface."

"Well, the solution seems to bring out some good Worthington pumps to pump up the water and irrigate the soil."

"That wouldn't do any good," said the engineer. "It is so hot here that the sun would evaporate the water before it had done the soil any good and would leave it caked and dry."

"But the nights are cool. Why not pump the water up and irrigate at night when it will have time to sink into the soil? They really ought to be able to raise food. There must be a way if there is water underneath the soil."

When he met King Ibn Saud of Arabia aboard ship on the way back, Roosevelt told him he thought American companies could be found who would help water the desert.

The King looked blank and uninterested. "I am an old man, agriculture is not for me," he said. "Perhaps my nephew will be interested when he comes to rule."

"But," said the President when he told me about it, "you know, there is something in that idea. The reason the Near East is so explosive is because the people are so poor. They haven't enough to eat. They haven't enough possible occupations. They need a food supply and they need to raise it themselves. That one thing, I think, would do more than anything else to reduce the explosive qualities of these areas. Look what the Jews have done in Palestine. They are inventing new ways of using the desert all the time."

He paused reflectively, then went on, "When I get through being President of the U.S. and this damn war is over, I think Eleanor and I will go to the Near East and see if we can manage to put over an operation like the Tennessee Valley system that will really make something of that country. I would love to do it."

"There is plenty for you to do here," I replied.

"Well, I can't be President forever, and I don't know any people who need someone to help them more than the people in the Near East."

VIOLET MCNEAL   [1947]

Violet McNeal admired the medicine men, and she knew what their job was like. Born on an Iowa farm in 1888, she was sixteen when she met Will, who smoothly deluded her into taking opium, "married" her, and later used her as his pitchman, a role which she performed with such effectiveness that she was envied by all competitors.

Medicine Men

During the course of the winter all the big medicine men who worked in the East, as well as those who worked in the hinterlands of California, would visit Los Angeles to refresh themselves with the climate and renew old acquaintances.

Among the visitors were Will Cooper, of Tanlac fame, who buttoned his coat with twenty-dollar gold pieces and his vest with tens; Phenomenal Kraus, known to thousands for his watch chain made of solid gold nuggets, in each of which a diamond was set; and Wonderful Walton, whose private nickname was the Iron Gall Kid.

Big Foot Bill Wallace was another of the rare ones. He always began his pitch with the words, "I'm Big Foot Bill from over the hill; I never worked and I never will." He then loaded down the natives with what he claimed were electric belts. They looked swell, being covered with purple satin. Their gimmick was an area of zinc, dosed with vinegar, which produced a temporary tingle when placed next to the skin. Wallace had to keep on the move because in some instances the suckers developed sores on their backs and began looking for their benefactor with a scatter-gun.

Professor Herzog was an old-timer who dispensed a hair tonic, offering as proof of its virtues the fact that his own hair had grown down to the level of his waist. This unusual growth was achieved, he explained, by application of the tonic after his original crop of hair had all but disappeared. He also sold Resurrection Oil, a medicinal substance allegedly capable of making old muscles young if applied with sufficient energy.

Henry Gale was famous across the country for his corn cure, a preparation known to the trade as "corn slum." Its chief ingredient was collodion, which had very little effect on corns. Gale had supplied himself with a couple of pseudo corns whittled from a horse's hoof. They were rather startling as to size but were triangular in shape and fitted the average yokel's conception of what a corn should look like. After making his pitch Gale would summon to his chair on the platform some yokel who had shown particular interest in his remarks. He would cut out the usually small corn of which the yokel complained, carefully palm it, and display one of the frightening items of equine origin. Considerably unsettled by the sight, his audience would then be prepared to listen to any reasonable solution to the corn problem. Surgery, Gale told the natives solemnly, was not necessary. They could avoid the horror of the knife by applying his preparation nightly for three nights. At the end of that time the corn either would be dissolved or could be lifted without difficulty from its socket. When he planned to be in a town more than a week Gale would add, "Repeat applications if necessary in stubborn cases."

Gale was quite a ladies' man. He was small in stature and about twenty-five years old when he reached his peak as a pitchman. Girls would cluster in droves at the edge of his crowd, waiting for him to end his pitch. The more there were, the better he liked it, and he made no distinction between those who were married and those who were not. The period during which he favored any one girl with his attention seldom lasted more than two weeks. Not long after visiting Los Angeles he made the mistake of attempting a semi-permanent arrangement. While pitching in the South he picked up a doctor's wife and took her with him to Florida. This attachment endured for several weeks, although it terminated eventually, as had the others, in a separation more desirable to him than to his partner. Several months later Gale made his second mistake when he returned to the same town from which he and the doctor's wife had fled. He had no more than begun his pitch when the doctor, apparently narrow-minded about the whole affair, stepped up and fairly blew him apart with a sawed-off shotgun.

In a class by himself was Ray Black, who ballyhooed with a skull, a Bible and a rope. First he set up a folding table which held his satchel of medicine, called a "med case" or "med keister." Then he spread out the skull, Bible, and rope on the ground nearby. It was impossible for the curious natives to resist this assortment of articles. Black paid no attention to the yokels as they began to gather. He kept his back to them. Frowning, and pausing at intervals to study different effects, he would arrange and rearrange the items, as absorbed as if he were alone in the world. When a sidelong glance assured him he had enough of a crowd to start, he would wheel around and go into his pitch.

Black's pitch was the lengthiest known to the medicine business. Sometimes he lectured for as long as five hours without a break, escorting his hearers on a tour of the world which neglected none of the major points of interest. I asked him once why he pitched for five hours instead of breaking it up into three or four pitches of one hour each.

"Vi," he said, "if they stay with me to the end, they're sure to buy. When I get through with them their heels are round. After standing for five hours their backs are aching and they're certain they have lumbago or kidney trouble."

Black's pitch bore down heavily on kidney trouble. He was traveling one time in Australia, he told his listeners, when he observed some beautiful birds which were strange to him, although they somewhat resembled parrots. These birds were drinking water from various springs in a remote section of the country. He became so interested in the lovely fowl that he made inquiries of the natives. The birds, he learned, were known to have a life span of at least five hundred years. Nor were the curious powers of the springs associated solely with longevity. The natives collected the crystals from the edge of the springs, finding them a sure-fire medicine for kidney trouble. Black had, he asserted, gathered huge quantities of the crystals and brought them back to this country.

Black always closed his pitch with a shocker. "Kidney trouble," he would say, "sneaks up on you like a snake in the grass. Like a thief in the night. It spares neither rich nor poor. The Archbishop of Canterbury was descending the steps of that great English cathedral when he fell down like an ox smitten in the shambles, stone dead! They held an autopsy; there was nothing wrong with his stomach, heart, or lungs. But, gentlemen, when they turned him over and looked at his kidneys—" Ray would lower his voice impressively— "gentlemen, they looked just like a rotten tomato."

On with the sale! The price of the "precious little box of crystals" was one dollar. The crystals themselves were manufactured from Epsom salts, with a dash of flavoring to disguise the taste.

Black could neither read nor write. He had to draw his name when he signed a document. Nevertheless, he enjoyed posing as if he were reading. One day he was sitting in a hotel lobby and a yokel stepped over to him and said, "Mister, don't you know your paper is bottom side up?" Black lifted eyes filled with disgust. "What of it? Any damned fool can read a paper right side up. Reading it this way exercises my eyes and my brain."

Another pitchman category included the Gummy-Ga-Ho men. Standing on a box, they worked from a grip set on a tripod. They sold a glue for mending dishes and furniture. It actually did the work, although the margin of profit was greater than the yokels supposed.

Then there were the cheap razor-strop-dressing pitchmen. They sold a cheap razor strop and a small box of salve which contained a quantity of carborundum. For the purpose of demonstration they sharpened their razors at home until they could split a hair. They also worked from a tripod or a table. After rubbing some salve on the strop, they would give the razor a couple of light swipes. Part of their equipment was an old toupee. They plucked a hair from the toupee, held it up, and dramatically sliced off sections of it. The wonderful "kangaroo-hide" razor strop and dressing sold for one dollar, of which seventy-five cents was profit.

Another group of particular interest was the Look-Back pitchmen. One of them who visited Los Angeles used a rattlesnake for his ballyhoo, draping the reptile—the fangs of which had been removed —around his neck. The Look-Backs were cardboard boxes about one and a half by four inches in size, punctured with a couple of holes. Inside the box was a mirror. A Look-Back pitchman always began his pitch with the warning that the lecture was for men only. Anyone using the little box, he pointed out, would be able to see behind him. He called two or three men up from the audience, and of course the mirror enabled them to look to the rear. The pitchman called attention to the fun which could be had at parties, as the owner of a Look-Back could tell his friends what was happening while his back was turned. The Look-Back had other possibilities, he added. Adjustment of the mirror enlarged the field of vision in peculiar and unusual ways. Here the lecturer usually frowned and shook his head. Certain evil-minded men had discovered that a minor alteration in the mirror's position permitted them to look through keyholes and over transoms. He, the lecturer, would not be a party to any such use of the device. He absolutely refused to make the adjustment required for such an unworthy purpose, and he was sure no one in his audience would consider it. The Look-Backs sold like hot cakes for ten or fifteen cents. There was never a complaint from low-minded characters who failed to get the hang of tilting the mirror for keyhole-peeping purposes.

Hal the Healer was one of the best of the "painless" tooth extractors. His method was simple and infallible. He put his left arm around the chump's neck, with the edge of his hand just above the Adam's apple. He pulled the tooth with his right hand and choked off the chump's wind with his left. At Hal's signal his band would strike up a lively tune, and if the chump did get out a gurgle or two, no one heard him. After it was all over the chump was so pleased to be rid of his aching molar he never said a word.

The first medicine woman I ever heard of was Madame du Bois or, as she was sometimes known, Madame du Plat. She and her husband pulled teeth and sold medicine from a great chariot and had a brass band.

Not all of the old medicine men and performers were narcotic addicts, but most of them were heavy drinkers. One of them, a painless dentist, never could get through his lecture and the extracting without two or three drinks. So he had three colored bottles and glasses put on the platform, when he had gone as long as he could without a bracer, he would look up and pretend he had heard someone say something. "I heard you," he would say sternly. "You say it is harmful—this wonderful painkiller. No. It is as harmless as a mother's milk. I'll show you." He would proceed to pour out a slug of whisky and put it down the hatch, frowning, meanwhile, at the imaginary yokel whose doubts had given him this opportunity. He would pull this off with different variations two or three times during his lecture.

Successful pitchmen all had quick wits. One "doctor" I remember got up to sell hair restorer. He was as bald as an egg. As he was getting warmed up in his lecture someone in the audience shouted, "Why don't you use some of that stuff yourself?" He was too old a hand to let the audience get to laughing. "Young man," he replied, "I heard you. You asked why I didn't use some of this wonderful hair restorer myself. Would to God I had been able to! But I didn't know of it until I had lost every hair on my head." His voice grew sad. "It was too late. If I had heard someone like myself speaking before I became totally bald, my hair would have been saved. Let this be a lesson to you." The heckler was one of the first to buy.

Those were the days of the tapeworm. A medicine show would not have been a show without several large glass containers with enormous tapeworms gracefully arranged inside. We got our tapeworms at the stockyards, where for five dollars a butcher would rescue a generous assortment of all sizes. We whittled a wooden or cork stopper for our jars. Bent wires, around which the worms were draped, were suspended from the stopper. Worms and stoppers were eased gently into the one- or two-quart jars, leaving just enough room for the grain alcohol. I never saw a yokel who could resist stopping to look at a bunch of tapeworms, and of course nearly every member of the audience was sure he had a tapeworm by the time he had heard the lecture.

The medicine men sold a preparation which really would remove a worm if the patient happened to have one. When this rare but happy occurrence took place, both "doctor" and yokel were proud. An announcement to that effect would be made by the doctor from the platform the following night, with the proud native standing beside him to offer embarrassed but elated verification. If there was no worm, the "doctor" had an alibi. This was an exceptional case in which the medicine had dissolved the tapeworm entirely. This, however, was a rather hit-or-miss proposition, so some wise guy manufactured an artificial tapeworm out of some kind of composition. It was rolled tightly, placed in a large capsule, and swallowed by the patient as the first step in the treatment. Next came a dose of the famous worm remedy. Well, the gelatin capsule melted, the physic acted, and there was never a miss. The "doctor" had his money, the native had a glance at his tapeworm, and everybody was satisfied.

These medicine men were my idols. They made lots of money and spent lots of money. I think I never saw more wealth in one small place than I saw when Will and I went to visit Phenomenal Kraus. As casually as if they had been jelly beans, Kraus poured half a cup of unset diamonds on the table for us to look at. No one ever knew when a hasty departure might become advisable, and diamonds were quick collateral anywhere.

For some reason the wives of the medicine men didn't make much impression on me. They were lovely ladies, bejeweled and beautifully dressed, but they didn't do anything. They weren't spectacular.

ALINE B. SAARINEN [1958]

*A well-known art critic, wife of the late architect Eero Saarinen, Aline
B. Saarinen is an expert on art and art collectors. This excerpt from* The
Proud Possessors *describes the great connoisseur of Oriental art whose
collection is displayed in* The Freer Gallery *in Washington, D.C. Six
years after graduating from Vassar College in 1935, Mrs. Saarinen received an M.A. from the Institute of Fine Arts, New York University, and
went on from there to work on* Art News *and the* New York Times.

Charles Lang Freer

Fastidiousness was his persistent and inviolate characteristic. The
Vandyke beard which he wore in early life was meticulously
trimmed and the closely cropped, almost imperceptible mustache of
later years was impeccably groomed. His pince-nez had the most
delicate of rims. It pained him when a young niece was sloppy in
appearance and penmanship, failing to comb her hair and close
her "a's" and "o's." He could not suffer a chef who knew nothing of
"pastry-work," and indeed, although over the years he raised their
salaries from $60 to $100 a month, many of his chefs were returned
to New York from his Middle Western home having survived but
a single meal. His finicky scrutiny missed no detail, from the flat
silver and the ivory dishes with gold edges on his table to the size
of the monograms embroidered on his sheets and pillowcases by
the nuns of a nearby convent. The color of the single rose in a vase
by the bathtub of a lady house guest was as carefully considered as
the frequent order for the best imported caviar from New York.
Personal inconveniences irritated him. But although he was impatient with inefficient servants and irascible with stupid acquaintances, he framed his public complaints against such indignities as a
washroom on a train being as "cold as a refrigerator car" with
punctilious politeness. He was aghast at crude manners, disgusted
by rowdiness and offended at anything but the most chivalrous conduct toward women.

MARJORIE HOUSEPIAN [1958]

Marjorie Housepian was born in New York City in 1923, graduated from Barnard College in 1944, and published her best-selling novel A Houseful of Love while she was working in the president's office at her alma mater. She is currently teaching at Barnard, raising her three sons, and working on a new novel.

Levon Dai in Council Bluffs

When Levon Dai went to Council Bluffs to give a lecture to the Ladies Auxiliary of the First Presbyterian Church, the family received an urgent letter from him, pleading for some details about Armenian history. "These people seem to be under some misconception about us," Levon Dai had written. "Be good enough to send me a brief summary of our history so that I may enlighten them with facts. Please send it by return mail, as my lecture is Tuesday night." Uncle Boghos was indignant at the idea of Levon Dai, who had spent his childhood avoiding school whenever possible, enlightening anybody. "This will teach you the value of an education," Boghos said. "What luck that fellow has, though; imagine it. Why could someone not ask *me* to go out and give a lecture?"

It was true enough that Levon Dai had been fortunate. He arrived in Council Bluffs and found a delegation of ladies waiting to greet him at the railroad station, several of them carrying placards.

WELCOME MR. LEVON LEVONIAN
TO COUNCIL BLUFFS
Come and hear him Tuesday night, 8 P.M.
First Presbyterian Church
Come early for potluck supper
Also grab bag and door prize

No sooner had the lavender-haired lady, Mrs. Slater, introduced Levon Dai to the others than he discovered himself to be the center of a controversy that must have been raging for some time before his arrival. It seemed that several of the ladies, led by one Mrs. Portlemaine, who was a neighbor of Mrs. Slater's and in the manner of neighbors given to finding matters for controversy, decided that Mrs. Slater was running the Ladies Auxiliary too singlehandedly. Levon Dai could see that instead of thanking her for her willingness to manage their tedious affairs, they were in effect sabotaging her efforts for the sake of something which they called "the democratic process." Mrs. Slater could not open her mouth to make a suggestion without Mrs. Portlemaine's demanding that the matter be brought to a vote. It seemed to Levon Dai to be some sort of malicious game.

Now Levon Dai was tired when his train arrived in Council Bluffs. For all the long day that he had been sitting in the train rolling toward Iowa, he had been looking forward to nothing more than a bit of supper, a warm bath and a refreshing sleep in a soft bed such as Mrs. Slater had intimated in her letter would be provided for him. He was not in the least prepared to have Mrs. Portlemaine say, after the introductions were complete, "Well now, Mr. Levonian, I believe the ladies have decided to give you a tour of the city before it gets too dark. This is my car, right here, and Mrs. Slater will follow us in hers."

"Now, Sarah," Mrs. Slater said peevishly, "I thought it was all settled that Mr. Levonian should come home with me now in my car and rest up. He must be all tired out after his trip, and we can have the tour in the morning."

"It seemed to me, Eloise," said Mrs. Portlemaine, "that we discussed all this at the meeting this afternoon, and decided to take Mr. Levonian on a tour in *my* car this *evening*. However, if you are unconvinced, the democratic process dictates that we should put it to a vote. I move that we take Mr. Levonian in my car for a tour of the city before it gets dark. Second?"

"Second," said a small voice whose owner Levon Dai could not trace.

"Allinfavoursayaye," said Mrs. Portlemaine, jabbering so fast that Levon Dai could make very little of it, "Nays? Motioniscarried. All right, Eloise, Mr. Levonian will ride with me and you just follow along with Mrs. Price and the others."

"Just hold your horses a minute there, Sarah," said Mrs. Slater, arching her voice for a fight, if one was necessary. "The democratic process may dictate that we should bring this to a vote, but parliamentary procedure dictates that the chairman should conduct the voting. *I* am chairman, I believe, duly elected by democratic process?"

There was some slight commotion among the ladies. One or two of Mrs. Slater's friends tittered, causing Mrs. Portlemaine's faction to mumble among themselves before the latter conceded defeat, temporarily. "All right, Eloise, I was merely trying to save time, since it was all settled anyway," said Mrs. Portlemaine not too graciously. "I'm sure Mr. Levonian would rather see the city than stand here waiting for parliamentary procedure to take its course, but please do conduct the voting."

"Will someone make a motion that we take Mr. Levonian directly home so that he can rest for his long day tomorrow?" asked Mrs. Slater, looking squarely at her group of followers.

"I so move," said a tall, gray lady.

"Second," said another voice.

"I should like to discuss the motion," said Mrs. Portlemaine loudly, gathering her forces for a filibuster.

As parliamentary procedure took its slow, circuitous course, Levon Dai shifted from one foot to another and wondered whether it would be unseemly to sit down on his new suitcase. His new shoes were hurting him and he was confused, although he understood enough to realize that he ought to begin orienting himself to giving up the idea of a bath and a soft bed in the near future. He was also worried, as it began to dawn on him that he had made no preparation for his speech on Tuesday night, and he had no idea what it was that they expected of him. Presently, however, he perceived that through the good offices of a box-shaped lady who was carrying a placard, the discussion began to reach a compromise. This lady was an arbiter, and Levon Dai was pleased to note that the species existed, even in Iowa.

"In view of the stalemate," the square lady said, "I move that we take Mr. Levonian to *my* house for some supper. I'm sure we must all be starved." Levon Dai was indeed starved, and he was everlastingly grateful to the square lady, especially as her suggestion seemed to strike everyone except Mrs. Slater and Mrs. Portlemaine as a splendid one, and the motion was carried without further discussion and with only two "nays."

In the days that followed, Levon Dai spent a good deal of time waiting around for the ladies to decide what to do with him, for although he was staying at the home of Mrs. Slater, Mrs. Portlemaine was a close enough neighbor to challenge Mrs. Slater's monopoly of her guest. However, he was relieved to observe that whenever Mrs. Portlemaine insisted that an issue be voted upon, and the discussion became deadlocked, the square lady could be counted upon to inject a note of compromise. Levon Dai decided that the democratic process would be a gruesome thing indeed without someone like the square lady to pull it together now and again.

The day after his arrival, Levon Dai was taken on a tour of the city, and introduced to many prominent personages about the town, including the President of the Chamber of Commerce, the Chief of Police, and the owner of the local Pierce Arrow agency. He was taken to tea at the Presbyterian Church rectory, and as this was in September, before the elections for mayor, he was warmly and publicly greeted by the candidates of both major parties and by the incumbent, who presented him with the keys to the city. The Mayor made a little speech, telling Levon Dai how happy he was to welcome the first genuine Armenian to this cosmopolitan city, etc., etc., and how they were all looking forward to hearing about his exciting adventures, and since Levon Dai was extremely flustered at the unexpected fuss that was being made over him and had no speech prepared, he countered with the first thing that came into his head, which was Aesop's fable about the fox and the crow.

"I am overcome with the renowned honors you are bestowing upon me in the name of my people," Levon Dai said. "There are no words in English with which I can thank you. I can only tell you, as we say in our language . . ." And he launched upon Aesop's story in Armenian. This made a tremendous hit with the ladies, who had all gathered behind the Mayor during his presentation, and everyone shouted "Bravo!" and applauded very loudly. Mrs. Slater told Levon Dai later that it had been the greatest thrill for everyone to hear him speak to them in this strange and exciting tongue, and she hoped he would inject some of it into his talk on Tuesday evening.

When the evening came for his talk, Levon Dai was in an even greater state of agitation. The information he had asked for had not yet arrived from New York, and Levon Dai had been spending so much time being feted that he had not had an opportunity to write a proper speech. His English was quite halting, and it was not possible for him to speak at any great length without reading something already prepared. When it was nearly time to go to the church, Mrs. Slater told Levon Dai that the ladies would be greatly disappointed if he did not wear his turban and robes. It was very difficult for Levon Dai to try to explain to Mrs. Slater that Armenians did not wear turbans, for he had tried before, and she seldom appeared to understand anything Levon Dai said to her.

"I do hope you'll wear your turban, Mr. Levonian," said Mrs. Slater, "and your *sari*—is that what you call the long white garment your people wrap around themselves?" Levon Dai perceived that she would have him swathed in the manner of Mahatma Gandhi.

"My dear lady," he said, for the third time and somewhat exasperated, "I believe you are referring to a *charshaff*, which is quite different from a *sari*. The Indians wear *saris*, Turkish women wear *charshaffs*. Armenians, Mrs. Slater, wear *suits*, just as the Americans. I have no turban, nor have I a *charshaff*!" Mrs. Slater was already rummaging around in the bottom drawer of her linen cupboard and apparently had heard not a word of what Levon Dai said.

"You didn't bring it with you? What a shame," said Mrs. Slater. "But never mind. Here—how would this runner do for a turban, do you think it's long enough?" She produced a long narrow piece of linen cloth and insisted that Levon Dai should wrap it round his head. "Just try it," Mrs. Slater said when he began to object. "I know it's not exactly right, but the girls will be terribly disappointed if you don't *look* authentic. Now, if I can just find a sheet we could use as a—what did you say that word was?"

"*Charshaff*," said Levon Dai wearily, resigning himself to Mrs. Slater's dogged misunderstanding.

"*Charshaff*," repeated Mrs. Slater, at the same time triumphantly producing an old sheet. "I'm certainly learning fast! Here now— I'm sure you'll look as authentic as can be once you get these wrapped around you. But please do hurry, Mr. Levonian, it's almost six-thirty."

So at seven o'clock there was Levon Dai, wrapped most appropriately for a Turkish bath, and in a very poor frame of mind for speech-giving. The turban had not surrendered without a severe struggle, and he was perspiring from the effort it had taken to keep it from sliding up, since the back of his skull was rather flat. Half a dozen safety-pins were managing to hold it more or less in place, but he was afraid to move his head for fear of jogging the whole thing loose again. The sheet, at the same time, was a constant threat to his modesty, and because Levon Dai felt that his reputation was at the mercy of the safety-pins which were holding him together, he murmured a little prayer to the safety-pin manufacturer before embarking for the church and then, as he later said, "I put myself in his and God's hands and stopped worrying. What more could I do?"

There was little more Levon Dai *had* to do, as it turned out. From the moment that Mrs. Slater ushered him proudly into the hall a small cry went up among the ladies, indicating that his wrappings, at any rate, met with their approval. "How thrilling that you have worn your native costume, Mr. Levonian!" Mrs. Portlemaine had

come up to shake his hand, and when Levon Dai on an impulse
raised it to his lips, he could see that in just such small gestures lay
the success of his visit. Levon Dai had never been addicted to hand-
kissing, but he swears that on this occasion he kissed more than
forty-seven hands, not counting those he was certain sneaked in for
a second round. The necessity for keeping his head still also lent
a certain dignity to Levon Dai's bearing, which he tried to capitalize
on, although when standing up he had to keep one hand clutched
to his stomach in a somewhat modified Napoleonic gesture, to keep
the sheet from slipping around too much. During the pot-luck
supper the ladies kept up a steady barrage of questions, but Levon
Dai saw that like Mrs. Slater most of them did not listen for an
answer. As for the others, he found he could save himself a great
deal of trouble by pretending not to understand what they said, or
at most by saying, "That is a very interesting question, Madame,
but it is difficult for me to answer it in English. As we say in Armenian—" this last was usually obscene and could therefore not be
translated, but for Levon Dai it added a sort of zest to the evening,
and the ladies nodded understandingly and told him he was fascinating. Before very long Levon Dai found he was enjoying himself
immensely.

Presently the time came for him to speak, and Mrs. Slater delivered a long and elaborate introduction, after which everyone applauded and Levon Dai gathered his sheet close about him and stood
up, only to discover that she had merely been presenting someone
called the Chairman of the Programs Committee. This lady then
began what Levon Dai took to be a eulogy of herself, so he relaxed
and after a few moments was near to falling asleep when he heard
his name called, twice, and realized that she had in fact introduced
him to the audience, and so once again he gathered his robes, rather
hastily this time, and made for the rostrum.

Up to this time he had given no thought at all as to how he was to
begin, and when he found himself looking at fifty-odd upturned and
expectant faces, Levon Dai later confessed that he was momentarily
tempted to fling his accursed sheet and turban aside and flee the
hall in disgrace, but such was not basically his character, and so he
took a deep breath and spoke.

"My dear ladies and gentlemen," he said, "I wish to tell you a
story, and I shall tell it to you in Armenian, for that is the language
in which it was intended to be told. But first, I shall explain to you
what the story says. The story is of a man who had no homeland,

and he therefore wandered for many years over the face of the earth in search of one. Through the hot deserts of Arabia he roamed, and across the green hills of Cyprus; into the land of the Nile and thence over mountains into the heart of Europe, and finally through small villages on the coast of France. And in each place he found something of perfection. The deserts offered infinite space; the hills rendered him peace; while the Nile possessed an ancient and consuming culture. In the mountains his eyes were filled with scenes of overwhelming beauty, and in the villages by the sea he ate fish and fowl which were unexcelled in their taste. And still he was not satisfied, and still he searched.

"At last, after crossing a vast ocean and wandering through many strange and shapeless cities, he came upon one which was in no way distinguished, for it offered neither greatness in size, nor beauty of landscape. It boasted no store of antiquity, nor did it offer succulence to the palate, or unlimited space to the eye, or solitude to the mind. It was, in fact, a very ordinary city, and one in which a stranger would come to rest only quite by accident. And yet it was here that he found the very thing for which his soul had hungered: the kindness, the generosity, and the friendship of the people."

Here Levon Dai paused to wipe his forehead with the back of his hand. A trumpet-like noise broke the hush, and he saw that Mrs. Portlemaine was blowing her nose. Thus far, it was his words that had directed him, almost unconsciously, to the point he discovered himself to be making. Now that he could see his audience so deeply moved, he sensed within himself an unfamiliar emotion, which may have been partly relief, and in some measure a realization that his words were not totally untruthful. Mrs. Slater, he noticed, was not the only lady dabbing her eyes with her handkerchief, and he suddenly felt for them all a feeling of warmth and affection as he thought of how he must be affecting them at that moment. A tear or two stole into his own eyes, which he wiped away with a gesture so elaborately touching that his audience was moved all the more. "And now," he said, hurrying to capitalize on the moment, "now I shall tell you this story in my own language."

When spoken slowly, the Armenian language is hauntingly musical. Levon Dai spoke very slowly. In a kind of melodious epilogue his voice bled the already softened senses. An operatic tenor could not have surpassed the sob in his voice, nor could a violinist have more deftly used the crescendo and the sudden pianissimo as he brought his words to an end. There was a long moist silence before Levon

Dai could bask in the glow of the applause, which might have continued indefinitely had Mrs. Slater not interrupted to say, rather apologetically, that there was a little more to the program. The square lady was called on to deliver a short essay on the virtues of reforestation, followed by Mr. Portlemaine, who rendered one of his original poems with a musical accompaniment on the organ.

> Let nature thrill
> To rock and rill
> And silvery tassels fair
> Enslave the night
> With newborn light
> And breathe the good clean air.

Everyone had been given a mimeographed copy, and joined in on the chorus:

> Oh, I-O-WAA, oh, I-O-WAA,
> We-e sing to you to-day, ay, ay.
> The-ere may be more
> In the world in store
> But from you we'll never stray, ay, ay.

It was all anticlimactic, however, according to Levon Dai, and when the raffle and grab bag finally brought the program to an end and there was no longer any compulsion for the ladies to keep their seats, he was virtually mobbed by well-wishers who shook his hand until it threatened to disintegrate, and told him that Council Bluffs was his very own.

Now it should be mentioned that there were some husbands in the audience, as this fact is important to the story of why Levon Dai stayed in Iowa. Ladies may praise, flatter and even lionize, but if one is practical, in the end it is from a man that one most often receives the opportunity for success—businesswise. So, very fortunately for Levon Dai, among those who squeezed his hand that evening was one Abner Kingsley, a ruddy-faced, bald-headed gentleman most prosperously engaged in the the dry-cleaning business, owning a chain of shops throughout Pottawattamie County. His greeting, Levon Dai later said, habitually consisted of clearing his throat with a sound resembling that of a rather belligerent dog barking.

"Arf arf," said Mr. Kingsley, "Levonian, m'boy, you laid it right on the line. Right on the line. More power to you, m'boy, arf arf. Like your spirit. Like your gumption. Like your running all over t'hell 'n' gone 'n' wanting to settle right here. Nothing wrong with right here.

Best place in the world. Great opportunities. Could use a boy like you 't my place. Come around t'morrow. Keep up the fight. Arf."

As yet Levon Dai had no intention of remaining in Council Bluffs, but what harm would there be in going to see Mr. Kingsley? None, thought he.

"Learn the business inside out," said Mr. Kingsley the next day. "Start 't the bottom. I did. Work y' way up. I did. What's wrong with that, heh? Arf!"

Nothing wrong with that, thought Levon Dai. Already he had been booked for two more talks. The Methodists wanted him and the Rotary Club had put in a bid via Mr. Portlemaine that very morning. So for several months Levon Dai spent two or three evenings a week giving talks at churches and clubs all over the county, while by day he learned the dry-cleaning business inside and out. Inside, Levon Dai spotted, pressed and sorted. Outside, for several hours each day he walked up and down in his sheet and turban with a sandwich sign to back and front which read:

> *Abracadabra!*
> Klothes Kleaned like Magik
> AT KINGSLEY KLEANERS
> Try us and See
> You'll say "Allah be praised!"

With his salary in addition to honorariums here and there Levon Dai accumulated a tidy cashbox, especially since he had not yet any living expenses, for as long as he was a town celebrity Mrs. Slater and Mrs. Portlemaine continued to feud over him, and Mrs. Slater was loath to let him go as a guest for fear that Mrs. Portlemaine would grab him up herself. At Christmastime Levon Dai further ingratiated himself with the citizens by going from church to church expertly tying the turbans on the heads of little boy shepherds in the Christmas pageants—free of charge.

There is no need to go into detail about his meteoric rise to success. Within two years, Levon Dai was managing Mr. Kingsley's shops. And gradually, as he accumulated more capital, and as Mr. Kingsley grew closer to retirement, he bought out the shops, one by one, and eventually acquired and expanded the dry-cleaning plant itself, which did the work not only for Kingsley Kleaners but for all the cleaning establishments within a radius of fifty miles. Levon Dai became a Mason, and a leader in the Rotary Club, and now, although we heard that as a civic responsibility he still tied the turbans on the shepherd boys at Christmas, there was no thought of his wearing a costume himself, or giving lectures.

ELIZABETH HARDWICK   [1960]

Elizabeth Hardwick, who went to the University of Kentucky and did graduate work at Columbia University, has published two novels and edited the selected letters of William James. Her articles on a variety of subjects appear frequently in The New Yorker *and elsewhere.*

The Life and Death of Caryl Chessman

> They rode together in harmony, Abraham and Isaac, until they came to Mount Moriah. But Abraham prepared everything for the sacrifice, calmly and quietly; but when he turned and drew the knife, Isaac saw that his left hand was clenched in despair, that a tremor passed through his body—but Abraham drew the knife. Then they returned again home, and Sarah hastened to meet them, but Isaac had lost his faith. No word of this had even been spoken in the world, and Isaac never talked to anyone about what he had seen, and Abraham did not suspect that anyone had seen it.
> KIERKEGAARD, *Fear and Trembling*

The "abominable and voluptuous act known as *reading the paper*," Proust called it. In a bleary, addicted daze I followed the last years in the life of Caryl Chessman and, with increasing interest—or *consumption,* perhaps one should call the taking in of the flesh and blood of a person through the daily press—his last months. After the shock of his pointless execution, after his exit from the front pages, Chessman still did not entirely remove himself from public contemplation to make room for the young criminals who seemed to spring from the earth just as his bones were lowered into it. Even during the triumphal procession, soon after his death, of Tony and Margaret—the short, little couple, their hands raised as if in a benediction—the ghostly, beaky, droopy, heart-shaped face remained, creating one of those accidental juxtapositions whose significance is everything or nothing.

I wondered how Chessman had appeared in the newspapers during his arrest and trial as "the red light bandit." I went back to the files of the New York *Herald Tribune* and looked up the dates of his tragic history. January 23, 1948, when Chessman was arrested in a stolen car and identified as the man who made assaults on two women—there was nothing in the paper; May 18th, 1948, when he was convicted on seventeen of eighteen charges—nothing; June 25, 1948, when he was given two death sentences—no mention of the case; July 3, 1948, when, at the age of twenty-seven, he entered Death Row in San Quentin prison—blankness in the *Herald Tribune* on this matter. To the East at least, Chessman had been nonexistent as a criminal, as a case, as a doomed young man. He had to bring himself forth from the void of prison, from nothingness, from non-existence. This condition of his nothingness, his nonexistence, makes his remarkable articulation, his tireless creation of himself as a fact, his nearly miraculous resurrection or birth—which it was we do not know—a powerfully moving human drama. With extraordinary energy, Chessman made, on the very edge of extinction, one of those startling efforts of personal rehabilitation, salvation of the self. It was this energy that brought him out of darkness to the notice of the Pope, Albert Schweitzer, Mauriac, Dean Pike, Marlon Brando, Steve Allen, rioting students in Lisbon (Lisbon!)—and, perhaps by creating his life, Chessman had to lose it. The vigor of his creation aroused fear, bewilderment, suspicion. As he tells us in his accounts of his fellow convicts on Death Row, it is usually the lost, the cringing, the deteriorated who are finally reprieved. A man needs a measure of true life in order to be worth execution.

People on the street, talking about the case, found Chessman's energy, his articulation of his own tragic trap, his stubborn efforts on his own behalf, truly alarming. These efforts were not mitigating; indeed they were condemning. He had trained himself to sleep only a few hours a night so that he could write his books, study law, work on his case. But suppose another condemned man wanted his sleep, couldn't bother to work on his own destiny, hadn't the strength or the talent to bring himself from darkness to light—what then? Lest his very gifts save him, some people wanted him executed in order to show the insignificance of personal vigor before the impersonal law. And, true, his energy is very uncommon among habitual criminals. "Flabby, bald, lobotomized" Lepke; dreamy, paretic gangsters; depressed, deteriorated murderers; goofs putting bombs on planes. Chessman was a young hoodlum who was able, in the last decade of his life, to call upon strange reserves of strength. His early violence and his late effort at personal integration seem to have come from the same mysterious source. Life is haunted by one so peculiarly instructive, a history so full of fearful symbolism.

Cell 2455, Death Row, Chessman's autobiography, is a work of genuine and poignant interest. (Its faults as literature are those almost inevitably found in naturalistic first novels by young men who are writing from harsh experience: occasional sentimentality, strained efforts at rhetorical decoration, cultural pretentiousness. Its virtues are of the same genre—power, natural expressiveness, authenticity.) This is an oddly American book. The need to confess violent thoughts is softened by the cream of despairing sentiment, remembered hopes, perfect loves, and the incongruent beauties of the jungle. I had not thought of reading it until after the execution. It had not seemed likely that Chessman would have sufficient objectivity to tell us what we wanted to know about him; or that, if he had the intention to give a serious picture, he would have the words at hand. Almost unwillingly one discovers that he really had, as he said, a great deal to tell. The life of a chronic offender, existence reduced to chaos or ruled by tides of compulsion, reform school, jail, parole, jail once more, and death at the end of it—that history he is abundantly able to record.

The aim of this aching revelation was to save the author from the gas chamber and that it did not do. Its other aim—to picture the life of a young criminal—is accomplished with exceptional truth. Careening cars, gun fights, arrests, escapes, loyalties and betrayals, horror, confusion, defiance, manic decision, hopeless cruelties: there it is. But it is not a collage. In the center is a person, young, monstrously careless, living in hell, acting out these sordid images and twisted yearnings. Chessman is himself and also a national and international phenomenon of our period. Someone like him will be in the news tomorrow in New York, in Paris, in Moscow. His story has an uncanny application at a hundred points. You never doubt his existence or that of his companions, desperate boys named Tuffy or Skinny, and coarse girls, defiantly self-debasing. These are harsh portraits, very unlike the social worker's case history, the TV delinquents, who cannot avoid a false tidiness and handsomeness as they sweat to render an image not their own. The kindly, manly interviewer, the restless kid, the nagging, hysterical parents—the truth is so much worse than the "problem." We know convicts and condemned men are people, but we are always certain they are not the people in the movies. Their restless, self-devouring emptiness, so like our own, has an unbearably great importance because of their crimes against others and their torture to themselves. Chessman's books, particularly *Cell 2455*, and many passages from his other books about his case, could not possibly be negligible because of the information he was peculiarly able to impart. And beyond that, the fact that he, from whom nothing could have been expected, was able to write them at all is a circumstance of compelling interest. It seems to suggest that only through "art," through some difficult and utterly personal expression is reclamation and prevention possible. This is a world beyond the therapy of the basketball court, the recreation center, the social worker's hopeful sympathy. Its energy alone could only be used up in some violent dedication.

The Story: Chessman's family, his early years, are not what one would expect. He was an only child who loved his parents and was loved by them. Perhaps this love lends itself to interpretation because of his tendency to idealize his parents and his failure to make them real. About his mother: "Hallie was a dreamer, at heart a poetess with both feet firmly planted on the ground and her soft, searching blue eyes in the heavens." In any case, the affection on both sides was real and lasting. Chessman was spared the blight of neglect, abandonment, beatings, drunkenness; his severe delinquency does not easily yield its secret and the family situation is a clue to his strength rather than his weaknesses. His parents urged him to "do the right thing," to return to reform school when he had escaped and so on, but he does not record any pressure more coercive than their mere hopes and pleas. They were feeble, trusting people. They believed whatever excuse their son gave for staying out all night and were always surprised and dismayed to learn he had been "getting into trouble." Chessman's schemes, his plans, his hopes, all expressed in the vigorous distortions of his own personality, were of a degree of vitality and daring beyond anything the parents could call upon. They were frail, harmless branches blown about by a genuine tornado. To the tornado, they are the idealized calm, pitiful and innocent. He defends and destroys them at the same time. After he was grown, Chessman learned that his mother was a foundling. She did not know who she was. He set out to find her. With the money he got holding up brothels, he hired a dectective to trace his mother's origins. Nothing was discovered.

Early, he contracted bronchial asthma. He was nursed and protected by his parents, but in his own mind the asthma was a profound indication of weakness and shame. "The need to be strong became more demanding with each passing attack." A few years later, an attack of encephalitis left Chessman tone deaf. "The disease

ravaged [his] personality as well as his physical self." This was followed by tantrums at school, cruelty, and hatred of himself because
of aggressive feelings. His mother was injured in an automobile
accident and became permanently paralyzed. Disasters multiplied.
All the family resources were spent on the mother's illness. When
Chessman was fifteen, his father attempted suicide, "with a prayer
for forgiveness." The family went on the dole. With the humiliation
of food packages, Chessman began his criminal activity. He told his
credulous parents that he had a paper route and got up early in the
morning to rob stores of provisions left outside. The dole, the food
packages, the search for new doctors and new operations for the
mother are pretexts for crime; he does not pretend they were more
than that.

All pretexts are gradually discarded. Motivation is hidden and
justification is not even attempted beyond the hunger of vanity and
the compulsion of destructiveness. "He committed nine burglaries,
he purchased food with forged personal checks and got, in addition
to the food, a dollar or two back in cash." Because of his childhood
illnesses and physical weaknesses, Chessman convinced himself that
he wouldn't live long and that his thefts and forgeries would be
punished by God. His guilt was relieved and, waiting as he was upon
his final and eternal judgment, he could hope his parents would not
discover his misdeeds. Not long after, he went to a doctor for a simple stomach-ache and had his illusion of imminent death destroyed.
He was told he was sound and healthy. "These words had an almost
paralyzing effect. . . . They meant he wouldn't die!" His parents,
after all, would have the sorrow of his disgrace. "God had no right to
punish his parents for what he had done! Already they had been
made to suffer too much. Already they had made too many sacrifices
for him. He, alone, deserved punishment." (These are youthful sentiments, recalled later. Chessman died an atheist, rejecting religious
rites and burial and saying that for him to call upon God would be
hypocrisy. One of his lawyers thought this his worst trait of character.)

It is hard to avoid the thought that Chessman's conscious feelings
about his parents masked other feelings of great distress to himself.
Shortly after his discovery that he would have to live, he began to
risk everything. And the story of his life, at the point of its greatest
recklessness and violence, becomes more truthful. Self-knowledge
increases, as nostalgia, adolescent emotions, acceptable fears and
longings withdraw.

Cars: "That night he stole two cars and committed three burglaries." The young offender's dreams are alive with the embraces of warm, fat, forbidden cars. The car is freedom, power, exhilaration, madness. "Driving was a joyous form of creative expression. Driving made him free. Driving was his personal, triumphant accomplishment." Yet, the pleasure of driving is no greater than the joy in wrecking. ". . . he practiced driving or 'tooling' these hot heaps. He learned to corner, to broadside, to speed and snap-shift them. He purposely rolled and crashed them. He sent them hurtling through traffic at high speeds. He sought out patrol cars and motorcycle cops and taunted them into chasing him, just for the thrill of ditching them, just for the hell of it, and for practice." The car is escape—and capture. No sooner are Chessman and the other reform boys out of jail than they are in a stolen car, running through a stop light, alerting the police, who start after them and put them back in jail. The car is not stolen, altered, driven, to provide accommodation for the criminal on the run. It is wrecked just when it would be most useful. It is driven conspicuously, not stealthily.

Capture: Capture is courted with all the passionate energy that just a few weeks previously went into escape. "I stepped into a stolen car the Glendale police had staked out and was promptly arrested by two detectives with drawn guns." Or "I wanted peace and I unhesitatingly declared war to find it. I wanted to get even, to have one last defiant fling, and to go out in a blaze of ironically stolen glory." There is no meaning, no purpose, no gain. "Repeatedly we had had it impressed upon us that the road we followed led not to riches but to prison or the grave. Soon we reached the point where we were unable to justify the continuation of our collective effort without frankly admitting that our goal was merely to raise as much violent, dramatic, suicidal hell as possible. . . ."

He was put in reform school, released in April, 1937. He came home to his weak, lenient, kind parents. "The next day he was home and his homecoming was a happy one. . . . Not a word of censure did he hear. His parents' sole concern was for his future and how it could be made a success. And they were immensely pleased at how sturdy and healthy he appeared." Freedom is brief. The need to get back in conflict with the law begins almost at the prison gate, after the handshake with the paroling officer, after the lecture. Paroled in April, in May he had stolen a car and more armed robberies began. All of this culminated years later in his arrest and identification as the "red light bandit," an armed robber who flashed a red light into cars parked on "lovers' lanes," robbed the couple, and twice sexually assaulted the women. "After nine years of criminal violence and penal servitude following his release from reform school, he had come to the condemned row at San Quentin prison, twice condemned to death."

San Quentin at last. Prison is a part of the cycle; escape and capture, alternate back and forth, "naturally." Capture is rest from the manic push. The glum, exhausted face of the young outlaw is as revealing as his arrogant, excited mask during the chase. There is no sensible plan, no criminal organization; it is crime and punishment, escape and capture, parole and violation. San Quentin, the ultimate, the final, appears early in this grim dialogue. With Chessman, the exhilaration of violence gives way to extraordinary exertion in handling the fact of imprisonment.

Cruelty and threats have no meaning to men who live by cruelty and threats. They merely provide self-justification. The desire to be strong, not to bend under punishment, keeps criminal defiance alive. "I preferred to stand on my own feet, even if it was in hell." Independence, fearlessness, distorted into horrors, have a monstrous power over the convict. Chessman certainly died with "dignity," and that was the best he could do for himself, even if his kind of fearlessness is a tragic example of strength. Even his last words make much of the crippling "courage" he had lived by. "When you read this, they will have killed me. I will have exchanged oblivion for an unprecedented twelve year nightmare. And you will have witnessed the final, lethal, ritualistic act. It is my hope and my belief that you will be able to report that I died with dignity, without animal fear and without bravado. I owe that much to myself."

The woe of his crimes and the waste of his life lay upon Chessman's soul. He feels that society does not understand the young criminal. It is his mission to explain. "It is the story of a grinning, brooding, young criminal psychopath in definitely willing bondage to his psychopathy." The fate is personal, mysterious. "My father had failed to grasp the real reason for my many clashes with authority. He would never understand what drove me. He never would be fully aware of the jungle."

And what drove him? What was the jungle? "I ventured the thought that perhaps after one spends a while in a jungle world he gets so he cannot or does not want to believe there is anything better, or that it is attainable in any case. Maybe hate has a lot to do with it. Hate for everybody, for himself."

"But there are periods of self-doubt when you know yourself for what you really are—an angry, hating, fighting *failure*. Usually then you curse your doubts and blaspheme the imagery [*sic*] of the self you see."

His history is appalling. "Yes, I have been in reform schools, jails, and prisons most of my life. Yes, I had committed many, many crimes and had ample warning of what to expect if I kept on. Yes, I had kept on nevertheless. No, I was not guilty of the crimes for which I was sentenced to death. I was not the red light bandit. . . . Yes, I would say I was not the red light bandit even if I were."

The Thing is describable but inexplicable. "I was one of the trees in this dark and forbidding forest. I knew what it meant to live beyond the reach of other men or God. I had 'proved' everything I had felt the need to prove: that I couldn't be scared or broken or driven to my knees, that I didn't give a damn. But here is where the tragedy lies: this felt need is compulsive and negative only. It is a need to prove one can do without—without love, without faith, without belief, without warmth, without friends, without freedom. This negative need to prove becomes progressively greater and greater . . . the ultimate (conscious or unconscious) need is to prove that one can do without even life itself."

How is society to heal such a desperate sickness? Chessman puts himself in the position of a leper who is also a physician. He studies his own pains and deformations; he does not find the answer. Each offender is different from every other. The salvation of the meanest or the mildest is as complicated and difficult as the life of every non-criminal man. It is tedious, discouraging, even hopeless. Society is too dull, too rigid, too tired to make the effort. We do not even want to reform the criminal because of our anger that we have sometimes tried and failed. Every account of jails, of guards and matrons seems to show that reform is not believed in or encouraged. If a man might be saved by eight hours at the piano, the warden is sure to put him in the jute mill to teach him his lesson. The senseless determination of the prison officials to keep poor Chessman from writing is one of the most depressing and telling aspects of this sad case. One of the wardens at San Quentin, admitting that Chessman was not a difficult disciplinary problem, said, "So far as I'm concerned, our only problems with him have been literary."

The Case: There was a large element of the sacrificial in Chessman's execution. Even if he was absolutely guilty, the way of stating the charge and the decision to give the death penalty were severe beyond anything we are accustomed to. Further, the fact that the unusual severity of the sentence, in a case where murder was not involved or kidnaping either in any sense in which the world understands the term, could not be modified after exhaustive litigation suggests again the sacrificial and symbolic nature of the case. In Mark Davidson's study in *The Californian* he says, ". . . Chessman was not convicted of rape, because in both of the robbery-attack offenses for which he was condemned, the victims persuaded the bandit not to pursue coitus. The bandit instead had them perform *fellatio*. . . ." It has been widely suggested that Chessman's execution was society's punishment of its own perverse sexual wishes or deeds.

The mystery and force of Chessman's character were probably more outraging than the sordid crime itself. This older juvenile posed the question for which we have no answer. Why had he been a hoodlum at all? His cockiness, his loquaciousness, his cleverness, his energy, his talents only made his life more mysterious and more repulsive. His command of the word repelled the jurors. One of them twelve years later told a reporter that Chessman was just "as vicious as ever." When asked how she could know this, she replied, "After all, I seen his picture in the papers and he still has that same mean look, don't he?" He went on talking, defying, acting as his own lawyer, writing books, trying society's patience more and more. His life represents our defeat, our dread of the clear fact that we do not know how to deal with the senseless violence of the young. It is not too hard to understand organized crime, but how can you understand two young boys who kill an old couple in their candy store for a few dollars? In our rich society, the smallness of the sums for which people are killed shows a contempt for money as well as for human life. The nihilism at the bottom of Chessman's fate, his brains, what the newspapers called his "evil genius," made him a fearful and dreadful example. His cleverness undid him. His fight for his life was stubborn, cocky, pugnacious—and defiant.

In a sacrificial death, the circumstances that the mass fears and dreads and violently condemns may arouse involuntary feelings of wonder and grief in others. There was something almost noble in the steely, unyielding effort Chessman had made to define and save himself. He was a real person. He had breathed life into himself. One could only say that when he died this poor criminal was *at his best*. It was dismal to think his struggle counted for nothing. His ordeal was a tangle of paradoxes. He had spent twelve years in the death house because the law hesitated to deny him every possibility for reversal of the sentence. Those were horrible years, awaiting the answer. Would it have been better if he had been executed six months after his sentence? No, it would not have been better. And yet twelve years are twelve years, a unique suffering that cannot be denied. Somehow a justice complicated enough to delay twelve years to study the "technicalities" should have been complicated enough to refuse death simply because so many delays were legally possible. A part of the protest was a cry against rigidity and against the element of meanness in the law's refusal to place the case in a human context. And there was the *feeling* that Chessman might be innocent.

The Claims for Innocence: (1) The transcript of the trial was deeply impugned by the death of the court stenographer before he had transcribed more than a third of his private notes. The transcription and the enlargement were done, without Chessman's approval, by a relative of the prosecutor. (2) The description of the red light bandit, given before the arrest, did not entirely fit Chessman. (3) He was identified not in the line-up, but in handcuffs. (4) He had committed a wide variety of crimes, none of them involving attacks on women before this arrest. (5) He said he was innocent of the crimes for which he was sentenced to death.

After Chessman died in the death chamber, Governor Brown said he was sorry he had had no power to stay the execution and claimed he said this even though he was fully satisfied of Chessman's guilt. It was reported he then went for a lonely, sorrowing ride in the country. A detective who worked on Chessman's case and later married one of the victims attended the execution at San Quentin and said, when the death was at last accomplished, "I'm satisfied."

The end was reported with prodigal fullness. As I gluttonously read a dozen newspapers—a dozen newspapers all telling the same story of the gas pellets, the winks, the final lip-read good-byes, the last struggles of the body—I remembered a hanging that had taken place in my youth. On the morning a Negro was to be hanged in the courthouse yard, other Negroes stayed at home from their work for fear of the way the wind might blow. That same morning a relation of mine went downtown to shop in a department store. The Negro who would ordinarily have been operating the elevator was at home, quietly waiting for the dangerous day to pass. My relation fell down the elevator shaft and suffered ghastly damage to her body and mind.

MARION MAGID   [1963]

Marion Magid, who graduated from Barnard College in 1953, and is now living in New York City, writes frequently about the theater. Her articles have appeared in such magazines as Midstream *and* Commentary.

The Innocence of Tennessee Williams

A European whose knowledge of America was gained entirely from the collected works of Tennessee Williams might garner a composite image of the U.S.: it is a tropical country whose vegetation is largely man-eating; it has an excessive annual rainfall and frequent storms which coincide with its mating periods; it has not yet been converted to Christianity, but continues to observe the myth of the annual death and resurrection of the sun-god, for which purpose it keeps on hand a constant supply of young men to sacrifice. Its young men are for the most part beautiful and fawnlike; an occasional rough customer turns up, but in the end he, too, is revealed as beautiful and fawnlike. Its women are alternately in a state of heat or jitters; otherwise they are Mediterranean. The country does not observe the traditional Western sexual orientation which involves the pursuit of the female by the male; instead, its young men reluctantly allow themselves to be had on those occasions when there is no way of avoiding it and when the act is signaled and underscored by portents of Elizabethan proportions. They are right in general to be of two minds regarding the sexual embrace, for it is as often as not followed by the direst consequences: cannibalism, castration, burning alive, madness, surgery in various forms ranging from lobotomy to hysterectomy, depending on the nature of the offending organ.

Perhaps the European would not be very far wrong. A culture does not consistently pay the price of admission to witness a fable which does not ensnare some part of the truth about it. Perhaps that feverish tropical set by Jo Mielziner is the land of heart's desire for Americans, as Italy has been the land of heart's desire for Englishmen, huddled all winter long around their shilling meters and damp fireplaces. In any case, watching the ladies in flowered hats queuing up for a matinee of *Sweet Bird of Youth* inevitably raises questions: How much do they understand? How much do they suspect? What do all these goings-on mean to them? Do they flock to a new play by Tennessee Williams because it is sensational, because it is "poetic," because it is both at the same time and the one quality redeems the other? Finally, do they find anything of their own experience—of love, marriage, desire, loneliness—reflected in that peculiar mirror which Williams holds up to nature?

Probably they do. Tennessee Williams is not our best, but our only American playwright since O'Neill. His imagination, magnetized though it is by the outlandish and the outré, is a kind of fever chart of our national ailments. There is, for instance, an image which runs obsessively through Williams' plays—the beautiful young man at bay, the quarry ringed by his pursuers. The mind, the sensibilities, the stomach, all recoil from this image when it is served up with obvious relish in a darkened theater, snakily choreographed by Kazan or distended on wide screen in all the glory of M.G.M. technicolor. Yet that image is frighteningly akin to the one emblazoned not so long ago on all the front pages of the land: Meredith ringed by the Mississippi National Guard on the campus at Ole Miss; and in the background, blurred figures with clenched fists. Who knows what goes on behind those flat faces with steel-rimmed eyeglasses and slits for mouths? One has a sense that Williams dwells closer to that knowledge than other dramatists writing about us, for us, today. Though Williams has not, so far as I know, delivered himself of a single pronouncement on the question of integration, though his signature is never to be found on a petition or a full-page ad in the *New York Times,* he seems to have located the trouble spots more precisely than Arthur Miller, for instance, who deals so conscientiously with "social" questions. Williams is American in his passion for absolutes, in his longing for purity, in his absence of ideas, in the extreme discomfort with which he inhabits his own body and soul, in his apocalyptic vision of sex, which like all apoclyptic visions sacrifices mere accuracy for the sake of intensity. Intensity is the crucial quality of Williams' art, and he is perhaps most an American artist in his reliance upon and mastery of surface techniques for achieving this effect.

One result is that Williams' plays cannot be talked about except in their performance. Ever since 1947, when *A Streetcar Named Desire* was produced under the direction of Elia Kazan and starring Marlon Brando, Jessica Tandy, and Kim Hunter, with a stage setting by Jo Mielziner, the pattern for rendition of a Williams play has remained as fixed as a Kabuki dance. Other hands than Kazan's have since dimmed the lights, set the underbrush to quivering, and on occasion

gilded the lily, yet the results have always been, when successful—
that is, when "like a play by Tennessee Williams"—approximations
of that *ur*-Williams production.

There is first of all the matter of lighting. As Eric Bentley observed, Kazan sees the world, especially Williams' world, as phan-
tasmagoria. "Don't turn the lights on," Blanche gasps in *Streetcar*
and Kazan passed the word on to the electricians. Nor have they
been turned on since. Doing so would dispel the shadows, the
evanescence, the sense of undefined shapes and meanings lurking in
the foliage. In Hollywood, the word "air" is used to designate atmosphere, the intangible stuff of which dreams are made. Directors in
the throes of creation have been known to cry out for "more air"—
which means the opposite of what it seems to mean: not clarity nor
breathing space nor the light of day, but the baying of bloodhounds,
the waving of palm fronds, the lonely clarinet solo, the voices of off-
stage potion peddlers raised in song. The milieu of Williams' plays
lends itself especially well to this hot (Southern) "air" treatment.
One suspects that, after *Streetcar*, Williams worked with an image
in his mind's eye closer to the South of Broadway than to the actual
South.

The second element is timing. Kazan is the virtuoso of a certain
kind of tension on stage. His method might be called the technique
of unexpected syncopation. The regular to-and-fro buildup of a cli-
mactic scene, particularly of an encounter between two actors, is
slightly distorted. Pauses are a trifle longer than expected, or a trifle
shorter. Long speeches are broken up in eccentric ways, so that unexpected words ring out in the electric silence. No Williams play is
complete without the participation of at least one, preferably more,
actors who have been trained at the Actors' Studio or temples of the
same persuasion, where they have perfected their versions of this
curious syncopation.

This mode of diction has by now become a convention of contemporary American theater in the past two decades. Its components
are mainly twofold: since it was originally developed by the Group
Theater in its attempt to render "realistically" the rhythms of ur-
ban, and especially New York, life, it has more than a trace in it of
Yiddish inflection as well as Yiddish phrasing; at the same time it has
been updated by hipster gesture and talk. The diction can now be
heard nightly on those serious hour-long television dramas which
frequently give the impression of being dubbed, so many preparatory
lip movements does the actor go through before he works around to

the crisis of utterance. This nervous medley acts as an assurance to the spectator that harrowing as the content is of what is spoken, what is unspoken is even worse. What is said is the less important half; the better half is the silence.

Williams writes the ideal "line" for this mode of delivery. It is a long line, which achieves its most striking effects through a Steinian repetitiveness, through the use of unexpected archaisms, and the insertion of unexpected "literary" words and ironically elegant turns of phrase. It is a stylized rendering of Southern diction, which is more self-conscious, more evasive, but also more imaginative than Northern speech. The odd thing is that nearly all of Williams' characters speak this language, regardless of class or place of origin, and it is to be heard even in the grunts of Stanley and Mitch in their more pensive moments.

When a Williams libretto is placed in the hands of an actor whose rendition is tailored to it, the result is an orgy of syncopation just this side of hysteria. It has been remarked that Williams writes great parts for actresses, but only for a certain kind of actress. She must bring to the part a fund of that particular kind of nervous intensity that we associate with Geraldine Page, Maureen Stapleton, or Lois Smith. The champion performance of all time in The Syncopated Mode was the one given by Geraldine Page in *Summer and Smoke* in 1951. It was this performance which brought her stardom and spawned legions of imitations that are still among us—actresses who express emotion by plucking at their forearms and the ever-present brooch at their throats, who issue declarations with an upward inflection and ask questions with a downward one.

The actress who lacks this particular intensity is as fatally out of place as a prima donna singing in English with an Italian opera company. A case in point was that of Shelley Winters, who played the female predator in *The Night of the Iguana*. Miss Winters is not on the brink of hysteria, she does not even seem neurotic, much less bizarre. Dressed in blue jeans and a hastily buttoned man's shirt, she romped through the part of the bitch hotelkeeper looking like nothing so much as a plump athletics counselor at a girl's camp. Common sense as well as the sense of humor rebelled against the idea that she represented that ogre-female, the hideous embodiment of the life force, which is central to Williams' vision of life. Lacking its center, the play slowly fell apart.

All of which are some of the reasons why a successful Williams play in full regalia does not seem written and produced so much as masterminded; it is more like the perfect crime than an artistic undertaking. Williams' vision is not only fulfilled, it is overfulfilled by Kazan's technique, which is to keep the play in a state of constant explosive motion. Perhaps this is one reason why it does not linger in the mind. Its effect is all in the seeing and quivering at the moment of seeing, a series of shocks to the eye and to the nervous system which renders the viewer captive. Occasionally one has an impulse to shout "Stop!" when some particularly questionable assertion has been made onstage, but it has already flitted away, been swallowed up in the chiaroscuro. It is this shimmering motion that most of the critics praise when they invoke Williams' good qualities —his "elusiveness," his "poeticism." It is as though on Broadway that larger ambiguity which is a characteristic of great art can be achieved merely by a blurring of outline. Dim the lights, provide a clarinet solo or the tinkling of a jukebox, buttress the action with a gathering storm and if possible add a symbol or two which seems to flicker on and off like a neon light, saying: "I may look like an iguana, but what I really am is a symbol." Then all efforts to discern what the playwright is actually saying will be dismissed as pedantry, offensive to the "magical" nature of the theatrical occasion.

Lately, however, Williams has been getting a bad press, though for the wrong reasons. Certain of his motifs have become so insistent and so unmistakable that they no longer quite scurry away unnoticed into the underbrush. Yet Williams' vision has not really changed so much between *Streetcar*, which was hailed as our only American tragedy, and *Sweet Bird of Youth*, which outraged even Kenneth Tynan. It seems unjust of the critics to have taken Williams to their bosoms when he hinted coyly at the unspeakable and to chide him when he speaks a bit more clearly about it.

The total effect of Williams' work has been to plunge ordinary conceptions of the male-female relation into such disorder that the services of a Harry Stack Sullivan seem needed to straighten them out again. The first of these grand subversions was the figure of Stanley Kowalski, which appeared before the American public and before the world in the person of Marlon Brando. Though numerous actors have since played the part, Brando remains forever etched in memory as the embodiment of American malehood, and Kowalski is probably the most famous male figure in modern drama. Doubtless at this moment Brando's Korean counterpart is playing the role in whatever passes at the Seoul Repertory Company for a torn T-shirt.

Kazan, who likes to get down to brass tacks, described Kowalski in his celebrated notes to the production of *Streetcar* as "a walking penis." Whatever that would look like (the imagination is certainly compelled), Brando's rendition of it came out as something more ambivalent. His mincing interpretation of the role may even have struck sophisticated members of the audience as a brilliant example of post-Freudian insight: the walking phallus must necessarily take on some suspicious mannerisms: we all know about overcompensation, and what is brutality but the fear of cowardice and impotence?

Leaving Brando's performance out of it and taking Kowalski at face value, as written by Williams—what are we to make of him? Even forgetting temporarily certain cultural data—that members of the lower middle class are rather more inclined toward the sham genteel in their sexual mores than toward the nobly savage, and that it is primarily college graduates who are as conscientious about their sex life as though it were some humanist obligation—one still wonders how Stella and Stanley ever got together. How did Stella ever get over those initial hurdles—Stanley's table manners, Stanley's preferences in dress, Stanley's recreational interests, Stanley's friends, Stanley's stupidity? If we accept Stanley as ape, the character of Stella ceases to be interesting except clinically. Williams claims allegiance with Lawrence in his philosophy of sex, yet in the creation of Kowalski he forgets utterly Lawrence's basic lesson—that profound sexual experience civilizes, humanizes, lends grace and delicacy. Lady Chatterley is attracted specifically by the natural aristocracy of the gamekeeper which his skill and power as a lover only confirm. Despite his presence on the stage in satin pajamas and his continued invocation of the "colored lights" we do not really believe in the instinctive animal beauty (purity?) of Stanley in bed because out of it he behaves with such benighted cruelty. Did Stanley rape Stella, too, just by way of a how-do-you-do? Do all women burn to be raped? Is this the locker-room fantasy that is Williams' version of animal purity?

"They come together with low, animal moans," the stage directions say. Earlier Stella launches into the first of those hushed sexual confidences which run through all of Williams' plays and ring such an astonishingly false note. "I can hardly stand it when he's away for a night," says Stella. "When he's away for a week I nearly go wild. . . . And when he comes back I cry on his lap like a baby. . . ." It is hard to know what is more unpleasant in this image: the overt sentimentality it expresses, or the latent brutality it masks: a fascination with the image of the helpless creature under the physical domination of another, accepting his favors with tears of gratitude. That the emotion of gratitude is not the predominant one that women feel for their lovers seems to have escaped Williams, fixated as he seems to be upon the delights his heroes must be capable of affording. Later Stella's breathless sexual confidences will be echoed by Serafina delle Rose, describing her husband's prodigious feats in bed, and by Margaret describing the absolute "indifference" of Brick, which makes him the perfect lover. When there is no woman on the scene to give testimony, the heroes themselves oblige with weary chronicles of the services they have rendered scores of women: Val in *Orpheus Descending* refusing to serve any longer as "stud" to women like the impatient Carol; Chance Wayne in *Sweet Bird of Youth* describing the legions of lonely women whom he has taught about love; Shannon in *Night of the Iguana* confiding his rape at the hands of an adolescent girl. At the center of most of Williams' plays there is the same slightly repellent pas de deux: the man austere, eager to keep his purity; the woman turning to him like Potiphar's wife unto Joseph.

The foregoing belongs, in Williams' world, to the category of "corruption." When he describes "pure" love, one expects hoots from the gallery—but perhaps again the gallery is hungering for any version of that fabled sentiment that Williams can manage to offer. "Pure" love in Williams—which antedates the hero's initiation into "corruption" (spoken darkly, with a faint slurring)—generally takes place in aquatic environs when both the hero and the heroine were very young. The heroine—Val's chance encounter on a houseboat off the Florida coast, Chance Wayne's true love by the Gulf Stream—is generally an exceedingly pale girl with long blond hair—ethereal to the point of incorporeality. In *Sweet Bird*, dramatizing one of those fervid paradoxes that Williams so loves, Heavenly, the "corrupted" pure love, rides at the head of a political caravan, dressed "all in whaat . . . laak a virgin . . ." though she's had that—operation— (spoken darkly and crooningly) "done" on her. . . . How strange to find Williams, the disciple of Lawrence, talking about physical (corrupt) and spiritual (pure) love.

In any event it is difficult to credit those dossiers of sexual achievement that Williams' heroes carry around with them like traveling salesmen with a new fall "line." They seem, when actually confronted with it, to go to great lengths to avoid going to bed with women. They would, in general, prefer to go bowling, to throw each other high forward passes, to wander off in quest of correspondences in the world of nature to their own sense of themselves. When authentic warmth is generated in the plays of Tennessee Williams, it it most often on the occasion of an encounter between two men, and at the expense of their temporarily absent womenfolk—as, for instance, in the moving and very beautiful scene between Brick and Big Daddy in *Cat on a Hot Tin Roof*. It takes Brick three long acts to be persuaded into bed, and it is only the threat of having his liquor supply cut off that finally does it; in the play *Night of the Iguana,* two acts elapse and the hero goes off reluctantly, as to a martyrdom, only when his resistance has been worn down through sheer fatigue; in *Sweet Bird of Youth* the bribe of a checkbook and the use of the Cadillac are necessary before Chance Wayne succumbs to the Princess. The filmed version, recording the moment in close-up and with a directness mercifully lacking in the theater, had Paul Newman's classic features wearing an expression of which the verbal equivalent could only have been "aw shucks!" as Geraldine Page undulated rapidly toward the windows to pull down the blinds. Surely even a gigolo enjoys his job somewhat, and Alexandra del Lago is supposed to be a famous and alluring movie queen; but the feeling communicated is of a child being forced to stay indoors and practice his scales for an hour before he will be released to go out and play with the other kids.

Indeed, Williams' heroes seem more compelled by the mysteries of the nursery and bathroom than by the mysteries of the boudoir, or any more epic battleground. Throughout his plays there is a continuous fascination with the intricacies of bodily processes, the unlovely data of mortality, which suggests a small boy eavesdropping on the talk of a couple of old maid aunts. In almost every Williams play there recurs the clinical-medical set piece, in one version or another; sometimes for comic purposes, as in the detailed evocation of Big Daddy's "spastic colon," which provides a sort of running gag to the play; or for darker purposes, as in the dark references to the imminent demise of Lady's husband in *Orpheus Descending,* or the hushed recitation of what the knife did to the young life of Heavenly Findley. Williams is one of the few dramatists writing who can get a nervous laugh from the audience simply by showing a group of pregnant women onstage. That shrouded Southern setting becomes a metaphor for an equally threatening landscape—the landscape of the body, interior and exterior, made actual in *Summer and Smoke* when Dr. John, standing before an anatomy chart, gives the hypnotized Alma a lesson in reality. (". . . and this is the sex.") This landscape of the body seems as fevered as any acreage on the Mississippi delta plain, with its mysterious shadows and weird foliage—the digestive tract, the reproductive tract, the respiratory tract, the alimentary canal. Stanley, whose colored lights leave something to be desired in the way of characterization, is never so convincing as when he is banging on the bathroom door and screaming about his kidneys. Shannon, the unfrocked priest of *Night of the Iguana,* keeps an all-night vigil with a woman who obviously—as she herself might say—feels more than friendship for him, and whiles away the long hours before dawn regaling her with stories, among which is the episode, observed in his travels, of a destitute beggar eating human offal. And earlier, he has described with similar precision how his moral turpitude stems from the moment his mother discovered him practicing the "little boy's vice."

The effectiveness of the beggar episode in the play—which is intended, it seems, to provide the final documentation of Shannon's and Williams' vision of life as hell—is considerably weakened by the fact that Shannon seems to have told his once devastating story numerous times before, in fact whenever he's had one too many, and its power as a Dantesque hallucination has run out. Earlier, Shannon —are we to take him as a ruined saint?—in a gesture of defiance against the busload of ladies who have been tormenting him with sexual or other claims, pees on everyone's luggage to the unbounded glee of the audience and of the two Mexican houseboys onstage who are retained by the management to crouch in feline postures and speak occasional sentences in Spanish. Only after he has accomplished these various demonic acts and been, in addition, lashed to his hammock in the most objectionable exploitation of Christian symbolism since Chance Wayne got castrated on Easter Sunday, does he go off to splash in the waves with Shelley Winters.

What, then, are we to make of the "serious" import of the play— with all this bathroom behavior mixed up with an apparent concern with the themes of the loss of faith and regaining of faith? To be sure, Shannon is provided with one of those incredible biographies that Williams gives his heroes-at-the-end-of-their-rope to explain how they got there. He was once a man of God who sinned in the attempt to find "purity." But when he hurls a challenge at God— "you senile delinquent"—and a perceptible stir goes through the audience, and when he later flings a crucifix to the ground, we are in the presence of nothing more than that most unpleasant of travesties—blasphemy without travail, without the prior justification of the

loss of a deeply held faith: in short, a black mass with costumes by
Motley for the titillation of a sensation-hungry audience. It is hard
to judge whether the fraud or the foolishness cries out louder in this
play, hailed by critics as Williams' "gentlest" thus far. There is al-
ways this distinct unease engendered by Williams' ultimate visions—
Sebastian devoured by the street urchins, the castration of Chance
Wayne, Val torn to pieces by the rabid mob, the madness of Blanche.
It is not only because of their intrinsic unpleasantness. Mutilation
and violent death are hardly news in an age whose experience of
Gehenna makes even Williams' hallucinations seem pastel-colored.
What turns the violent and shocking aspects of Williams' plays into
something repellent is the sense one has of a disproportion. His view
of life seems in excess of its own ostensible causes—rather as though
a man were to do in a series of women because his girl friend had
failed to keep an appointment. The plays simply do not seem sufficiently somber or profound to warrant their catastrophes; they do
not bear witness that the author has wrestled sufficiently with his
own demons to give his vision authority. If he had, Williams might
have succeeded in creating something like the tragic hero. Wistful,
charming, poignant though his characters are, they lack a certain
dignity, a grandeur appropriate to their own tragic ends. Instead of
resisting them, shaping them, finally transcending them, Williams
seems to welcome all too eagerly the most hectic images that flock
to his imagination or come across his path in his various sojourns
around the globe—as a very chic decorator welcomes something
really new in the way of tropical decorations for the patio. And there
is ultimately that particular unease produced by evasion—the feeling
one always has that his most gothic revelations are themselves masks
for a meaning still further hidden.

Perhaps the best illustration of this last point is provided by *Cat
on a Hot Tin Roof*—Williams' best play since *The Glass Menagerie*.
Here is Williams' finest writing—blessedly free of that false incanta-
tory note and straining after effect which mark his other plays. It is
lyric and authentic in its evocation of the American mythology of
brilliant halfbacks, beauty queens, and sports announcers. There is
an absence of the conspicuously "Southern" or of the Berlitz Italian
or Spanish, that Williams usually depends upon for "earthy" atmosphere. Moreover, it is the last of Williams' important plays to be
anchored in reality—that bedrock which the theater deserts at its
peril—the reality of houses, families, marriage, children, money.
Maggie the Cat is the best in Williams' gallery of jumpy Southern

women, a more detailed and psychologically accurate portrait than Blanche, whom she somewhat resembles. In general, Williams seems to have written this play with a control that he has not had before or since. Yet the play is astonishingly flawed at its center. It appears to be an Ibsenian play of unmasking, of revelation, of the stripping away of lies to reveal truth. Yet at the crucial moment, the unmasking is evaded. Williams seems to have toyed with the keys of a locked door, dangling them one by one, only to decide at the end that what is behind the door had best remain hidden.

Cat on a Hot Tin Roof is about a marriage that is falling apart. The husband, Brick, who was once a star athlete and later a sports announcer is now an alcoholic who refuses to sleep with his wife, Margaret. His wife loves him and wants to have a child by him because (among other reasons) the inheritance of the family estate depends on it. But Brick refuses to yield, is interested in nothing but alcohol which gives him peace, that "click" in the head which signifies the end of struggle. Each member of the family has his own version of why Brick drinks and why he will have nothing to do with his wife, but all agree this his behavior is related to the recent death of Skipper, Brick's best friend. The hostile members of the family, Brick's brother and his wife, have hinted darkly that Brick's and Skipper's friendship was "not normal." Margaret knows further details. She believes that though Skipper loved her husband "that" way, her husband did not respond in kind. She feels herself responsible for having alienated her husband, because it was her attempted seduction of Skipper which triggered his collapse and death. Only Brick knows the truth, and he refuses to talk.

Since the play announces its theme to be that of "mendacity," and since the crucial scene is the confrontation between Brick and Big Daddy in which they both agree that final disclosures must now be faced, one expects that this scene will reveal the answer to the question that everyone is asking: is Brick homosexual or isn't he? Astonishingly enough, though the characters circle this question for almost the length of an act in a carefully choreographed minuet of confrontation and confession, the question remains unanswered. Big Daddy succeeds in extracting from Brick only the admission that a final conversation he had with Skipper was the immediate cause of his death. And this admission is made to seem sufficient. Brick in turn tells Big Daddy what everyone has kept from him—that he is dying—and there is a sense of the restoration of balance, a lie exchanged for a lie, a truth for a truth.

But the failure to answer the question of Brick's homosexuality makes the play totally incoherent. Is it a play about a man unjustly accused by a society which is right (yes, homosexuality is evil, but this wasn't it) or a play about a man justly accused by a society which is wrong (no, homosexuality is not evil, it is only wicked tongues that make it out to be so)? In place of what would seem to be Brick's obligatory speech—the one in which he faces the real nature of his feelings for Skipper one way or another—there is an eloquent and finely ironic explanation of how "pure" love is no less "abnormal" than homosexual love, being so rare. In view of the fact, however, that we do not know whether this speech proceeds from the lips of a man who is telling the truth or from the lips of a man who is alternatively either lying or self-deluded, we cannot credit it. If Brick were, in fact, homosexual, or were unable to face the fact that he is homosexual, the assertion would be patently false—there would then, indeed, be no such thing as "pure" love between men. If he were, on the other hand, neither lying nor self-deluded, then there might. But the assertion cannot possibly hold for all three cases. It seems moreover crucial to the meaning of the play to know whether Brick is weak and self-deluded or whether he is the last example of the pure in heart. Are we to conclude from the author's ambiguities that he finds the two identical?

Most of the daily newspaper critics were so delighted to spot the old-fashioned well-made revelation scene that they missed the point that nothing was, in fact, revealed, and talked rhapsodically about how Williams had once again probed with his scalpel the most hidden places of the human heart, etc., etc. Only Walter Kerr of the New York *Herald Tribune* seemed to have noticed that the play evaded its own questions—that the love that dare not speak its name, so to speak, was still wearing a pseudonym. Williams answered by saying that ". . . some mystery should be left in the revelation of character in a play just as a great deal of mystery is always left in the revelation of character in life . . ." which is tantamount to saying that *Oedipus Rex* might on the whole have been a more profound tragedy if the rumor that Oedipus was sleeping with his mother had remained unconfirmed.

Why did Williams avoid answering this question in the play? Partly for the sake of expediency, the same expediency that permitted him to allow Kazan to tinker with the third act of the play so that it was sweetened, assuaged, and its real meaning—the bitterness and terror of marriage—somewhat masked. An audience that will

accept the unproved allegation of homosexuality, that is even prepared to accept an absent or dead homosexual figuring in someone
else's psychic drama, is still not quite prepared to accept a real live
red-blooded American husband as homosexual, and one who moreover gets into bed with the heroine at the final curtain. By evading
the real nature of Brick's feelings for Maggie—by leaving open the
possibility that Brick's aversion for her is on ethical rather than psychological grounds—Williams avoided writing the important American play, the one about the American family and its woebegone sons,
the story of American adolescence which so frequently persists into
middle age. But he managed instead neatly to insure the nice lady's
comment to her husband when the curtain fell: ". . . how sweet,
they've gotten together again. . . ."

Williams does not surrender to his audience; rather he establishes
the communion between his myths and theirs. He avoided being
specific about Brick's homosexuality not only because it is not "nice"
to confront an audience with such home truths, but because he
shares that curious American aversion to facts: the view that somehow or other people are different from what they do or say, from
what experience has turned them into—that a man is defined by
something other than his actions. America is after all the home of
the new start, the second chance, and there is a kind of gloomy,
adolescent optimism, reflected in the culture, which clings to the possibility that people may change—that with enough love (which
means forgiveness) they may one day become beautiful, good, and
happy. Williams' failure to pinpoint the character of Brick is a gesture of misguided benignity in his behalf. Like America, Williams
lacks ultimately the conviction of his own neurosis.

This same hedging before specifics has always been evident in the
critical reception of Williams. There are real and apparent themes
in Williams, and the critics have invariably seized upon the apparent
ones. They are easier to take, and by now sufficiently orthodox, even
sacrosanct, to avoid danger: the failure of communication, the de-
struction of the dreamers by the practical men, how hellish life can
be for the lonelies and the losers. Oddly enough, adumbrating these
themes, reviewers frequently congratulate Williams on having once
again "affirmed the dignity of the human spirit," the one thing that
he has not succeeded in doing. For Williams has never created a
character who recovered from the wounds and desolation of childhood.

A play like *Period of Adjustment*—Williams' rather touching attempt to adjust his world view to the comic and the domestic by sheer will power—is particularly revealing in the clarity with which it shows, or shows up, the true nature of his obsessions. It is a banal, ordinary, and even vulgar play about, of all things, how scary the wedding night can be. The play is in effect a mild dirty joke sustained for two acts; but the embarrassment that it occasions is the embarrassment of hearing a dirty joke told by someone fairly prudish. What emerges into the open is that shrinking and fastidious side of Williams which has made him so adept at capturing the ironic self-observations of women who are too smart to believe in their own delusions, but too weak to do anything about them, and who are sustained by a certain delicacy of hope. Though it has the requisite Williams touches, the play offers an entirely conformist, trivial view of love as a kind of soothing ointment. Its burden is that somehow or other human beings—weak, frail, tormented, and uncertain as they are—can offer each other at least the comfort of bodily warmth. The bride in the play is a nurse and the controlling image is that the world is a hospital.

The play is about false and true ideas of manhood, and here we observe a curious thing. Williams has always carried with him, in suspension as it were, the corrective to his own distortions of the masculine. He knows, as do most of us, the truth about the excessive blustering of American malehood—the notorious fear of seeming soft or sissyish, the mistrust of hair worn too long, of demonstrations of affection or tenderness among men, the longing to go off with the boys and all the other apparatus of stag party camaraderie—that all of this is not an expression of authentic masculinity, but of its opposite. Yet this knowledge has never inhibited Williams' more lurid perpetrations of the masculine ideal—the crudities of Stanley Kowalski, the grotesque cavortings of "normalcy" in *Cat* and *Streetcar*, the gratuitous obscenity of Big Daddy when he talks about women. It is as though Williams were aware of the reality, but helpless before the fantasy. Even in *Period of Adjustment*, which amounts to a course of instruction in that very truth, Williams stacks the cards to thwart his own purpose. He offers us two "typical" American couples engaged in working out the ambiguities and problematics of the married state. The first man is married to a woman presented as so incredibly homely that her appearance onstage in a nightgown instantly provokes gales of laughter from the audience; a laughter which is sustained by the author's relish for the details of synthetic correction that she has undergone to make herself bearable. The second man is in such an advanced state of anxiety that he literally has the shakes.

The play ends with an extraordinary scene. The stage is divided in two: on either side of the partition, two beds are invitingly made up, and the two protagonists, with many a backward glance, hop into the sack with their all-too-willing wives. After the first recoil the viewer comes to the astonishing realization that only in America could an entire play be constructed on the question of whether four consenting adults will or will not succeed in making love to one another on a given night. Where one would expect a domestic comedy by a sophisticated modern author in 1960 to begin, Williams' play ends.

And Williams has, one must recall, the reputation for being our sexiest American playwright. What could, in fact, be more innocent? Coprophilia, cannibalism, homosexuality, exhibitionism, fetishism, violation of the Mann Act, turn out in Williams to be masks for some other horror, darker than any of these: the catastrophe of normal adult sexuality. In the end, Williams' vision is revealed as a shocked outcry, a child's refusal to accept the fact of sex, that, yes, grownups really do it. Perhaps this ultimately is what the ladies in flowered hats understand about Williams—that beneath the mantle of the swashbuckling libertine, the initiate, the participant in the dark mysteries, there beats a heart as virginal as their own, as their husbands', as America's—that country where the women's magazines on every newsstand carry side by side starry-eyed evocations of the "act of love" and "Eric's strong arms . . ." and the most lurid clinical how-to-do-it manuals of the practice and fulfillment of heterosexual love.

III ❧ FATHERS, SONS, AND BROTHERS

EDITH WHARTON   *[1909]*

Edith Wharton's story about a father whose son is more like him than either of them knows is both poignant and funny. Born in New York in 1862, educated by private tutors, Mrs. Wharton became a prolific short story writer and novelist before her death in 1937.

His Father's Son

I

After his wife's death Mason Grew took the momentous step of selling out his business and moving from Wingfield, Connecticut, to Brooklyn.

For years he had secretly nursed the hope of such a change, but had never dared to suggest it to Mrs. Grew, a woman of immutable habits. Mr. Grew himself was attached to Wingfield, where he had grown up, prospered, and become what the local press described as "prominent." He was attached to his brick house with sandstone trimmings and a cast-iron area-railing neatly sanded to match; to the similar row of houses across the street, with "trolley" wires forming a kind of aerial pathway between, and to the vista closed by the sandstone steeple of the church which he and his wife had always attended, and where their only child had been baptized.

It was hard to snap all these threads of association, yet still harder, now that he was alone, to live so far from his boy. Ronald Grew was practicing law in New York, and there was no more chance of his returning to live at Wingfield than of a river's flowing inland from the sea. Therefore to be near him his father must move; and it was characteristic of Mr. Grew, and of the situation generally, that the translation, when it took place, was to Brooklyn, and not to New York.

"Why bury yourself in that hole I can't think," had been Ronald's comment; and Mr. Grew simply replied that rents were lower in

Brooklyn, and that he had heard of a house there that would suit him. In reality he had said to himself—being the only recipient of his own confidences—that if he went to New York he might be on the boy's mind; whereas, if he lived in Brooklyn, Ronald would always have a good excuse for not popping over to see him every other day. The sociological isolation of Brooklyn, combined with its geographical nearness, presented in fact the precise conditions that Mr. Grew sought. He wanted to be near enough to New York to go there often, to feel under his feet the same pavement that Ronald trod, to sit now and then in the same theaters, and find on his breakfast table the journals which, with increasing frequency, inserted Ronald's name in the sacred bounds of the society column. It had always been a trial to Mr. Grew to have to wait twenty four hours to read that "among those present was Mr. Ronald Grew." Now he had it with his coffee, and left it on the breakfast table to the perusal of a "hired girl" cosmopolitan enough to do it justice. In such ways Brooklyn attested the advantages of its nearness to New York, while remaining, as regards Ronald's duty to his father, as remote and inaccessible as Wingfield.

It was not that Ronald shirked his filial obligations, but rather because of his heavy sense of them, that Mr. Grew so persistently sought to minimize and lighten them. It was he who insisted, to Ronald, on the immense difficulty of getting from New York to Brooklyn.

"Any way you look at it, it makes a big hole in the day; and there's not much use in the ragged rim left. You say you're dining out next Sunday? Then I forbid you to come over here to lunch. Do you understand me, sir? You disobey at the risk of your father's malediction! Where did you say you were dining? With the Waltham Bankshires again? Why, that's the second time in three weeks, ain't it? Big blow-out, I suppose? Gold plate and orchids—opera singers in afterward? Well, you'd be in a nice box if there was a fog on the river, and you got hung up halfway over. That'd be a handsome return for the attention Mrs. Bankshire has shown you—singling out a whipper-snapper like you twice in three weeks! (What's the daughter's name—Daisy?) No, sir—don't you come fooling round here next Sunday, or I'll set the dogs on you. And you wouldn't find me in anyhow, come to think of it. I'm lunching out myself, as it happens—yes, sir, *lunching out.* Is there anything especially comic in my lunching out? I don't often do it, you say? Well, that's no reason why I never should. Who with? Why, with—with old Dr.

Bleaker: Dr. Eliphalet Bleaker. No, you wouldn't know about him—he's only an old friend of your mother's and mine."

Gradually Ronald's insistence became less difficult to overcome. With his customary sweetness and tact (as Mr. Grew put it) he began to "take the hint," to give in to "the old gentleman's" growing desire for solitude.

"I'm set in my ways, Ronny, that's about the size of it; I like to go tick-ticking along like a clock. I always did. And when you come bouncing in I never feel sure there's enough for dinner—or that I haven't sent Maria out for the evening. And I don't want the neighbors to see me opening my own door to my son. That's the kind of cringing snob I am. Don't give me away, will you? I want 'em to think I keep four or five powdered flunkeys in the hall day and night—same as the lobby of one of those Fifth Avenue hotels. And if you pop over when you're not expected, how am I going to keep up the bluff?"

Ronald yielded after the proper amount of resistance—his intuitive sense, in every social transaction, of the proper amount of force to be expended, was one of the qualities his father most admired in him. Mr. Grew's perceptions in this line were probably more acute than his son suspected. The souls of short thick-set men, with chubby features, mutton-chop whiskers, and pale eyes peering between folds of fat like almond kernels in half-split shells—souls thus encased do not reveal themselves to the casual scrutiny as delicate emotional instruments. But in spite of the disguise in which he walked Mr. Grew vibrated exquisitely in response to every imaginative appeal; and his son Ronald was always stimulating and feeding his imagination.

Ronald in fact constituted Mr. Grew's one escape from the element of mediocrity which had always hemmed him in. To a man so enamored of beauty, and so little qualified to add to its sum total, it was a wonderful privilege to have bestowed on the world such a being. Ronald's resemblance to Mr. Grew's early conception of what he himself would have liked to look might have put new life into the discredited theory of prenatal influences. At any rate, if the young man owed his beauty, his distinction and his winning manner to the dreams of one of his parents, it was certainly to those of Mr. Grew, who, while outwardly devoting his life to the manufacture and dissemination of Grew's Secure Suspender Buckle, moved in an enchanted inward world peopled with all the figures of romance. In this company Mr. Grew cut as brilliant a figure as any of its noble phantoms; and to see his vision of himself projected on the outer world in the shape of a brilliant popular conquering son, seemed, in retrospect, to give to it a belated reality. There were even moments when, forgetting his face, Mr. Grew said to himself that if he'd had "half a chance" he might have done as well as Ronald; but this only fortified his resolve that Ronald should do infinitely better.

Ronald's ability to do well almost equaled his gift of looking well. Mr. Grew constantly affirmed to himself that the boy was "not a genius"; but, barring this slight deficiency, he had almost every gift that a parent could wish. Even at Harvard he had managed to be seven desirable things at once—writing poetry in the college magazine, playing delightfully "by ear," acquitting himself creditably of his studies, and yet holding his own in the sporting set that formed, as it were, the gateway of the temple of Society. Mr. Grew's idealism did not preclude the frank desire that his son should pass through that gateway; but the wish was not prompted by material considerations. It was Mr. Grew's notion that, in the rough and hurrying current of a new civilization, the little pools of leisure and enjoyment must nurture delicate growths, material graces as well as moral refinements, likely to be uprooted and swept away by the rush of the main torrent. He based his theory on the fact that he had liked the few "society" people he had met—had found their manners simpler, their voices more agreeable, their views more consonant with his own, than those of the leading citizens of Wingfield. But then he had met very few.

Ronald's sympathies needed no urging in the same direction. He took naturally, dauntlessly, to all the high and exceptional things about which his father's imagination had so long ineffectually hovered—from the start he *was* what Mr. Grew had dreamed of being. And so precise, so detailed, was Mr. Grew's vision of his own imaginary career, that as Ronald grew up, and began to travel in a widening orbit, his father had an almost uncanny sense of the extent to which that career was enacting itself before him. At Harvard, Ronald had done exactly what the hypothetical Mason Grew would have done, had not his actual self, at the same age, been working his way up in old Slagden's button factory—the institution which was later to acquire fame, and even notoriety, as the birthplace of Grew's Secure Suspender Buckle. Afterward, at a period when the actual Grew had passed from the factory to the bookkeeper's desk, his invisible double had been reading law at Columbia—precisely again what Ronald did! But it was when the young man left the paths laid out for him by the parental hand, and cast himself boldly on the world, that his adventures began to bear the most astonishing resemblance to those of the unrealized Mason Grew. It was in New York that the scene of this hypothetical being's first exploits had always been laid; and it was in New York that Ronald was to achieve his first triumph. There was nothing small or timid about Mr. Grew's imagination; it had never stopped at anything between Wingfield and the metropolis. And the real Ronald had the same cosmic vision as his parent. He brushed aside with a contemptuous laugh his mother's entreaty that he should stay at Wingfield and continue the dynasty of the Grew Suspender Buckle. Mr. Grew knew that in reality Ronald winced at the Buckle, loathed it, blushed for his connection with it. Yet it was the Buckle that had seen him through Groton, Harvard and the Law School, and had permitted him to enter the office of a distinguished corporation lawyer, instead of being enslaved to some sordid business with quick returns. The Buckle had been Ronald's fairy godmother—yet his father did not blame him for abhorring and disowning it. Mr. Grew himself often bitterly regretted having attached his own name to the instrument of his material success, though, at the time, his doing so had been the natural expression of his romanticism. When he invented the Buckle, and took out his patent, he and his wife both felt that to bestow their name on it was like naming a battleship or a peak of the Andes.

Mrs. Grew had never learned to know better; but Mr. Grew had discovered his error before Ronald was out of school. He read it first in a black eye of his boy's. Ronald's symmetry had been marred by the insolent fist of a fourth former whom he had chastised for alluding to his father as "Old Buckles"; and when Mr. Grew heard the epithet he understood in a flash that the Buckle was a thing to blush for. It was too late then to dissociate his name from it, or to efface from the hoardings of the entire continent the picture of two gentlemen, one contorting himself in the abject effort to repair a broken brace, while the careless ease of the other's attitude proclaimed his trust in the Secure Suspender Buckle. These records were indelible, but Ronald could at least be spared all direct connection with them; and that day Mr. Grew decided that the boy should not return to Wingfield.

"You'll see," he had said to Mrs. Grew, "he'll take right hold in New York. Ronald's got my knack for taking hold," he added, throwing out of his chest.

"But the way you took hold was in business," objected Mrs. Grew, who was large and literal.

Mr. Grew's chest collapsed, and he became suddenly conscious of his comic face in its rim of sandy whisker. "That's not the only way," he said, with a touch of wistfulness which escaped his wife's analysis.

"Well, of course you could have written beautifully," she rejoined with admiring eyes.

"*Written?* Me!" Mr. Grew became sardonic.

"Why, those letters—weren't *they* beautiful, I'd like to know?"

The couple exchanged a glance, innocently allusive and amused on the wife's part, and charged with a sudden tragic significance on the husband's.

"Well, I've got to be going along to the office now," he merely said, dragging himself out of his chair.

This had happened while Ronald was still at school; and now Mrs. Grew slept in the Wingfield cemetery, under a life-size theological virtue of her own choosing, and Mr. Grew's prognostications as to Ronald's ability to "take right hold" in New York were being more and more brilliantly fulfilled.

II

Ronald obeyed his father's injunction not to come to luncheon on the day of the Bankshires' dinner; but in the middle of the following week Mr. Grew was surprised by a telegram from his son.

"Want to see you important matter. Expect me tomorrow afternoon."

Mr. Grew received the telegram after breakfast. To peruse it he had lifted his eye from a paragraph of the morning paper describing a fancy-dress dinner which the Hamilton Gliddens' had given the night before for the housewarming of their new Fifth Avenue palace.

"Among the couples who afterward danced in the Poets' Quadrille were Miss Daisy Bankshire, looking more than usually lovely as Laura, and Mr. Ronald Grew as the young Petrarch."

Petrarch and Laura! Well—if *anything* meant anything, Mr. Grew supposed he knew what that meant. For weeks past he had noticed how constantly the names of the young people were coupled in the society notes he so insatiably devoured. Even the soulless reporter was getting into the habit of uniting them in his lists. And this Laura and Petrarch business was almost an announcement. . . .

Mr. Grew dropped the telegram, wiped his eyeglasses, and reread the paragraph. "Miss Daisy Bankshire . . . more than usually lovely . . ." Yes; she *was* lovely. He had often seen her photograph in the papers—seen her represented in every attitude of the mundane game: fondling her prize bulldog, taking a fence on her thoroughbred, dancing a *gavotte,* all patches and plumes, or fingering a guitar, all tulle and lilies; and once he had caught a glimpse of her at the theater. Hearing that Ronald was going to a fashionable first night with the Bankshires, Mr. Grew had for once overcome his repugnance to following his son's movements, and had secured for himself, under the shadow of the balcony, a stall whence he could observe the Bankshire box without fear of detection. Ronald had never known of his father's presence; and for three blessed hours Mr. Grew had watched his boy's handsome dark head bent above the fair hair and averted shoulder that were all he could catch of Miss Bankshire's beauties.

He recalled the vision now; and with it came, as usual, its ghostly double: the vision of his young self bending above such a shoulder and such shining hair. Needless to say that the real Mason Grew had never found himself in so enviable a situation. The late Mrs. Grew had no more resembled Miss Daisy Bankshire than he had looked like the happy victorious Ronald. And the mystery was that from their dull faces, their dull endearments, the miracle of Ronald should have sprung. It was almost—fantastically—as if the boy had been a changeling, child of a Latmian night, whom the divine companion of Mr. Grew's early reveries had secretly laid in the cradle of the Wingfield bedroom while Mr. and Mrs. Grew slept the sleep of conjugal indifference.

The young Mason Grew had not at first accepted this astral episode as the complete canceling of his claims on romance. He too had grasped at the high-hung glory; and, with his tendency to reach too far when he reached at all, had singled out the prettiest girl in Wingfield. When he recalled his stammered confession of love his face still tingled under her cool bright stare. His audacity had struck her dumb; and when she recovered her voice it was to fling a taunt at him.

"Don't be too discouraged, you know—have you ever thought of trying Addie Wicks?"

All Wingfield would have understood the gibe: Addie Wicks was the dullest girl in town. And a year later he had married Addie Wicks. . . .

He looked up from the perusal of Ronald's telegram with this memory in his mind. Now at last his dream was coming true! His boy would taste of the joys that had mocked his thwarted youth and his dull middle age. And it was fitting that they should be realized in Ronald's destiny. Ronald was made to take happiness boldly by the hand and lead it home like a bride. He had the carriage, the confidence, the high faith in his fortune, that compel the wilful stars. And, thanks to the Buckle, he would also have the background of material elegance that became his conquering person. Since Mr. Grew had retired from business his investments had prospered, and he had been saving up his income for just such a purpose. His own wants were few: he had brought the Wingfield furniture to Brooklyn, and his sitting room was a replica of that in which the long years of his married life had been spent. Even the florid carpet on which Ronald's first footsteps had been taken was carefully matched when it became too threadbare. And on the marble center table, with its beaded cover and bunch of dyed pampas grass, lay the illustrated Longfellow and the copy of Ingersoll's lectures which represented literature to Mr. Grew when he had led home his bride. In the light of Ronald's romance, Mr. Grew found himself reliving, with mingled pain and tenderness, all the poor prosaic incidents of his own personal history. Curiously enough, with this new splendor on them they began to emit a faint ray of their own. His wife's armchair, in its usual place by the fire, recalled her placid unperceiving presence, seated opposite to him during the long drowsy years; and he felt her kindness, her equanimity, where formerly he had only ached at her obtuseness. And from the chair he glanced up at the discolored photograph on the wall above, with a withered laurel wreath suspended on a corner of the frame. The photograph represented a young man with a poetic necktie and untrammeled hair, leaning against a Gothic chairback, a roll of music in his hand; and beneath was scrawled a bar of Chopin, with the words: *"Adieu, Adèle."*

The portrait was that of the great pianist, Fortuné Dolbrowski; and its presence on the wall of Mr. Grew's sitting room commemorated the only exquisite hour of his life save that of Ronald's birth. It was some time before the latter event, a few months only after

Mr. Grew's marriage, that he had taken his wife to New York to hear the great Dolbrowski. Their evening had been magically beautiful, and even Addie, roused from her usual inexpressiveness, had waked into a momentary semblance of life. "I never—I never—" she gasped out when they had regained their hotel bedroom, and sat staring back entranced at the evening's vision. Her large face was pink and tremulous, and she sat with her hands on her knees, forgetting to roll up her bonnet strings and prepare her curl-papers.

"I'd like to *write* him just how I felt—I wisht I knew how!" she burst out in a final effervescence of emotion.

Her husband lifted his head and looked at her.

"Would you? I feel that way too," he said with a sheepish laugh. And they continued to stare at each other through a transfiguring mist of sound.

The scene rose before Mr. Grew as he gazed up at the pianist's photograph. "Well, I owe her that anyhow—poor Addie!" he said, with a smile at the inconsequences of fate. With Ronald's telegram in his hand he was in a mood to count his mercies.

III

"A clear twenty-five thousand a year: that's what you can tell 'em with my compliments," said Mr. Grew, glancing complacently across the center table at his boy.

It struck him that Ronald's gift for looking his part in life had never so completely expressed itself. Other young men, at such a moment, would have been red, damp, tight about the collar; but Ronald's cheek was a shade paler, and the contrast made his dark eyes more expressive.

"A clear twenty-five thousand; yes, sir—that's what I always meant you to have."

Mr. Grew leaned carelessly back, his hands thrust in his pockets, as though to divert attention from the agitation of his features. He had often pictured himself rolling out that phrase to Ronald, and now that it was on his lips he could not control their tremor.

Ronald listened in silence, lifting a hand to his slight mustache, as though he, too, wished to hide some involuntary betrayal of emotion. At first Mr. Grew took his silence for an expression of gratified surprise; but as it prolonged itself it became less easy to interpret.

"I—see here, my boy; did you expect more? Isn't it enough?"

Mr. Grew cleared his throat. "Do *they* expect more?" he asked nervously. He was hardly able to face the pain of inflicting a disappointment on Ronald at the very moment when he had counted on putting the final touch to his bliss.

Ronald moved uneasily in his chair and his eyes wandered upward to the laurel-wreathed photograph of the pianist.

"*Is* it the money, Ronald? Speak out, my boy. We'll see, we'll look round—I'll manage somehow."

"No, no," the young man interrupted, abruptly raising his hand as though to check his father.

Mr. Grew recovered his cheerfulness. "Well, what's the trouble then, if *she's* willing?"

Ronald shifted his position again and finally rose from his seat and wandered across the room.

"Father," he said, coming back, "there's something I've got to tell you. I can't take your money."

Mr. Grew sat speechless a moment, staring blankly at his son; then he emitted a laugh. "My money? What are you talking about? What's this about my money? Why, it ain't *mine*, Ronny; it's all yours—every cent of it!"

The young men met his tender look with a gesture of tragic refusal.

"No, no, it's not mine—not even in the sense you mean. Not in any sense. Can't you understand my feeling so?"

"Feeling so? I don't know how you're feeling. I don't know what you're talking about. Are you too proud to touch any money you haven't earned? Is that what you're trying to tell me?"

"No. It's not that. You must know—"

Mr. Grew flushed to the rim of his bristling whiskers. "Know? Know *what*? Can't you speak out?"

Ronald hesitated, and the two faced each other for a long strained moment, during which Mr. Grew's congested countenance grew gradually pale again.

"What's the meaning of this? Is it because you've done something . . . something you're ashamed of . . . ashamed to tell me?" he gasped; and walking around the table he laid his hand gently on his son's shoulder. "There's nothing you can't tell me, my boy."

"It's not that. Why do you make it so hard for me?" Ronald broke out with passion. "You must have known this was sure to happen sooner or later."

"Happen? What was sure to hap——?" Mr. Grew's question wav-

ered on his lip and passed into a tremulous laugh. "Is it something
I've done that you don't approve of? Is it—is it *the Buckle* you're
ashamed of, Ronald Grew?"

Ronald laughed too, impatiently. "The Buckle? No, I'm not
ashamed of the Buckle; not any more than you are," he returned
with a flush. "But I'm ashamed of all I owe to it—all I owe to you—
when—when—" He broke off and took a few distracted steps across
the room. "You might make this easier for me," he protested, turning back to his father.

"Make what easier? I know less and less what you're driving at,"
Mr. Grew groaned.

Ronald's walk had once more brought him beneath the photograph on the wall. He lifted his head for a moment and looked at it;
then he looked again at Mr. Grew.

"Do you suppose I haven't always known?"

"Known—?"

"Even before you gave me those letters at the time of my mother's
death—even before that, I suspected. I don't know how it began . . .
perhaps from little things you let drop . . . you and she . . . and re-
semblances that I couldn't help seeing . . . in myself. . . . How on
earth could you suppose I *shouldn't guess?* I always thought you
gave me the letters as a way of telling me—"

Mr. Grew rose slowly from his chair. "The letters? Do you mean
Dolbrowski's letters?"

Ronald nodded with white lips. "You must remember giving them
to me the day after the funeral."

Mr. Grew nodded back. "Of course. I wanted you to have everything your mother valued."

"Well—how could I help knowing after that?"

"Knowing *what?*" Mr. Grew stood staring helplessly at his son.
Suddenly his look caught at a clue that seemed to confront it with a
deeper difficulty. "You thought—you thought those letters . . . Dolbrowski's letters . . . you thought they meant . . ."

"Oh, it wasn't only the letters. There were so many other signs.
My love of music—my—all my feelings about life . . . and art . . . And
when you gave me the letters I thought you must mean me to know."

Mr. Grew had grown quiet. His lips were firm, and his small eyes
looked out steadily from their creased lids.

"To know that you were Fortuné Dolbrowski's son?"

Ronald made a mute sign of assent.

"I see. And what did you intend to do?"

"I meant to wait till I could earn my living, and then repay you . . . as far as I can ever repay you . . . for what you'd spent on me. . . . But now that there's a chance of my marrying . . . and that your generosity overwhelms me . . . I'm obliged to speak."

"I see," said Mr. Grew again. He let himself down into his chair, looking steadily and not unkindly at the young man. "Sit down too, Ronald. Let's talk."

Ronald made a protesting movement. "Is anything to be gained by it? You can't change me—change what I feel. The reading of those letters transformed my whole life—I was a boy till then: they made a man of me. From that moment I understood myself." He paused, and then looked up at Mr. Grew's face. "Don't imagine that I don't appreciate your kindness—your extraordinary generosity. But I can't go through life in disguise. And I want you to know that I have not won Daisy under false pretenses—"

Mr. Grew started up with the first expletive Ronald had ever heard on his lips.

"You damned young fool, you, you haven't *told* her—?"

Ronald raised his head with pride. "Oh, you don't know her, sir! She thinks no worse of me for knowing my secret. She is above and beyond all such conventional prejudices. She's *proud* of my parentage—" he straightened his slim young shoulders—"as I'm proud of it . . . yes, sir, proud of it. . . ."

Mr. Grew sank back into his seat with a dry laugh. "Well, you ought to be. You come of good stock. And you're your father's son, every inch of you!" He laughed again, as though the humor of the situation grew on him with its closer contemplation.

"Yes, I've always felt that," Ronald murmured, gravely.

"Your father's son, and no mistake." Mr. Grew leaned forward. "You're the son of as big a fool as yourself. And here he sits, Ronald Grew!"

The young man's color deepened to crimson; but his reply was checked by Mr. Grew's decisive gesture. "Here he sits, with all your young nonsense still alive in him. Don't you begin to see the likeness? If you don't I'll tell you the story of those letters."

Ronald stared. "What do you mean? Don't they tell their own story?"

"I supposed they did when I gave them to you; but you've given it a twist that needs straightening out." Mr. Grew squared his elbows on the table, and looked at the young man across the gift books and dyed pampas grass. "I wrote all the letters that Dolbrowski answered."

Ronald gave back his look in frowning perplexity. "*You* wrote them? I don't understand. His letters are all addressed to my mother."

"Yes. And he thought he was corresponding with her."

"But my mother—what did she think?"

Mr. Grew hesitated, puckering his thick lids. "Well, I guess she kinder thought it was a joke. Your mother didn't think about things much."

Ronald continued to bend a puzzled frown on the question. "I don't understand," he reiterated.

Mr. Grew cleared his throat with a nervous laugh. "Well, I don't know as you ever will—*quite*. But this is the way it came about. I had a toughish time of it when I was young. Oh, I don't mean so much the fight I had to put up to make my way—there was always plenty of fight in me. But inside of myself it was kinder lonesome. And the outside didn't attract callers." He laughed again, with an apologetic gesture toward his broad blinking face. "When I went round with the other young fellows I was always the forlorn hope— the one that had to eat the drumsticks and dance with the leftovers. As sure as there was a blighter at a picnic I had to swing her, and feed her, and drive her home. And all the time I was mad after all the things you've got—poetry and music and all the joy-forever business. So there were the pair of us—my face and my imagination— chained together, and fighting, and hating each other like poison.

"Then your mother came along and took pity on me. It sets up a gawky fellow to find a girl who ain't ashamed to be seen walking with him Sundays. And I was grateful to your mother, and we got along first-rate. Only I couldn't say things to her—and she couldn't answer. Well—one day, a few months after we were married, Dolbrowski came to New York, and the whole place went wild about him. I'd never heard any good music, but I'd always had an inkling of what it must be like, though I couldn't tell you to this day how I knew. Well, your mother read about him in the papers too, and she thought it'd be the swagger thing to go to New York and hear him play—so we went. . . . I'll never forget that evening. Your mother wasn't easily stirred up—she never seemed to need to let off steam. But that night she seemed to understand the way I felt. And when we got back to the hotel she said to me: 'I'd like to tell him how I feel. I'd like to sit right down and write to him.'

" 'Would you?' I said. 'So would I.'

"There was paper and pens there before us, and I pulled a sheet toward me, and began to write. 'Is this what you'd like to say to him?' I asked her when the letter was done. And she got pink and said: 'I don't understand it, but it's lovely.' And she copied it out and signed her name to it, and sent it."

Mr. Grew paused, and Ronald sat silent, with lowered eyes.

"That's how it began; and that's where I thought it would end. But it didn't, because Dolbrowski answered. His first letter was dated January 10, 1872. I guess you'll find I'm correct. Well, I went back to hear him again, and I wrote him after the performance, and he answered again. And after that we kept it up for six months. Your mother always copied the letters and signed them. She seemed to think it was a kinder joke, and she was proud of his answering my letters. But she never went back to New York to hear him, though I saved up enough to give her the treat again. She was too lazy, and she let me go without her. I heard him three times in New York; and in the spring he came to Wingfield and played once at the Academy. Your mother was sick and couldn't go; so I went alone. After the performance I meant to get one of the directors to take me in to see him; but when the time came, I just went back home and wrote to him instead. And the month after, before he went back to Europe, he sent your mother a last little note, and that picture hanging up there. . . ."

Mr. Grew paused again, and both men lifted their eyes to the photograph.

"Is that all?" Ronald slowly asked.

"That's all—every bit of it," said Mr. Grew.

"And my mother—my mother never even spoke to Dolbrowski?"

"Never. She never even saw him but that once in New York at his concert."

The blood crept again to Ronald's face. "Are you sure of that, sir?" he asked in a trembling voice.

"Sure as I am that I'm sitting here. Why, she was too lazy to look at his letters after the first novelty wore off. She copied the answers just to humor me—but she always said she couldn't understand what we wrote."

"But how could you go on with such a correspondence? It's incredible!"

Mr. Grew looked at his son thoughtfully. "I suppose it is, to you. You've only had to put out your hand and get the things I was starving for—music, and good talk, and ideas. Those letters gave me all that. You've read them, and you know that Dolbrowski was not only a great musician but a great man. There was nothing beautiful he didn't see, nothing fine he didn't feel. For six months I breathed his air, and I've lived on it ever since. Do you begin to understand a little now?"

"Yes—a little. But why write in my mother's name? Why make it appear like a sentimental correspondence?"

Mr. Grew reddened to his bald temples. "Why, I tell you it began that way, as a kinder joke. And when I saw that the first letter pleased and interested him, I was afraid to tell him—*I couldn't* tell him. Do you suppose he'd gone on writing if he'd ever seen me, Ronny?"

Ronald suddenly looked at him with new eyes. "But he must have thought your letters very beautiful—to go on as he did," he broke out.

"Well—I did my best," said Mr. Grew modestly.

Ronald pursued his idea. "Where *are* all your letters, I wonder? Weren't they returned to you at his death?"

Mr. Grew laughed. "Lord, no. I guess he had trunks and trunks full of better ones. I guess Queens and Empresses wrote to him."

"I should have liked to see your letters," the young man insisted.

"Well, they weren't bad," said Mr. Grew drily. "But I'll tell you one thing, Ronny," he added. Ronald raised his head with a quick glance, and Mr. Grew continued: "I'll tell you where the best of those letters is—it's in *you*. If it hadn't been for that one look at life I couldn't have made you what you are. Oh, I know you've done a good deal of your own making—but I've been there behind you all the time. And you'll never know the work I've spared you and the time I've saved you. Fortuné Dolbrowski helped me do that. I never saw things in little again after I'd looked at 'em with him. And I tried to give you the big view from the start. . . . So that's what became of my letters."

Mr. Grew paused, and for a long time Ronald sat motionless, his elbows on the table, his face dropped on his hands.

Suddenly Mr. Grew's touch fell on his shoulder.

"Look at here, Ronald Grew—do you want me to tell you how you're feeling at this minute? Just a mite let down, after all, at the idea that you ain't the romantic figure you'd got to think yourself. . . . Well, that's natural enough, too; but I'll tell you what it proves. It proves you're my son right enough, if any more proof was needed.

For it's just the kind of fool nonsense I used to feel at your age—
and if there's anybody here to laugh at it's myself, and not you. And
you can laugh at me just as much as you like. . . ."

MARGARET SANGER   [1920]

*Margaret Sanger, who was educated at Corning and Claverack College
in Hudson, New York, and the Nurses Training School of White Plains
Hospital, is the founder and President Emeritus of the International
Planned Parenthood Federation and a well-known pioneer in legalizing
and disseminating information on birth control. In* Woman and the New
Race *she considers the father's plight.*

Planned Fatherhood

The effect of the large family upon the father is only less disastrous
than it is upon the mother. The spectacle of the young man, happy
in health, strength and the prospect of a joyful love life, makes us
smile in sympathy. But this same young man ten years later is likely
to present a spectacle as sorry as it is familiar. If he finds that the
children come one after another at short intervals—so fast indeed
that no matter how hard he works, nor how many hours, he cannot
keep pace with their needs—the lover whom all the world loves will
have been converted into a disheartened, threadbare incompetent,
whom all the world pities or despises. Instead of being the happy,
competent father, supporting one or two children as they should be
supported, he is the frantic struggler against the burden of five or
six, with the tragic prospect of several more. The ranks of the physically weakened, mentally dejected and spiritually hopeless young
fathers of large families attest all too strongly the immorality of the
system.

PEARL S. BUCK   [1936]

*Born in West Virginia and soon taken to the Orient by her missionary
parents, Pearl Sydenstricker Buck lived in China until the age of seventeen. Her experiences there form the background of many of her best-*

known novels, as well as of her biography of her father, "Andrew," who fought like an "angel" in China, always accompanied by her mother, "Carie." (Miss Buck's comments on "the education of men and women" appear on p. 27.)

Fighting Angel

What Andrew never knew, and what I did not know until I grew up and saw for myself, was that, with all his seeming tranquillity, he was a warrior with the best of them, a son of God continually going forth to battle, a fighting angel. One of my earliest memories in that square mission bungalow was of Monday afternoons devoted to what was called "station meeting," a gathering of the resident missionaries. On Sunday everyone had been religiously whetted by three church services—not only religiously whetted but physically exhausted and emotionally strained. Monday was the day after. I have sat, hundreds of Mondays, a small bewildered child, looking from one stubborn face to the other of my elders, listening to one stubborn voice and then another. What the quarrel was about I never in those days quite knew because it so continually changed. A great deal of it was about money—whether Mr. Wang, the evangelist at the West Gate chapel, should get ten dollars a month instead of eight, for instance. I hoped for ten because I rather liked round-faced merry little Mr. Wang who brought me packages of sweet rice cakes on New Year's Day. Hours went into the discussion of two dollars. But it seemed the two dollars would give Mr. Wang notions—he might want twelve some day—there would be luxuries, perhaps—mission money was sacred—a trust. Mr. Wang must have only eight dollars. Carie got up and went out, her face very red. I followed timidly.

"What's the matter, Mother?" I wanted to know.

"Nothing," she said, pressing her lips together. "Nothing—nothing at all!"

But I saw everything in her face. I went back, crushed, only to find Mr. Wang was quite forgotten now and they were arguing over repainting the church door or about an appropriation for tracts or over opening a new station. Andrew was always wanting to expand the Work, to open more stations, and the others did not want him to do it. Listening to them, my heart swelled with helpless tears. It seemed to me they were always against Andrew and Carie, those men and women with their leathery skins and hard mouths and bitter determined eyes. Andrew sat there, never looking at them, but always out of the window, across the valley to the hills, that brow of his white and serene, his voice quiet and final. Over and over again he was saying, "I feel it my duty to push further into the interior. I regret if it is against your will, but I must do my duty."

Thus Andrew did his share of quarreling, but in his own fashion. He never obeyed any rules at all, because they always seemed to conflict with what was his duty, and he always knew his duty. The others might vote and decide, for the Work was supposed to be carried on by a sort of democratic decision of all the missionaries, subject to their financial boards in America. But Andrew listened only to God. Lack of money never stopped him. If he had no money, and he never had it, he wrote to anybody he knew who had any, asking for it shamelessly. If he got it, and he often did, he was supposed by mission rule to report it and put it into the common budget. But though he would report it if he thought of it, he never gave it up and he used it as he liked—always to push on into the interior, to open up new little centers for his preaching. I have seen other lesser and more bureaucratic missionaries grow almost demented trying to control Andrew. They shouted bitter words at him, they threatened him with expulsion if he did not cease disobeying rules, over and over they called him a heretic, once even called him insane because he seemed to hear nothing they said. He was a rock in the midst of all the frothing—unmoved, unresentful, serene, but so determined, so stubborn in his own way, that I know there have been those who, seeing that high, obstinate, angelic tranquillity, have felt like going out and groaning and beating their heads against a wall in sheer excess of helpless rage. But Andrew did not know even that they were angry with him. Had he not told them God's will? He must obey God's will.

Well, God's will led him along the line of battle all his life. He waged continual war—battle and skirmish, but no retreat. One of his wars, which time and his own determination won him at last, was on the subject of an educated Chinese clergy. When he went to China he found the Chinese clergy for the most part very nearly illiterate. They had been coolies, servants, gatemen in mission compounds, humble men who were easily converted and who more easily stepped into the slight supremacy of standing in a pulpit and haranguing a passing crowd. Andrew was shocked to the soul. He was a scholar and a lover of learning, and he perceived the intellectual quality of the Chinese and how little Chinese of worth and standing could respect these ignorant men. It was, he felt, to bring the Church into contempt.

It seems absurd now, more than half a century later, to realize what a tremendous uproar Andrew made by such a belief. He was called a heretic, he was denounced for liberalism and modernism, for not believing in the power of the Holy Ghost, for trusting to men's brains rather than to God's power—all the hue and cry familiar through centuries to those who have dared to differ from orthodox religion. For, cried the orthodox—do they not always so cry?—God could do anything. He could make a gateman into a great preacher. Human knowledge was nothing but deception, "filthy rags," St. Paul had taught them to call all human righteousness.

Andrew, his head high above the surge, began to gather about him a little group of young intellectuals, five or six, whom he taught in a class in his own study. They were already learned in their own language. He taught them history, religious philosophy, Hebrew, Greek, homiletics—all the things he himself had been taught in seminary. He continued that class over years, its members changing. He never used an uneducated man in any of his churches. Fifty years after he began that war he saw a thriving theological seminary established and he closed his class. His world had caught up to him.

Then there was that question of religious denominations. One of the astounding imperialisms of the West has been the domination over the Chinese of Methodists, Presbyterians, Baptists, and what not, to the number of well over a hundred different types of the Protestant Christian religion alone. This has been, in China, more than a spiritual imperialism—it has been physical as well. There has been much talk of political spheres of influence, of Japan and Germany and England and France, dividing China into areas for trade and power. But the missionaries divided China, too. Certain provinces, certain areas, were allotted to certain denominations for propaganda and there was supposed to be no overstepping.

Andrew was, of course, a born overstepper, because he always did as he pleased. He went where he pleased to preach. If some irate Methodist missionary pointed out that in a certain town there was already a Methodist chapel and that therefore Andrew had no right there, he pshawed and preached on briskly. Accused, he said calmly, "The Methodists aren't accomplishing anything there. The man at their chapel is a stick. I can't let all the people in that town go without the Gospel." Yes, I know he was maddening.

For, illogically, he could be merciless on any who stepped into his preserves. A bogey of our childhood was a certain one-eyed Baptist missionary who, I know now, was a harmless good man, not more obstinate in his ways than others, but who throughout my childhood I felt was a spirit of darkness. I gathered that impression from Andrew because the man believed in and taught immersion as the one true baptism, while Andrew, being Presbyterian, only sprinkled the heads of his converts. But the one-eyed Baptist went about in Andrew's territory telling everybody sprinkling was wrong.

It was a nice situation, humorous only to the impartial observer. For the ignorant people, believing that if a little water was a good thing for the soul, more was better, too often followed the one-eyed man, to Andrew's intense fury. Moreover, it seemed there were certain passages in the New Testament which disconcertingly supported the one-eyed missionary's theory that Jesus walked people entirely under the water. The only thing that really helped Andrew was that a good many of the Chinese were disinclined to get themselves wet all over, especially in the winter, so that immersion was unpopular except in the hot season.

The war went on year after year, and it was the more difficult because Carie maintained a friendship with the pleasant wife of the Baptist. We sat silent through many a meal while Andrew with unwonted fluency said what he felt about other denominations, especially about the folly of immersion, and most especially about the lunacy of telling ignorant people they must be immersed. In his defense it must be said that it was of course extremely trying for him to labor to secure a good Presbyterian convert in one season only to discover upon the next visit that he had been immersed into a Baptist. It was like harboring a cuckoo in the nest. One taught and labored and suffered all the trouble of instilling the fundamentals of Christianity into a heathen and at least one should be able to put down a new member in the statistics. It was nothing short of religious thievery when the member was added to the Baptist glory.

After thirty years of strenuous warfare, the situation was settled one morning by the one-eyed missionary being found dead in his bed of heart failure. Andrew felt he was completely vindicated. He was at the breakfast table when the sad news was brought in by the compound gateman. He poured tinned cream into his coffee and put in a little extra sugar before he answered. He secretly loved sugar and was very stern with himself about it. But this morning he stirred it up. Then he looked around at us all and said in a voice of calm and righteous triumph, "I knew the Lord would not allow that sort of thing to go on forever!"

Afterwards he was a complete and untiring advocate of denominational union. But that is the story of another war and he died before it was finished.

The truth is that the early missionaries were born warriors and very great men, for in those days religion was still a banner under which to fight. No weak or timid soul could sail the seas to foreign lands and defy danger and death unless he did carry his religion as a banner under which even death would be a glorious end. The early missionaries believed in their cause as men these days do not know how to believe in anything. Heaven was actual, a space filled with solid goods. Hell did burn, not only for the evil unbelieving, but far more horrible, for those who died in ignorance. To go forth, to cry out, to warn, to save others—these were frightful urgencies upon the soul already saved. There was a very madness of necessity, an agony of salvation. Those early missionaries were fighting in a desperate cause—to save those who were being born more quickly, dying more swiftly than they could possibly be saved. They laid vast plans, they drew up campaigns over hundreds of thousands of miles, they sped swiftly from soul to soul. They even estimated two minutes to a soul to tell them the way of salvation. "Believe on the Lord Jesus Christ—you believe? Saved, saved!"

It is not a thing to smile at, not even in these days of casual disbelief. It was a terrible thing, a crushing horror, not upon the blessed ignorant who died peacefully and went to hell all unknowing, but upon those frantic desperate men and women who felt upon themselves the responsibility of saving souls. None but the strong could have borne the burden—none but the strong, none but the blindly hopeful, could have eaten, could have slept, could have begotten children and lived out their days under such oppression.

But they were strong. I have not seen anywhere the like of Andrew and his generation. They were no mild stay-at-homes, no soft-living landsmen. If they had not gone as daring missionaries, they would have gone to gold fields or explored the poles or sailed on pirate ships. They would have ruled the natives of foreign lands in other ways of power if God had not caught their souls so young. They were proud and quarrelsome and brave and intolerant and passionate. There was not a meek man among them. They strode along the Chinese streets secure in their right to go about their business. No question ever assailed them, no doubt ever weakened them.

They were right in all they did and they waged the wars of God, sure of victory.

Ah well, they are all gone now! There are no more left like them. Those who take their place in our modern times are shot through with doubt and distrust of themselves and their message. They talk of tolerance and mutual esteem, of liberalizing education and of friendly relations and all such gentle feeble things. They see good in all religions and they no longer wage any more wars and they serve their lives out for a small security. There is no taste in them. I can hear Andrew reading sternly from the Book of Revelation, "So then because thou art lukewarm, and neither cold nor hot, I will spue thee out of my mouth!" The giants are gone.

My memory of that circle of half a dozen soberly dressed people is grim. Now, of course, after years away from them, after knowing what people are like in ordinary places, I realize the impossibility to which their human souls were stretched. The real story of life in a mission station has never yet been told. When it is told it must be told, if it is to be told truthfully, with such vast understanding and tenderness and ruthlessness that perhaps it never can be done justly. The drama in it is terrifying. Imagine two, four, five, six—rarely more—white men and women, some married to each other, the others starved without the compensation of being consecrated to celibacy, imagine them thrown together, hit or miss, without regard to natural congeniality of any sort, in a town or city in the interior of China, living together for years on end, without relief, in the enforced intimacy of a mission compound, compelled to work together, and unable, from the narrowness of their mental and spiritual outlook, to find escape and release in the civilization around them. Within those compound walls is their whole real world. Their real companionships are with each other, or else they live utterly alone. They seldom become proficient enough in the language to enjoy Chinese society or literature, even if their prejudice did not forbid it. There they are, struggling to maintain standards of Christian brotherhood, struggling against their own natural antipathies and desires, wasting their spirits in an attempt to be reconciled to that which is irreconcilable among them.

And what incredible stories, what pathetic, human, inevitable stories! They are hushed, guarded against, kept secret, for the sake of the Work, for the sake of the "home church," for shame's sake, for God's sake—but what stories!

There was that old white-haired gentle man who worked for so many faithful years, only to go at last so strangely mad, so quietly mad, shielded by his agonized loyal wife. The story crept out, as it always comes out, through servants. He had a concubine—a fresh-faced Chinese country girl. Yes, his wife knew. Yes, they had prayed over it in such distress, so long—there was that insatiable thirst in him for—for such things. It was hard to understand—he was so good, really. And then his wife had thought of old Abraham, longing for the young Hagar, and it seemed to her she was like Sarah, and Sarah gave Hagar to Abraham. And God was not angry—God understood. But the story came creeping out, and the old white-haired pair were hastily retired.

And there was the strange little gray-eyed, brown-haired, pallid Chinese child, running about with a native pastor's flock of children. And there was the tall lonely missionary whose wife was years away, educating her own children at home. No one ever knew how that story came creeping out of a little village. An enemy did it, perhaps. No one is without enemies in China. But when the Chinese pastor was asked why among his dark brood there should be the one pale child with foreign eyes, he answered candidly enough, "The white man who is my head lives a very lonely life. And did not David take another man's wife, yet he was the Lord's beloved?"

And there were the two old missionaries, man and wife for forty years, living dangerous, brave, sacrificing lives, and suddenly their life fell into pieces when they were old, and the man, sensitive and worn to his bones, cried out that he had hated his wife for years, that his flesh had revolted at hers, and he had lived in desperate unhappiness. He cried over and over only one thing, shuddering, "I don't want ever to hear her voice again. I don't want to feel the touch of her hand!"

And there is the story of that pleasant-looking missionary, subject for years to moods of mania, when he imagined his kind dark-eyed wife was unfaithful to him, and he would seize a knife from the table or a chair or anything at hand, and try to kill her. Their four little children grew up with the horrible secret and not one of them spoke, because their mother, after the mood was over and after he had made her do penance by crawling around him on her hands and knees, laid it upon them with passion that they were never to tell. So they never told. They grew up with a strange quiet tensity of look, but no one knew. Then the faithful wife died and the missionary married again, a gentle spinster, and she would not tell, and so it went until at last he revealed the truth himself in a fit, and all the years of torture came to life again in the shuddering words of the children, released at last to speak.

And no one has told the story of the spinsters for Christ's sake, the women who in the sweet idealism of their youth go out to lonely mission stations. Year by year they grow paler and more silent, more withered and more wistful, growing sometimes severe and cruel with their fellowmen, and sometimes, too, growing into miracles of pure and gentle selflessness. Most of them never marry, because no man ever asks them—there is none to ask them. Sometimes they marry a man inferior, an older widower, a rough river captain—even, sometimes, though this is never to be told, their Chinese associates. But that is so rare I think it truly need not be told.

And those missionary widowers, marrying so quickly when their wives die that even the polygamous Chinese wonder! The missionary cemeteries are full of wives. I think of one black shaft of a tombstone in a certain walled spot beside the Yangtze River where an old son of God lies buried with three wives and seven of his children about him. But the shaft is raised only to him. Yes, the blood of such white men runs hotter than the blood of the heathen, even though they are men of God.

Yet to understand the impossible narrowness of that mission life is to forgive every bond that is sometimes burst. In that hot foreign climate, in the storms of wind and dust, in the floods and wars and risings of mobs against them, in such uneasiness of life, in such impossibility of achieving what they have set themselves, in bitter isolation from their kind, in the inward oppression of their own souls, that oppression which looks out of their somber eyes and sounds in their voices, apathetic if they are not angry, the wonder is not that men of God quarrel with each other so often, but that they do not kill each other or themselves more often than they do.

They do sometimes kill themselves. There was that missionary wife who rose from her husband's bed after she had borne him eight children and ran in her white gown through the night on a Chinese street and leaped from a cliff into the Yangtze River. And there was that gay and pretty Southern girl who rose in another night and crept downstairs into her own kitchen and with a common chopping knife tried to cut her throat and could not die, and she went up into the attic, her husband and her four little children sleeping, and found a rope and hung herself, and she leaped from the window and the rope broke and still she could not die, and she staggered, dripping blood, upstairs again into the bathroom and found poison and so died at last. There are such stories, but nobody wants them told, for the Work must go on. I say the wonder is not that there are these stories and scores like them, but that there are not many more than there are. Conversion does not really change the needy human heart.

But of course I only came to know all this afterwards. In those days of my childhood I may as well confess I was afraid of Andrew and all of them. My own private real life was lived entirely elsewhere in a place where there was no God at all.

There were mornings, bright sunny spring mornings, when one woke up to imagination. Usually it was a day when Andrew was going away on a journey. I may as well tell still more of the truth. A certain relief came over us all when he was going away on one of his preaching tours. The servants ran briskly to fetch and pack. There was always a bedding roll to get ready, a long bag of brown homespun cotton cloth into which was put a thin mattress, a blanket, and a pillow. Andrew was fastidious about lice in inn beds. If he were traveling by land this bedding was thrown across the back of his white donkey. Then he, wearing a sun helmet and a light gray cotton suit, or earlier his Chinese robes, and carrying a cane under his arm to beat off dogs, would straddle the donkey and the bedding roll, his long legs dangling until his feet were not two inches from the ground. He always said drily that if the donkey tried to kick up he simply held his feet on the ground. But it was a sturdy beast and trotted off with dogged gaiety, its ears cocked wickedly, tail swishing. We watched that gaunt indomitable figure disappear down the cobbled, willow-shaded lane, and then a sense of peace fell over us all. The servants dawdled. Carie went to the organ and sang a long time or she read a book, and I—I went out into the garden and played all day there was no God. And Carie often helped unconsciously by saying at twilight, "We'll skip prayers tonight and take a walk instead—just for once God won't mind." God! There hadn't been any God all day.

On one such evening I carried imagination to a dangerous pitch. I decided not to say my prayers at all. I could not sleep for a long time, dreading the darkness. For in the darkness I knew of course there really was a God—there was that Eye that saw everything. But I stuck to my wickedness and fell asleep to wake, to my astonishment, perfectly safe, the peaceful summer sunshine streaming in my window. I never feared Andrew quite so much again. God had not done anything to me.

Now that I am no longer young, I know that Andrew never meant to frighten a little child or dreamed that he did. There were times, I remember now, when he came back from his long tours spent and weary but in a sort of glory of content, his work well done, God well served. He seldom saw beauty, and yet there were times when he said at supper, "The mountains were pretty today, covered with red and yellow azaleas everywhere." Sometimes he even brought back an armful of the flowers, if it so happened that his heart was content with what had happened to him. Sometimes he told us what he had seen—a small hill panther had crouched at the side of the road, and he had not known whether to go on or turn back, but he had promised to be at a certain village at noon and there would be those who waited for him. So he went on without seeming to notice, and the beast had not sprung. Wolves he saw often in winter, sometimes running down into the fields where the farmers chased them. But I was disappointed when I first saw a wolf because it looked like a big village dog and little more, except it was an odd dull gray in color.

In the spring Andrew was always gone. He grew restless as winter closed and as soon as the spring floods began to well into the canals from the river, swollen with melting snows in the upper gorges, he began to plan his long preaching tours by junk or upon his white ass. When Carie lay dying she said to me, knowing well enough that some woman would have to look after Andrew, "Look out for spring! About the first of April he gets hard to manage. It won't matter if he's eighty, he'll want to get away over the country and behind the hills preaching." Well, it was a good thing he always had the Gospel to preach so that he could go into all the world and be happy, feeling it was his duty. Not everyone is so lucky. But then I always said Andrew had a happy life. God always seemed to have told him to do what he would have wanted to do anyway.

SALLY BENSON [1943]

Sally Benson, who was born in 1900 in St. Louis, is known chiefly for her Junior Miss *stories and* Meet Me in St. Louis. *But she is also very*

knowledgeable in the ways of adults. What women truly think about
their sons is the subject of the following story.

He'll Outgrow It

When Mrs. Scott's son, Richard, wrote her that he was going to be
married, she spent the morning telephoning to her closest friends.
"Richard's going to be married, so he writes," she said, "and he's
already rented a small apartment. I suppose that Toledo was just
too much for him, living in a hotel and everything. I suppose he's
just lonesome and wants a *home*. Although goodness knows how he
can plan to have a home, moving about the way he does, six months
here and eight months there. . . . No, I've never met her. All I know
is that her name is Helen Voorhees and that he must be in love with
her, or he wouldn't be marrying her, would he?"

When she had finished telephoning, she sat down at her Governor
Winthrop desk and wrote Richard a letter on heavy pale-gray paper.
"My dear Richard:" she wrote, "Your news came as a surprise. I am
delighted, of course, that you appear to be so happy, and I hope
everything will turn out for you as splendidly as you seem to think
it will. I hope that 'Helen' (such a pretty name! 'Helen, thy beauty
is to me Like those Nicaean barks of yore, That gently, o'er a per-
fumed sea, The weary, wayworn wanderer bore To his own native
shore') understands that you are indeed a 'weary, wayworn wanderer' and that you have told her all about how you have to 'pull up
stakes' every few months, especially now when you may be called
goodness knows where on defense work. I am sure you *have* told
her, and I am sure she is a very remarkable young woman and understands that a consulting engineer's work makes this necessary.
I want you to be *fair* to her. Thank you, my dear boy, for asking me
to make the trip to Toledo for the wedding. There is nothing I would
like better to do, but I am going to curb my impatience, and who
knows but that someday in the distant future you can bring 'Helen'
home. I feel that I would rather see her for the first time in my own
little place, where I am surrounded by the memories of your dear
father and your own happy boyhood, and not in Toledo, a city about
which I know nothing and where, I am sure, I would feel *most*
strange. That is, I think I would, as I gather from your letters that
it is indeed a 'jumping-off spot.' Would you like me to send your
books on to you? There they sit on their cozy shelves in your bedroom, but I am sure they miss you! And the things in your bureau

and in the toy chest. What about them? Would you care for any of your pictures, or would you prefer that they remain on the walls of your bedroom, where they have hung for so long? I am afraid that in moving them spots will show where the wallpaper has faded, but that is a minor detail and deserves no consideration. Write me, my dear son, and I will do as you wish. Now, my fondest love to 'Helen' (my, what a popular name that was with young mothers of thirty years ago!) and tell her that I will write her soon. Affectionately, Mother."

In reply to her letter, Richard wrote that he would let her know about his things later. And Mrs. Scott, with set lips, dusted his books and put them in cartons, ready for shipping. She stripped the pictures from his walls and packed them in a barrel, together with his framed collection of butterflies, some shells, souvenirs of the summer they had spent at the shore, his school and college trophies, and the stuffed owl he had shot when he was ten. As the owl, its wings spread and its glassy eyes staring, had been his most prized possession, she sprayed it with Larvex, wrapped it in tissue paper, and placed it on the top of the barrel. Then she pushed the barrel and the boxes of books onto the sleeping porch, drew down the shades in Richard's room, and closed his door. Her face was stony. "This is the way he wants it," she thought.

Before Richard had been born, his room had been built expressly for him by adding an L-shaped wing to the ground floor of the house. It was a large, sunny room that faced south, and it had its own bath and a sleeping porch. To be sure, when he was a baby the room had been used solely as a playroom, and Richard had slept in a crib next to his mother's bed upstairs, so that she could hear him if he cried in the night. During this interval, Mr. Scott had been moved to the small, sparsely furnished guest room, where he had remained, without adequate closet space, until the day of his death. When Richard was six and had to be made into a little man, he was transferred downstairs to his own handsome quarters. For a week after the move, Mrs. Scott slept on the couch in the living room, and then, somewhat reassured by the fact that Richard was taking the change beautifully, she uneasily took to her own bed once more. Richard, his mother boasted, was a difficult child. It pleased her to remember that he was eighteen months old before his food stayed on his stomach for any length of time. By his eleventh birthday, he had run the gamut of children's diseases, knocked a chip off a front tooth, broken his ankle, got hopelessly behind in his arithmetic, and been run over

by a Mrs. Forman, who was innocently backing out of the Scotts'
driveway after a successful afternoon at bridge. Richard was only
bruised, but Mrs. Scott and Mrs. Forman had not spoken for years
afterward.

The day of Richard's wedding, his mother sat in the living room
of her house in Monroe, Connecticut, and thought about him. The
door that led to the screened side porch was open, and although it
was almost unbearably hot outdoors, the room was pleasant. A bowl
of stock and old-fashioned pinks on the low pine table gave a spicy
scent to the air, and the revolving spray made a cool sound as it
played on the lawn. The lilac bush by the window drooped in the
heat, and a fly buzzed and battered itself against the screen door of
the porch. Mrs. Scott sat very still, her small, square hands folded in
her lap, her feet, in their neat black oxfords, crossed daintily. In
spite of the weather she wore a thin black wool skirt that reached to
her ankles, a black silk blouse with a white collar of Irish lace, and
a black velvet band around her throat. Her hair was damp from the
heat and curled in soft rings at the nape of her neck.

The afternoon dragged on, and as the time of the ceremony drew
near she arose, and going to the door that led to Richard's room,
she opened it and stood on the threshold. The room looked strange
and uninhabited; the mattress on the bed had been folded over and
covered with newspapers; the bureau top and the bookshelves were
bare; and the blue-and-white wallpaper showed ugly spots where
the pictures had been removed. The air was close and smelled
strongly of camphor. For a few minutes she stood looking at the
narrow bed, at the boyish severity of the furnishings, the practical
gray of the rug, and the square solidity of the toy chest. It was a
boy's room, she thought, and nodded her head in satisfaction.

Mrs. Scott was glad she had written Richard, in reply to his suggestion that he and Helen might come East on their honeymoon,
that she was sure they would be better off by themselves. It was
shocking to think of jars of powder and creams on the bureau, indecent to think of scented feminine things hanging in the closet that
had known only the acrid smell of youth. Someday, she thought,
someday, if the marriage lasted and if he insisted on bringing Helen
home, she would move another bed into the guest room. It was the
most she would do.

She closed the door and went back to her chair, where she sat
watching the clock. When she was sure the wedding was over, she
sighed, and her eyes filled with tears. She went to her desk and began

to write. "My dear boy: So you are an old married man now! You will understand, I know, when I say that I cannot believe it. It was warm here today, but pleasantly so, and I felt for you this morning when I read of the 'hot spell' in the Middle West. I hope you weren't hurt by my seeming indifference to your suggested visit here, but to tell you the truth, my dear son, I didn't feel 'up to' the strain of entertaining 'newlyweds' (what a horrid word!). If, however, you could slip off for a few days sometime in the near future by yourself, I would love to see you and hear all your news, which must be very exciting indeed! This morning, Red Curtis passed the house on his way to play tennis. He is spending his furlough with his mother, and he looked well. He was surprised when I told him you were being married this very day, and he looked such a boy with his nice tan and his mop of red hair that it gave me a shock when I realized that there is only a few months' difference in your age and his. I am sure Mrs. Curtis is delighted to have him home with her once more. I told him I hadn't laid eyes on you for almost two years, but that it wouldn't be long, I hoped, before you were home for a brief visit. Write me, my dear boy, as I am anxious to know how things are working out for you. Affectionately as always, Mother. P.S. My very best to 'Helen,' too, of course!"

The summer drew to a close, and from time to time there were letters from Richard, and even, at first, long and detailed letters from Helen. Mrs. Scott answered Helen's letters conscientiously and briefly within a week after she had received them, but her letters to Richard were warm and bore the small bits of gossip that she thought he would want to hear.

It was the end of September when she received a letter from him that made her almost dizzy with happiness. It was still hot in Toledo, he wrote. They were pretty sick of their small apartment, but as he was about to be shifted around again, there was no sense in looking for another place. He thought it likely that he would be sent on to the plant in Bridgeport, and if it meant a short stay there, he and Helen had been debating whether or not it was worth while for her to make the move with him. Probably it would be better for her to stay with her family. The way it looked now, he would only be a month or so there, and then on to Detroit for a really decent stay of a year or more. There was the expense of moving, and money didn't grow on trees, and hotels cost such a hell of a lot. And what did she think?

Mrs. Scott answered cautiously. She suggested that if the stay in

Bridgeport was such a short one, it might be more practical if he came alone. In that case he could live at home and have his old room, which was perfect for one person but might not be too comfortable for Helen. There was the little car, too, she reminded him, which he was more than welcome to, and he could drive to work in about an hour. "I hesitate," she added, "to interfere in your plans, and if 'Helen' has made up her mind that she would be better off waiting for you in Toledo until you are more settled, I would not like her to change on my account. This is a rather dull little town in the winter, and I suppose, like all young women, she feels happier surrounded by her own friends."

She was not surprised when Richard wired her that he was coming East and coming alone. She flew into a fever of activity. She opened the windows of his room and let in the sharp autumn air. She unpacked his books and arranged them on the shelves: *The Call of the Wild, Mooswa, Kidnapped, Treasure Island, Les Misérables, Rob Roy, The Pirate,* the sets of Tennyson, Dickens, and Mark Twain. She brought bound volumes of *Popular Mechanics* down from the attic and arranged them on the lower shelves along with the "Motor Boys" and the "Aviation Boys" series. She polished his silver trophy cups and hung his rifle on the wall where it always used to be, between the picture of the dead moose and the photograph of the senior class at the Monroe Grammar School. She opened the toy chest and rearranged the Meccano sets, the small sailboats, the catcher's mask, and the boxes of games, noticing as she did so that the things looked almost new, as though they had not been played with very long or very hard. It reminded her how Richard had tired of his toys—more quickly than most boys. She brushed the stuffed owl and placed it on Richard's bureau. It was so large that there was scarcely any room left for his military brushes and his comb. She put fresh curtains at the windows and made his bed. When she had finished, she gave a last look around. The room had recaptured its personality and was what it had always been—a boy's room.

Yet, oddly enough, as she waited at the station for him the next day, she was nervous. And when he stepped off the train it was a moment before she recognized him. He looked taller and thinner, and as he kissed her, he seemed impatient and hurried. They drove away from the station in silence, over to the Post Road, under the fading elms. She glanced at him out of the corner of her eye and saw that his mouth was tired and petulant and that his clothes were almost shabby. When they turned onto the dirt road that led to the house, he smiled and drew a deep breath. The autumn sunlight was a warm gold, and the fields were rich with purple asters and harsh yellow goldenrod. Ahead of them the hills rose, bronze and hazy. "Smells good," Richard said.

"I've always thought this was a particularly pretty little spot," Mrs. Scott answered.

The house was clean and quiet. The kitchen clock and the clock on the mantelpiece in the living room sounded noisy as they entered. Mrs. Scott took Richard by the arm and pulled him toward his room. "It's just the same," she said. "Just as you left it."

He flung his suitcase on the bed and stood looking around, "Well, I'd better wash up," he said. He opened his bag and took out his razor, shaving brush and soap, hairbrushes and comb. He carried them to the bureau and moved the owl to one side. "Have I time for a bath?"

"Oh, of course," his mother answered. "Of course, dear. Will a half-hour be all right?"

"Sure thing." He took a clean shirt from the bag and laid it on the foot of the bed. Mrs. Scott watched him as he unfastened his tie. When he had loosened the top button of his shirt, he stopped.

"Oh!" his mother exclaimed. "Well, I have a few more things to do before dinner is ready, and I'll leave you to yourself."

When she left the room, he shut the door after her.

Although Mrs. Scott had planned the dinner with loving care, it was not a success. Richard ate the tender slices of roast beef, the late garden peas, the delicious brown biscuits, and the flaky apple pie without comment. His face was sulky, and she racked her brains to think of small, interesting bits of gossip that might make him laugh. He listened to her quietly, occasionally asking questions which showed that he was not sure what she was talking about. "Who's she?" or "I don't remember him. What did you say his name was?"

After dinner he went into the living room and listened to the radio while she washed the dishes. And later they sat listening to the radio together, scarcely speaking, until almost ten. Suddenly he switched it off and looked toward the clock. "If it's all right with you," he said, "I think I'll turn in."

She followed him to the door of his room. "I think you'll find everything."

"Oh, sure," he said. "Sure."

"I'm afraid I haven't had a chance to ask you about Helen." Her voice was as casual as though she had said she had forgotten to ask how his new bicycle worked.

"She's O.K. I wired her when I got to Bridgeport."

"Well, dear—" She lifted her face, and he kissed her on the cheek and closed the door.

Mrs. Scott pulled her rocking chair close to the fire and sat down. She breathed softly, so that she could hear Richard as he moved about the room. For almost an hour she sat, trying to imagine step by step what he was doing, what things his hands lingered on as they touched. His light still shone under the door, but he was so quiet that she wondered if he might not have fallen asleep.

She got up and opened his door. The first thing she saw was that the owl had been moved from the bureau, and in its place was the picture of a girl. She was not an especially pretty girl, and Mrs. Scott, staring at her, realized that she had nothing to fear.

Richard lay face down on his bed. He had not even undressed. As his mother stood in the doorway, he turned and lifted his head, and she saw that he must have been crying. He looked very young, almost as young as he had been when he cried because she would not let him have a canoe. She had given in finally about the canoe, and before very long he had tired of it and begged for a boat with an outboard motor. She sat down on the bed beside him. "My!" she said. "If you knew how funny you look in that little bed! If you hadn't rushed me so, the other one would have been here. I was saying to Mr. Norton at the furniture store only this morning that you'd probably outgrown it and that it certainly would not do for *two* people.

"You see," she went on hastily, "I've been rather daring and taken matters into my own hands. I decided it was rather—well, rather selfish of Helen not to be willing to come East with you. Sometimes I don't understand the young women of today."

Richard sat up, and his face was puzzled. "But Helen—" he began.

"I can understand your wanting to make excuses for her," his mother said. "But in my day a wife's place was with her husband. And if you want my opinion, she'd better give up her foolish ideas and come East as fast as she can. *Her* place is with you."

She rose briskly and walked toward the door, Richard's eyes were clear and he looked happy and excited. For some unaccountable reason her mind traveled upstairs to the storeroom, which was full of the other toys that he had begged for and that she had given him.

And she smiled when she remembered that they were as good as
new.

WINIFRED WELLES [1944]

*This fragile poem shows how subtly intermingled a brother and a lover
can become in a woman's mind. Winifred Welles (Mrs. Harold H.
Shearer), who was born in Connecticut and briefly attended Barnard College, was the author of five volumes of poetry, one published posthu-
mously. She died in 1939.*

White Valentine

Since you are dead, and I am gone
And that old house we knew now known
Only to strangers, I will cut
A paper heart for you, and put
A picture in its center. Faint,
And delicate, and small, I'll paint
Two figures there, and they will be
A miniature of you and me.
We're by my long gold mirror; bright
The bitter afternoon's cold light
Comes thinly through the windowpane
And strikes across us. A fine skein
Of leafless boughs and twigs is drawn
Across the sky; on the white lawn,
Their shadows in an intricate net
Are with a clear precision set.
It's winter, and we are at home
Together in my pale, blue room.
There you, a gaunt boy, gravely stand,
Sedately moving your thin hand.
I am the tall child in the chair,
Letting you brush my long, light hair.

Upon this shape of brittle lace
And gentle tints, there is no place

For the crude color of the heart.
This is a pastel day, apart
From all the later somber years,
The spite, mistrust, the sullen tears
And sad; from the crouched attitudes
Of separate terrors, from the feuds,
Shameful and harsh, between a brother
And sister close to one another,
But cleaved as woman and as man;
From all the honored daily plan,
That was the falsely mutual life
Of two not husband and not wife,
Caught frantic in a marriage mesh,
Which was of blood but not of flesh.
All that's their book, closed now forever,
This but a picture for the cover.

So, on my fragile valentine,
Let not one stain fall from that vine
Which, in the temples and the wrists,
Distorted, deviously twists;
Not one drop spatter from that flood
Which is the dense and scalding blood.
Here, decorated in white lace,
We share an instant all of grace,
And tenderness, and innocence.
Briefly, but ever, here relents
All taut devotion. On this heart,
We live released in trivial art,
Lovely, naïve.
                    It's winter weather,
And we are in my room together,
Amused, at peace; I in my chair,
You, standing, brushing my long hair.

LENORE G. MARSHALL　　　　　[1944]

Lenore G. Marshall, who was born in New York City in 1897 and graduated from Barnard College in 1919, now divides her time between her writing and her activities in such organizations as the National Committee for Sane Nuclear Policy. Her latest novel, The Hill Is Level, *was published in 1959.*

Flashlight

Tonight the lap of waves sliding in on the beach hardly rose to the veranda; all sound was embraced and confined below by the perpendicular cliffs that tumbled roughly from house to shore. It was a warm midsummery gentle night, so dark that the sandy trail and stepping stones of the hill merged with encroaching boulders and brambles; only the deep blue sky mapped by sharp stars was distinct and the windows of the little shingled salt-box house, gold oblongs with lamps alight inside.

The lamps were kerosene. Tim Crane went primitive on his vacation. So Mrs. Forrester, his mother-in-law, went primitive too. Luckily however her trusty flashlight was tucked away safely in the desk drawer behind her. She was feeling nervous about the lamps and candles for everyone, particularly Tim, pushed around in the crowded room with no thought at all of fires. Most of the group sat on the floor since there was an insufficient number of chairs or they got up and danced to the static of the radio. Tim strode over to a corner where he mixed drinks and as many women who could get near him drifted to the same corner. Somehow or other he had lost the cocktail shaker and was using a milk bottle. When he put it down, wet with alcohol, on the varnished table Mrs. Forrester could not restrain a distressed warning. "It will leave a ring, Timmy!" she called, regretting it as soon as she had spoken but as usual he acted as though he had not heard. Mrs. Forrester turned to see if anyone had noticed. "The landlady's furniture," she explained brightly to a young man beside her. "That Tim!" She wished to add, "You know they say a hero isn't a hero to his butler. It's the same to his mother-in-law," but she thought of it too late; the young man had already moved away and just then Tim knocked over a glass which broke. Not having possessions of her own Mrs. Forrester

minded such episodes although why should *she* bother?—for everything was Tim's, his rented summer cottage, his car, his liquor, his
favorite food, his friends; she didn't so much mind that everything
belonged to him as that he lost or broke everything. Even Mrs. Forrester perforce was his.

Mrs. Forrester's hair had been dyed back to its original color, dark
chestnut, because that way she felt better equipped, but repeated
chemicals had made it bushy and cottony, like brown mattress-
stuffing at large around her pinched and shrunken features. Her
hair marked her as rather a character, it proclaimed that this was
what she could make of herself in spite of the passage of time, it
was intended as a sign, gallant, undaunted, it grew out prominently
in a matted nest, giving the lie to the startled wan old bird face
within. She went everywhere with the Cranes. At parties she sat on
the last chair and nobody wanted to talk to her. She would be animated and strive to do her share but the others, all younger in years
although, she told herself firmly, no younger in interests, after the
first scrupulous politeness with which they addressed her, became
absent-minded; they would hunt with their eyes for an escape
around the room saying "Excuse me just a moment." She might sit
alone with no one beside her for as much as ten minutes at a time
but not relaxed, not resigned, not able to play the part of elderly
philosophical onlooker in spite of her detached smile, secretly deeply
embarrassed and under a strain waiting for a chance to get into
things. One enjoyed being in things. But it was as though Tim deliberately excluded her. Setting the pace as a tornado might, when
he wanted to argue people all argued, when he wanted to dance
they all danced, but he had a way of rarely hearing Mrs. Forrester,
addressing her only when necessary, never calling her by name,
which made her feel as though she did not quite exist. Of course he
was not actually rude. On the contrary Tim was the soul of courtesy
and boisterous good humor toward everyone, very popular; only he
and she knew about his blank innocence of her presence and that
this was in revenge for her sin of being there and dependent upon
him. She was always doing her best to placate him.

"My son-in-law's recent brilliant success," she would remark to
their guests, giving little fidgety preening pats to her spectacular
mop of thick hair, making a careful point of discussing Tim's work.
"You've heard about my son-in-law's latest discovery in chemistry,
haven't you? A great contribution! They've just made him a full-
fledged professor at Harvard. Full-fledged." At least there was an

inner satisfaction in letting him thus hear her showing appreciation of him, expatiating upon his experiments to whoever would
listen. "What he's getting at in his laboratory is this," Mrs. Forrester
always explained. She could have taken great delight in these conversations since she had a sort of inside track to the scientific world,
a favored position through her relationship to Tim, had it not been
for her constant foolish fear of him.

Mrs. Forrester looked across the room and for the life of her she
didn't know why she had called out so impulsively about a little
thing like the alcohol stain, wondering whether she had offended
him in public. At last she managed to catch Tim's gaze after hard
staring and she flashed him a smile.

"Anything I can do, Timmy?" she called.

Tim Crane was talking to handsome Mrs. Boris. He continued undisturbed, leaning over the girl in the chair. His wide shoulders, that
gave elegance even to a sports shirt, twitched very slightly; he
laughed at some remark of the girl's with extra hilarity.

The kerosene lamps made it hotter, and the tobacco-filled over-
crowded room gave one a sense of breathing in something solid. Mrs.
Forrester fluffed out her dark youthful hair, sitting erect on a stool,
her spine prodded by the desk drawer. Things were untidy and upset by this time, what with the cocktail shaker lost, books fingered
and put back in the wrong places, rugs pushed aside, that alcohol
ring on the table at the other end of the room. Tim's wife, somehow
diminishingly Mrs. Forrester's daughter, curled in the alcove, talking quietly, as though she were trying to hide. A gust of warm wind
blew in through an open window, bent a candle flame. A very good
thing indeed, Mrs. Forrester decided, that she had thought to conceal her flashlight in the desk before people came. One could never
tell when a flashlight would come in handy; besides, this was her
own flashlight, bought with her own money, not in any way Tim's.
It was a particularly good one, too, reliable, with a powerful bulb.
It gave a sense of security to have a thing like that within reach of
one's bed at night, in a tinder box house like this one. Tim could
keep his candles and lanterns, which were all very well for a man
with no imagination about what might happen; anyway this was
his house, if he wanted candles, of course that was his privilege.

"Anything I can get you?" Mrs. Forrester called out helpfully to
young Mrs. Boris, who was lounging in the deep chair across the
room. "A sandwich? Did Timmy offer you another drink?"

Tim got up. "What about a midnight swim?" he proposed to the room in general. "That's what I need on a hot night like this. Who's coming?"

They began to stir from sofas and cushions on the floor. For heaven's sakes, what nonsense, thought Mrs. Forrester, but she held her tongue.

"Wonderful idea," people were saying, dubiously at first, then more gaily. Tim's wife, Mrs. Forrester's daughter, jumped to her feet.

"How energetic!" sighed young Mrs. Boris. "Swell!" cried a stout, perspiring man.

"Everybody coming?" Smiling and commanding Tim stood among them, in the center of the disordered room.

"It's dark on the hill," a girl called from the veranda. "We'll break our necks on this path. What do you do about your rocks, Tim?"

"Who's got a flashlight?" Tim asked. He began rummaging around the room, pushing magazines and glasses about. "I lost mine." He laughed in amusement at himself.

Mrs. Forrester sat quietly on her stool against the desk, watching them get ready with kindly interest.

"We've got to have some light on those rocks," said Tim, still shoving at things. "Damned if I know where I put mine. You have a flashlight?" he said suddenly to Mrs. Forrester.

"No," she said quickly. "*I* haven't one either."

"Of course you have," said Tim. "You always have. Where is it?"

She knew what would happen. He would put it down somewhere on the dark beach and that would be the end of it. "I have no idea where it's gone to," she said.

"Oh, come along," cried Tim. "You know perfectly well where you put it. Stop hiding it."

The crowd stood around waiting. But of course he had no right to her flashlight. It was *hers*. She felt herself stiffening inside, resisting him, and suddenly she was in a panic, for in spite of the hot iron wall against him she had only her helplessness overwhelming her and spreading throughout her body. "No really, Timmy," she protested, trying to muster a casual voice for him and for those invading hordes surrounding her. "Really I've mislaid it. I was hunting for it just this morning. It's simply gone. Somebody must have taken it," she added boldly, as an afterthought.

Tim marched up to her the laugh still on his mouth. "Listen," he said, "nothing's going to happen to your old flashlight. We want it, that's all."

"But, Tim," she laughed too, cornered by his huge bulk above her, "be reasonable." She kept laughing for the sake of the party, looking up pleadingly from her straight stool. He was so close that she could not even rise. She could only laugh because there were all of those people around.

He took hold of her hair. He clutched humorously at her brown cottony hair and they could both feel his fingers fastening in its thick dry nest. The men and women chuckled and tittered, for he was just like a mastiff with a mouse in its paws, playing with the mouse as he shook her head loosely back and forth.

"Come along," he ordered jovially. No one could help roaring at the way the dyed cotton hair and the little pinched face jerked from side to side on the stringy neck.

Only Mrs. Forrester and Tim knew the moment that his playful clutch became deadly. Suddenly, although no one could see the wrenching force in his fingers, he was pulling the hair right up from the skull.

"You're hurting!" cried Mrs. Forrester, astonished. His fingers under the matted bush were really gripped, really pulling and lifting the hair from its roots, so that the roots strained, so that such a sharp pain struck Mrs. Forrester that she thought he would never stop until her whole scalp flew off, until her head was plucked from her shoulders; and Tim thought so too. He felt that awful gaudy pretentious wad in his hands and he did not want to let it go.

"Where's your flashlight?" he demanded.

She said: "In the desk drawer. Behind me."

It almost seemed that he was sorry she had told him; his fingers loosened slowly. But then he withdrew his hand from the disheveled tangle, stretched his fingers in freedom, and reached around her to the desk drawer behind. Her back had been pressed against it, guarding it like a shield. She leaned forward for him to open the drawer and he found the flashlight at once.

"Well, come on!" Timmy cried. "Everybody ready? All aboard who's going aboard!"

They pushed out of the door into the sweet pervading summer night. Below soft water lapped upon the beach and endless darkness rose up over the cliffs and extended and enveloped them altogether except for the sound of their steps scrambling down the path and their voices shouting, answering, diminishing. Mrs. Forrester stood alone in the doorway, her hands to her head.

"You'll see all right with that," she called after them, vainly trying to make herself heard above the chatter. "It's the best flashlight I ever had. Be careful. Please!"

DILYS LAING [1950]

Dilys Laing, who was a novelist as well as a poet, was born in North Wales in 1906 and died in New Hampshire in 1960. Educated chiefly by private tutors and at the Slade School of Art in London, in 1936 she married Alexander Laing, a writer, and moved to the United States. She became a citizen two years after her son was born in 1940.

Once Upon an Eternity

An angel stood in the sunflooded room beside the bookcase looking at my books.

Hello. Help yourself, I said. Read as many as you like.

Thank you, the angel said. I've just come out of that one. He pointed to Religio Medici.

There are others you may not have gone through, I suggested.

Undoubtedly, he replied with a charming smile. But I see through them all. Come with me and I'll show you something more profound.

He led me into the field and gave me a small flower. I realized that I would never learn the language in which it was written but the binding moved me to tears. The angel gently took the flower away and said, Come with me and I'll show you something close to you.

He took me to where a goat stood throwing back his bearded chin and looking at the world from upside down. Seeing me, the goat gathered himself, rose like a wave and butted me hard. Closer to me, indeed! I thought. He loves you, the angel laughed. Then he said, Come with me and I'll show you something farther from you.

He took me to a garden where a child sat on the grass petting a
young winged leopard. I sat down and played with the child
for several minutes before I realized that it was myself at
the age of two. Now come with me, the angel said, and I will
show you a thing more wonderful.

He took me to the barn and there on the side of it, on the weather-
bleached boards of grained silver, a man was wreathed and
crucified. Come with me, the angel said, and I will show
you a sadder thing.

He led me to an orchard and told me to look up into an apple tree.
There among the fruit I saw growing from one of the
branches a human foetus. Look close, the angel said. I looked
and saw in the pleated face of the rosepink monkey the fore-
shadowing of the features of my son.

I turned to the angel and asked, Is there no hope? And the angel
said, Break the branch.

As I broke the branch the wings of the angel withered and vanished.
The branch faded from my hand and I saw that the angel
was my son grown tall.

Your wings! I cried. What has happened to your wings?

He looked over first one shoulder then the other then shrugged them
both. Oh, those?

If it's not rubbers or raincoats, it's wings, he muttered. Mother, he
said reprovingly, you're always harping on trifles. Do try to
leave me alone. I have so much to do.

SHIRLEY JACKSON   [1953]

*Shirley Jackson and her husband Stanley Edgar Hyman boast that their
"major exports are books and children." Her own writings include not
only unsettling tales like "The Lottery," but also what she calls "disre-
spectful" stories about her progeny. Born in San Francisco in 1919, she
was graduated from Syracuse University in 1940 and now lives in Ben-
nington, Vermont. One day, in Vermont, her son Laurie came home from
school . . .*

Life Among the Savages

. . . with his jacket torn and an air of great innocent suffering. He was half an hour late, and he was accompanied by two of his friends, both of unsavory character; they strode manfully into the house and on into the study where my husband was peacefully doing research for an article on extinct fishes. I heard part of the conversation from upstairs where I was trying to dress Jannie after her nap. With my mind almost unoccupied, I listened without any real attention. "And they threw stones," one of Laurie's friends said in a thin, excited voice; he is somewhat older than Laurie, and he usually tells Laurie's stories for him when Laurie is too modest to tell them for himself, "and they said *terrible* language, and they *hit* Laurie, and *everything.*"

"Where were *you* all this time?" my husband asked. I could feel through the floor the righteous indignation mounting in the study. "Where were you two while these boys were hitting Laurie?"

There was a moment of quiet, and then Laurie's voice: "George was behind the tree, and William was running up here to tell you." Laurie apparently stopped to think for a minute. "I didn't run," he added finally, "because I *can't* very well, in these snow pants."

The enemy—I could see them from the upstairs front window— were still lingering outside, backing down the hill slowly, prepared to do further battle. Then I heard the front door slam. My husband issued forth, supported valiantly on either side by Laurie's two friends, while Laurie, with commendable discretion, stayed just inside the front door, yelling, "Here comes my *father!*"

Halfway up the hill, the enemy waited for my husband, and, although I could not hear, I could see them—my husband speaking fiercely and the enemy looking at him with wide, honest eyes. Presently the battle was resolved; my husband turned and stamped back to the house and the enemy went on down the hill, turning at a safe distance to call inaudible insults.

When my husband came inside, I went downstairs to meet him. "Well?" I said.

All of them began talking at once. "And they *hit* Laurie and *every*thing," his talkative friend said; "They even chased *me*," his other friend added.

"And these darn old snow pants," Laurie said at the same time, while over all of them rose the voice of my husband saying, "Ought to be taught better manners. Boy like that deserves a good whipping."

Jannie came down the stairs behind me, asking hopefully, "Was Laurie bad? I'm good, aren't I? Did Laurie do something *new* bad?"

When I had isolated the various political maneuvers into offense and defense, the story went something like this: Laurie and his two friends were walking home from school, entirely without malice, not hurting anybody and minding their own business. As a matter of fact, they stopped quite of their own accord to pick up the books of a little girl who had dropped them into a mud puddle. Furthermore, they were not even thinking any harm, because they were all three most unpleasantly surprised when the largest of the enemy, a boy named David Howell, came up behind them and pulled on the hood of Laurie's jacket. When Laurie said "Hey!"—and we all agreed he was perfectly justified—David spat at him, pronounced half a dozen forbidden epithets, and finally struck him. Laurie's two friends took no active part in the battle, partly because David was bigger than any of them and partly because, as they explained at great length, they felt strongly that it was Laurie's fight and interference would not be sporting. They had come home with Laurie, however, to be his witnesses and to see that justice was done.

"What did you do to David?" I asked my husband.

"I said you'd tell his mother," he said virtuously.

I have seen David's mother, have even spoken to her at P.-T.A. meetings. She is one of those impressive women who usually head committees on supervising movies, taking the entire sixth grade on a tour of one of our local factories, or outlawing slingshots, and I daresay she would be the first person everyone would think of if there should arise an occasion for the mothers to lift the school building and carry it bodily to another location. I felt very strongly, as a matter of fact, that bringing David's mother into this incident was a grave tactical error.

But there were the four of them looking at me trustingly—five, if you count Jannie, who was saying "Poor, poor Laurie," and rubbing his head violently.

"I'll phone her right away," I said, trying to make it sound resolute and threatening. After some unavoidable fumbling with the telephone book I found the Howells' number and finally, with everyone sitting around the phone expectantly, cleared my throat, straightened my shoulders, and briskly gave the number to the operator. After a minute, a strong, no-nonsense voice said "Hello?"

"Hello," I said faintly, "is this Mrs. Howell?"

"Yes," she said. She sounded quite civil, so I changed my mind and said as politely as I could, "Mrs. Howell, I don't know if your boy David has told you about attacking my son Laurie on his way home from school today, but I thought I'd better call you anyway and see if we can't do something about it." Realizing that I had ended a little weakly, I added, "Laurie is *quite* badly hurt."

Laurie looked up, gratified, and nodded. "Tell her I'm dead," he said.

"Mrs. Howell," I said into the phone, scowling at Laurie, "I *do* think that a boy so much bigger than Laurie—a boy so much bigger, as David is—I mean, David is so much bigger than Laurie that I *do* think—"

All this time Mrs. Howell had been silent. Now she said amiably, "I quite agree with you, of course. But I can't quite believe this of David; David is such a *quiet* boy. Is your little boy sure it wasn't David Williams or David Martin?"

"Are you sure it wasn't David Williams or David Martin?" I asked hopefully of the audience beyond the telephone. They all shook their heads violently, and one of Laurie's friends—the one who ran—said enthusiastically, "I know David Howell, and it was him all right. Anyway, he's always doing things like this. Two, three times now, he's hit Laurie. And me, too. He hits everybody."

"It was certainly your David," I said to Mrs. Howell. "They all agree on that. He picked a fight with Laurie on the way home from school and really hurt Laurie *quite* badly."

"Well," she said. "I'll certainly speak to David," she added after a minute.

"Thank you," I said, perfectly content to depart with this empty triumph, but my husband said, "Tell her he was fresh to me, too."

"He was fresh to my husband, too," I said obediently into the phone.

"Really?" Mrs. Howell said, as though David were fresh to her husband all the time and this was no surprise. "Well," she said again, "I'll certainly speak to him."

"Tell her he's hit me lots of times," Laurie said.

"Don't forget the bad words," one of Laurie's friends prompted.

"Make it really forceful," my husband said. "Why should he get away with a thing like this?"

"Will you see that this is stopped once and for all?" I demanded emphatically into the phone.

Her voice sharpened. "I *said* I'd speak to David," she repeated ominously.

"Thank you," I said hastily, and hung up.

We were congratulating one another on our victory when the phone rang. "This is Mrs. Howell," she said when I answered, and her voice had lost much of its civility. "I spoke to David," she went on. "I told you I would. And it seems that David was not entirely at fault." She dwelt on the last few words as though they gave her some fierce pleasure.

"I don't understand," I said. "Laurie was just walking along the—"

"I beg your pardon," she said, still with great relish. "What about the rock he threw at David?"

I looked at Laurie over the top of the phone, and he returned my glance with sober earnestness. "What rock?" I said, and Laurie's gaze did not waver, but an odd sort of reminiscent pleasure crept into his eye.

"Laurie," said Mrs. Howell plainly, "threw a rock and hit David in the head. There's a big big bump. David hadn't done *any*thing up to then. But if your little boy throws rocks, I can hardly blame—"

I retreated abruptly to safer ground. "Surely," I said, "you are not going to say that there is *any* excuse for a bigger boy hitting a smaller boy?"

"I shall certainly speak to David about that," she said stiffly. "But then, when Laurie's father called David a little sneak and said he ought to be horsewhipped—"

"What about what David called Laurie?" I countered tellingly. "It was so bad that Laurie wouldn't dream of repeating it."

Laurie and his two friends immediately said loudly what it was.

"Your husband said David ought to be horsewhipped," she said, not shaken, and almost, I thought, as though he were not actually the first person who had suggested major punishment for David, "and poor little David tried to tell him that Laurie had been throwing rocks. You really *ought* to do something about a child throwing rocks. None of *my* children throw rocks; it's something *I* can't stand. But poor little David—"

"David did so throw rocks," I said. "And if my husband said—"

"I did not say it," my husband said.

"Surely there is no excuse," she said, "for a grown man to pick on a poor little boy."

I backed up again. "What about poor little Laurie?" I asked. "He was *quite* badly hurt. Surely there is no excuse—"

"Poor little David—" she began.

"And my poor little—" I said, and then started again. "My husband, I mean. What about the names they yelled at *him?*"

I was suddenly reminded of the time Mrs. Howell had taken part in a local debate, holding and maintaining with absolute conviction the position that our state should secede from the United States to avoid having its natural resources completely depleted. "Furthermore—" she was saying.

"What a way to bring up a child," I said gently. "What kind of a mother are you?"

My audience, I perceived, was growing restless. Laurie's two friends were putting on their overshoes; Laurie himself had entered into an elaborately casual game with Jannie that had taken them almost to the kitchen doorway, and my husband was sauntering almost noiselessly back to the study.

"Now you listen to me," Mrs. Howell began, her voice rising, "now you listen to me—"

I hung up gracefully and followed Laurie into the kitchen.

"Laurie," I said sternly, "did you throw a rock at David?"

Laurie pondered, frowning, his head on one side and one finger thoughtfully tapping his cheek. "I forget," he said at last.

"Try to remember," I said threateningly. Laurie shook his head in despair. "I just forget," he said.

I went to the study door. "Did you call David a little sneak?" I demanded.

My husband looked up from his article on extinct fishes. "A little what?" he said.

"A little sneak."

"Don't be ridiculous," my husband said. "Why would I call what's-his-name a little sneak?" He turned back to his article. "Are you still worrying about *that?*" he asked.

The phone rang. I strode over and slammed it out of the receiver. "Well?" I said.

"If you think you can just hang up on people just because your son is a little bully and goes around throwing rocks and—"

"If you think you and your half-witted David can get away with picking on every child in the neighborhood just because he's overgrown and stupid—"

"If you would care to—"

"Perhaps *you* would like to—"

We hung up simultaneously. My husband opened the study door and looked out. "Who were you talking to?" he asked.

"Look," I said, "if you'd just take care of your own affairs and let Laurie fight his own battles and not come to me to—"

"I'm good, aren't I?" Jannie said. She came over and pulled at my hand. "I'm *good*, aren't I?"

My husband said loudly, "Let's box for a while, son. Get the gloves." Without looking at me he added, "We'll box out in the woodshed. Then," he said thoughtfully, "the noise won't bother Mother when she's on the phone."

"Aren't I?" said Jannie urgently. "*Aren't I?*"

I reached for the phone, and then hesitated. It was time to start the potatoes for dinner; I had a quick picture of Mrs. Howell peeling potatoes with one hand while she held a phone with the other, and I heard Laurie yelp as he walked into what was almost certainly a right cross.

"Want to help Mommy make dinner?" I asked Jannie.

Mrs. Howell and I met at the meat counter in the grocery the next morning; she smiled and I smiled and then she said, "How is Laurie today?"

"He seems much better, thanks," I said solemnly. "And David?"

"Fairly well," she said without turning a hair.

"Horrible little beasts," I said.

"Liars, all of them," she said. "*I* never believe a word they say."

We both laughed and turned to regard the meat. "They certainly do eat, though," she said mournfully. "I suppose it's hamburger again today."

"I was thinking about liver," I said.

"Will Laurie eat liver?" she asked with interest. "David won't touch it; do you cook it any special way?"

MAY SARTON   [1957]

May Sarton, who is a naturalized citizen, was born in Belgium in 1912. Although she chose to attempt the stage instead of attending college, she has received an honorary Litt.D. and has taught in more than eight colleges and universities.

A Celebration

I never saw my father old;
I never saw my father cold.
His stride, staccato, vital,
His talk struck from pure metal
Simple as gold, and all his learning
Only to light a passion's burning.
So, beaming like a lesser god,
He bounced upon the earth he trod
And people marvelled on the street
At this stout man's impetuous feet.

Loved donkeys, children, awkward ducks,
Loved to retell old simple jokes;
Lived in a world of innocence
Where loneliness could be intense;
Wrote letters until very late;
Found comfort in an orange cat—
Rufus and George exchanged no word,
But while George worked his Rufus purred—
And neighbors looked up at his light
Warmed by the scholar working late.

I never saw my father passive;
He was electrically massive.
He never hurried, so he said,
And yet a fire burned in his head;
He worked as poets work, for love,
And gathered in a world alive,
While black and white above his door
Spoke Mystery, the avatar—
An Arabic inscription flowed
Like singing: "In the name of God."

And when he died, he died so swift
His death was like a final gift.
He went out when the tide was full,
Still undiminished, bountiful;
The scholar and the gentle soul,

The passion and the life were whole.
And now death's wake is only praise,
As when a neighbor writes and says:
"I did not know your father, but
His light was there. I miss the light."

GINA BERRIAULT [1958]

*Gina Berriault worked as a journalist and reporter for the Pittsburgh
Courier before she turned to fiction and began raising her own family.
Though she often writes about adults and about women, she is particu-
larly attuned to laconic children like "The Stone Boy."*

The Stone Boy

Arnold drew his overalls and raveling gray sweater over his naked
body. In the other narrow bed his brother Eugene went on sleeping,
undisturbed by the alarm clock's rusty ring. Arnold, watching his
brother, felt a peculiar dismay; he was nine, six years younger than
Eugie, and in their waking hours it was he who was subordinate. To
dispel emphatically his uneasy advantage over his sleeping brother,
he threw himself on the hump of Eugie's body.

"Get up! Get up!" he cried.

Arnold felt his brother twist away and saw the blankets lifted in a
great wing, and, all in an instant, he was lying on his back under the
covers with only his face showing, like a baby, and Eugie was
sprawled on top of him.

"Whassa matter with you?" asked Eugie in sleepy anger, his face
hanging close.

"Get up," Arnold repeated. "You said you'd pick peas with me."

Stupidly, Eugie gazed around the room to see if morning had
come into it yet. Arnold began to laugh derisively, making soft,
snorting noises, and was thrown off the bed. He got up from the floor
and went down the stairs, the laughter continuing, like hiccups,
against his will. But when he opened the staircase door and entered
the parlor, he hunched up his shoulders and was quiet because his
parents slept in the bedroom downstairs.

Arnold lifted his .22-caliber rifle from the rack on the kitchen wall. It was an old lever-action Winchester that his father had given him because nobody else used it any more. On their way down to the garden he and Eugie would go by the lake, and if there were any ducks on it he'd take a shot at them. Standing on the stool before the cupboard, he searched on the top shelf in the confusion of medicines and ointments for man and beast and found a small yellow box of .22 cartridges. Then he sat down on the stool and began to load his gun.

It was cold in the kitchen so early, but later in the day, when his mother canned the peas, the heat from the wood stove would be almost unbearable. Yesterday she had finished preserving the huckleberries that the family had picked along the mountain, and before that she had canned all the cherries his father had brought from the warehouse in Corinth. Sometimes, on these summer days, Arnold would deliberately come out from the shade where he was playing and make himself as uncomfortable as his mother was in the kitchen by standing in the sun until the sweat ran down his body.

Eugie came clomping down the stairs and into the kitchen, his head drooping with sleepiness. From his perch on the stool Arnold watched Eugie slip on his green knit cap. Eugie didn't really need a cap; he hadn't had a haircut in a long time and his brown curls grew thick and matted, close around his ears and down his neck, tapering there to a small whorl. Eugie passed his left hand through his hair before he set his cap down with his right. The very way he slipped his cap on was an announcement of his status; almost everything he did was a reminder that he was eldest—first he, then Nora, then Arnold—and called attention to how tall he was (almost as tall as his father), how long his legs were, how small he was in the hips, and what a neat dip above his buttocks his thick-soled logger's boots gave him. Arnold never tired of watching Eugie offer silent praise unto himself. He wondered, as he sat enthralled, if when he got to be Eugie's age he would still be undersized and his hair still straight.

Eugie eyed the gun. "Don't you know this ain't duck season?" he asked gruffly, as if he were the sheriff.

"No, I don't know," Arnold sniggered.

Eugie picked up the tin washtub for the peas, unbolted the door with his free hand and kicked it open. Then, lifting the tub to his head, he went clomping down the back steps. Arnold followed, closing the door behind him.

The sky was faintly gray, almost white. The mountains behind the farm made the sun climb a long way to show itself. Several miles to the south, where the range opened up, hung an orange mist, but the valley in which the farm lay was still cold and colorless.

Eugie opened the gate to the yard and the boys passed between the barn and the row of chicken houses, their feet stirring up the carpet of brown feathers dropped by the molting chickens. They paused before going down the slope to the lake. A morning wind ran among the shocks of wheat that covered the slope. It sent a shimmer northward across the lake, gently moving the rushes that formed an island in the center. Killdeer, their white markings flashing, skimmed the water, crying their shrill, sweet cry. And there at the south end of the lake were four wild ducks, swimming out from the willows into open water.

Arnold followed Eugie down the slope, stealing, as his brother did, from one shock of wheat to another. Eugie paused before climbing through the wire fence that divided the wheat field from the marshy pasture around the lake. They were screened from the ducks by the willows along the lake's edge.

"If you hit your duck, you want me to go in after it?" Eugie asked.

"If you want," Arnold said.

Eugie lowered his eyelids, leaving slits of mocking blue. "You'd drown 'fore you got to it, them legs of yours are so puny," he said.

He shoved the tub under the fence and, pressing down the center wire, climbed through into the pasture.

Arnold pressed down the bottom wire, thrust a leg through and leaned forward to bring the other leg after. His rifle caught on the wire and he jerked at it. The air was rocked by the sound of the shot. Feeling foolish, he lifted his face, baring it to an expected shower of derision from his brother. But Eugie did not turn around. Instead, from his crouching position, he fell to his knees, and then pitched forward onto his face. The ducks rose up crying from the lake, cleared the mountain background and beat away northward across the pale sky.

Arnold squatted beside his brother. Eugie seemed to be climbing the earth, as if the earth ran up and down, and when he found he couldn't scale it he lay still.

"Eugie?"

Then Arnold saw it, under the tendril of hair at the nape of the neck—a slow rising of bright blood. It had an obnoxious movement, like that of a parasite.

"Hey, Eugie," he said again. He was feeling the same discomfort he had felt when he had watched Eugie sleeping; his brother didn't know that he was lying face down in the pasture.

Again he said, "Hey, Eugie," an anxious nudge in his voice. But Eugie was as still as the morning about them.

Arnold set his rifle on the ground and stood up. He picked up the tub and, dragging it behind him, walked along by the willows to the garden fence and climbed through. He went down on his knees among the tangled vines. The pods were cold with the night, but his hands were strange to him, and not until some time had passed did he realize that the pods were numbing his fingers. He picked from the top of the vine first, then lifted the vine to look underneath for pods and then moved on to the next.

It was a warmth on his back, like a large hand laid firmly there, that made him raise his head. Way up on the slope the gray farmhouse was struck by the sun. While his head had been bent the land had grown bright around him.

When he got up his legs were so stiff that he had to go down on his knees again to ease the pain. Then, walking sideways, he dragged the tub, half full of peas, up the slope.

The kitchen was warm now; a fire was roaring in the stove with a closed-up, rushing sound. His mother was spooning eggs from a pot of boiling water and putting them into a bowl. Her short brown hair was uncombed and fell forward across her eyes as she bent her head. Nora was lifting a frying pan full of trout from the stove, holding the handle with a dish towel. His father had just come in from bringing the cows from the north pasture to the barn, and was sitting on the stool, unbuttoning his red plaid Mackinaw.

"Did you boys fill the tub?" his mother asked.

"They ought of by now," his father said. "They went out of the house an hour ago. Eugie woke me up comin' downstairs. I heard you shootin'—did you get a duck?"

"No," Arnold said. They would want to know why Eugie wasn't coming in for breakfast, he thought. "Eugie's dead," he told them.

They stared at him. The pitch crackled in the stove.

"You kids playin' a joke?" his father asked.

"Where's Eugene?" his mother asked scoldingly. She wanted, Arnold knew, to see his eyes, and when he had glanced at her she put the bowl and spoon down on the stove and walked past him. His father stood up and went out the door after her. Nora followed them with little skipping steps, as if afraid to be left alone.

Arnold went into the barn, down along the foddering passage past the cows waiting to be milked, and climbed into the loft. After a few minutes he heard a terrifying sound coming toward the house. His parents and Nora were returning from the willows, and cries sharp as knives were rising from his mother's breast and carrying over the sloping fields. In a short while he heard his father go down the back steps, slam the car door and drive away.

Arnold lay still as a fugitive, listening to the cows eating close by. If his parents never called him, he thought, he would stay up in the loft forever, out of the way. In the night he would sneak down for a drink of water from the faucet over the trough and for whatever food they left for him by the barn.

The rattle of his father's car as it turned down the lane recalled him to the present. He heard the voices of his Uncle Andy and Aunt Alice as they and his father went past the barn to the lake. He could feel the morning growing heavier with sun. Someone, probably Nora, had let the chickens out of their coops and they were cackling in the yard.

After a while another car turned down the road off the highway. The car drew to a stop and he heard the voices of strange men. The men also went past the barn and down to the lake. The undertakers, whom his father must have phoned from Uncle Andy's house, had arrived from Corinth. Then he heard everybody come back and heard the car turn around and leave.

"Arnold!" It was his father calling from the yard.

He climbed down the ladder and went out into the sun, picking wisps of hay from his overalls.

Corinth, nine miles away, was the county seat. Arnold sat in the front seat of the old Ford between his father, who was driving, and Uncle Andy; no one spoke. Uncle Andy was his mother's brother, and he had been fond of Eugie because Eugie had resembled him. Andy had taken Eugie hunting and had given him a knife and a lot of things, and now Andy, his eyes narrowed, sat tall and stiff beside Arnold.

Arnold's father parked the car before the courthouse. It was a two-story brick building with a lamp on each side of the bottom step. They went up the wide stone steps, Arnold and his father going first, and entered the darkly paneled hallway. The shirt-sleeved man in the sheriff's office said that the sheriff was at Carlson's Parlor examining the Curwing boy.

Andy went off to get the sheriff while Arnold and his father waited on a bench in the corridor. Arnold felt his father watching him, and he lifted his eyes with painful casualness to the announcement, on the opposite wall, of the Corinth County Annual Rodeo, and then to the clock with its loudly clucking pendulum. After he had come down from the loft his father and Uncle Andy had stood in the yard with him and asked him to tell them everything, and he had explained to them how the gun had caught on the wire. But when they had asked him why he hadn't run back to the house to tell his parents, he had had no answer—all he could say was that he had gone down into the garden to pick the peas. His father had stared at him in a puzzled way, and it was then that he had felt his father and the others set their cold, turbulent silence against him. Arnold shifted on the bench, his only feeling a small one of compunction imposed by his father's eyes.

At a quarter past nine Andy and the sheriff came in. They all went into the sheriff's private office, and Arnold was sent forward to sit in the chair by the sheriff's desk; his father and Andy sat down on the bench against the wall.

The sheriff lumped down into his swivel chair and swung toward Arnold. He was an old man with white hair like wheat stubble. His restless green eyes made him seem not to be in his office but to be hurrying and bobbing around somewhere else.

"What did you say your name was?" the sheriff asked.

"Arnold," he replied, but he could not remember telling the sheriff his name before.

"Curwing?"

"Yes."

"What were you doing with a .22, Arnold?"

"It's mine," he said.

"Okay. What were you going to shoot?"

"Some ducks," he replied.

"Out of season?"

He nodded.

"That's bad," said the sheriff. "Were you and your brother good friends?"

What did he mean—good friends? Eugie was his brother. That was different from a friend, Arnold thought. A best friend was your own age, but Eugie was almost a man. Eugie had had a way of looking at him, slyly and mockingly and yet confidentially, that had summed up how they both felt about being brothers. Arnold had wanted to be with Eugie more than with anybody else but he couldn't say they had been good friends.

"Did they ever quarrel?" the sheriff asked his father.

"Not that I know," his father replied. "It seemed to me that Arnold cared a lot for Eugie."

"Did you?" the sheriff asked Arnold.

If it seemed so to his father, then it was so. Arnold nodded.

"Were you mad at him this morning?"

"No."

"How did you happen to shoot him?"

"We was crawlin' through the fence."

"Yes?"

"An' the gun got caught on the wire."

"Seems the hammer must of caught," his father put in.

"All right, that's what happened," said the sheriff. "But what I want you to tell me is this. Why didn't you go back to the house and tell your father right away? Why did you go and pick peas for an hour?"

Arnold gazed over his shoulder at his father, expecting his father to have an answer for this also. But his father's eyes, larger and even lighter blue than usual, were fixed upon him curiously. Arnold picked at a callus in his right palm. It seemed odd now that he had not run back to the house and wakened his father, but he could not remember why he had not. They were all waiting for him to answer.

"I come down to pick peas," he said.

"Didn't you think," asked the sheriff, stepping carefully from word to word, "that it was more important for you to go tell your parents what had happened?"

"The sun was gonna come up," Arnold said.

"What's that got to do with it?"

"It's better to pick peas while they're cool."

The sheriff swung away from him, laid both hands flat on his desk. "Well, all I can say is," he said across to Arnold's father and Uncle Andy, "he's either a moron or he's so reasonable that he's way ahead of us." He gave a challenging snort. "It's come to my notice that the most reasonable guys are mean ones. They don't feel nothing."

For a moment the three men sat still. Then the sheriff lifted his hand like a man taking an oath. "Take him home," he said.

Andy uncrossed his legs. "You don't want him?"

"Not now," replied the sheriff. "Maybe in a few years."

Arnold's father stood up. He held his hat against his chest. "The gun ain't his no more," he said wanly.

Arnold went first through the hallway, hearing behind him the heels of his father and Uncle Andy striking the floor boards. He went down the steps ahead of them and climbed into the back seat of the car. Andy paused as he was getting into the front seat and gazed back at Arnold, and Arnold saw that his uncle's eyes had absorbed the knowingness from the sheriff's eyes. Andy and his father and the sheriff had discovered what made him go down into the garden. It was because he was cruel, the sheriff had said, and didn't care about his brother. Was that the reason? Arnold lowered his eyelids meekly against his uncle's stare.

The rest of the day he did his tasks around the farm, keeping apart from the family. At evening, when he saw his father stomp tiredly into the house, Arnold did not put down his hammer and leave the chicken coop he was repairing. He was afraid that they did not want him to eat supper with them. But in a few minutes another fear that they would go to the trouble of calling him and that he would be made conspicuous by his tardiness made him follow his father into the house. As he went through the kitchen he saw the jars of peas standing in rows on the workbench, a reproach to him.

No one spoke at supper, and his mother, who sat next to him, leaned her head in her hand all through the meal, curving her fingers over her eyes so as not to see him. They were finishing their small, silent supper when the visitors began to arrive, knocking hard on the back door. The men were coming from their farms now that it was growing dark and they could not work any more.

Old Man Matthews, gray and stocky, came first, with his two sons, Orion, the elder, and Clint, who was Eugie's age. As the callers entered the parlor, where the family ate, Arnold sat down in a rocking chair. Even as he had been undecided before supper whether to remain outside or take his place at the table, he now thought that he should go upstairs, and yet he stayed to avoid being conspicuous by his absence. If he stayed, he thought, as he always stayed and listened when visitors came, they would see that he was only Arnold and not the person the sheriff thought he was. He sat with his arms crossed and his hands tucked into his armpits and did not lift his eyes.

The Matthews men had hardly settled down around the table,

after Arnold's mother and Nora had cleared away the dishes, when another car rattled down the road and someone else rapped on the back door. This time it was Sullivan, a spare and sandy man, so nimble of gesture and expression that Arnold had never been able to catch more than a few of his meanings. Sullivan, in dusty jeans, sat down in the other rocker, shot out his skinny legs and began to talk in his fast way, recalling everything that Eugene had ever said to him. The other men interrupted to tell of occasions they remembered, and after a time Clint's young voice, hoarse like Eugene's had been, broke in to tell about the time Eugene had beat him in a wrestling match.

Out in the kitchen the voices of Orion's wife and of Mrs. Sullivan mingled with Nora's voice but not, Arnold noticed, his mother's. Then dry little Mr. Cram came, leaving large Mrs. Cram in the kitchen, and there was no chair left for Mr. Cram to sit in. No one asked Arnold to get up and he was unable to rise. He knew that the story had got around to them during the day about how he had gone and picked peas after he had shot his brother, and he knew that although they were talking only about Eugie they were thinking about him and if he got up, if he moved even his foot, they would all be alerted. Then Uncle Andy arrived and leaned his tall, lanky body against the doorjamb and there were two men standing.

Presently Arnold was aware that the talk had stopped. He knew without looking up that the men were watching him.

"Not a tear in his eye," said Andy, and Arnold knew that it was his uncle who had gestured the men to attention.

"He don't give a hoot, is that how it goes?" asked Sullivan, trippingly.

"He's a reasonable fellow," Andy explained. "That's what the sheriff said. It's us who ain't reasonable. If we'd of shot our brother, we'd of come runnin' back to the house, cryin' like a baby. Well, we'd of been unreasonable. What would of been the use of actin' like that? If your brother is shot dead, he's shot dead. What's the use of gettin' emotional about it? The thing to do is go down to the garden and pick peas. Am I right?"

The men around the room shifted their heavy, satisfying weight of unreasonableness.

Matthews' son Orion said: "If I'd of done what he done, Pa would've hung my pelt by the side of that big coyote's in the barn."

Arnold sat in the rocker until the last man had filed out. While his family was out in the kitchen bidding the callers good night and the cars were driving away down the dirt lane to the highway, he picked up one of the kerosene lamps and slipped quickly up the stairs. In his room he undressed by lamplight, although he and Eugie had always undressed in the dark, and not until he was lying in his bed did he blow out the flame. He felt nothing, not any grief. There was only the same immense silence and crawling inside of him; it was the way the house and fields felt under a merciless sun.

He awoke suddenly. He knew that his father was out in the yard, closing the doors of the chicken houses so that the chickens could not roam out too early and fall prey to the coyotes that came down from the mountains at daybreak. The sound that had wakened him was the step of his father as he got up from the rocker and went down the back steps. And he knew that his mother was awake in her bed.

Throwing off the covers, he rose swiftly, went down the stairs and across the dark parlor to his parents' room. He rapped on the door.

"Mother?"

From the closed room her voice rose to him, a seeking and retreating voice. "Yes?"

"Mother?" he asked insistently. He had expected her to realize that he wanted to go down on his knees by her bed and tell her that Eugie was dead. She did not know it yet, nobody knew it, and yet she was sitting up in bed, waiting to be told, waiting for him to confirm her dread. He had expected her to tell him to come in, to allow him to dig his head into her blankets and tell her about the terror he had felt when he had knelt beside Eugie. He had come to clasp her in his arms and to pommel her breasts with his head. He put his hand upon the knob.

"Go back to bed, Arnold," she called sharply.

But he waited.

"Go back! Is night when you get afraid?"

At first he did not understand. Then, silently, he left the door and for a stricken moment stood by the rocker. Outside everything was still. The fences, the shocks of wheat seen through the window before him were so still it was as if they moved and breathed in the daytime and had fallen silent with the lateness of the hour. It was a silence that seemed to observe his father, a figure moving alone around the yard, his lantern casting a circle of light by his feet. In a few minutes his father would enter the dark house, the lantern still lighting his way.

Arnold was suddenly aware that he was naked. He had thrown

off his blankets and come down the stairs to tell his mother how he felt about Eugie, but she had refused to listen to him and his nakedness had become unpardonable. At once he went back up the stairs, fleeing from his father's lantern.

At breakfast he kept his eyelids lowered to hide the humiliating night. Nora, sitting at his left, did not pass the pitcher of milk to him and he did not ask for it. He would never again, he vowed, ask them for anything, and he ate his fried eggs and potatoes only because everybody ate meals—the cattle ate, and the cats; it was customary for everybody to eat.

"Nora, you gonna keep that pitcher for yourself?" his father asked.

Nora lowered her head unsurely.

"Pass it on to Arnold," his father said.

Nora put her hands in her lap.

His father picked up the metal pitcher and set it down at Arnold's plate.

Arnold, pretending to be deaf to the discord, did not glance up, but relief rained over his shoulders at the thought that his parents recognized him again. They must have lain awake after his father had come in from the yard: had they realized together why he had come down the stairs and knocked at their door?

"Bessie's missin' this morning," his father called out to his mother, who had gone into the kitchen. "She went up the mountain last night and had her calf, most likely. Somebody's got to go up and find her 'fore the coyotes get the calf."

That had been Eugie's job, Arnold thought. Eugie would climb the cattle trails in search of a newborn calf and come down the mountain carrying the calf across his back, with the cow running along behind him, mooing in alarm.

Arnold ate the few more forkfuls of his breakfast, put his hands on the edge of the table and pushed back his chair. If he went for the calf he'd be away from the farm all morning. He could switch the cow down the mountain slowly, and the calf would run along at its mother's side.

When he passed through the kitchen his mother was setting a kettle of water on the stove. "Where you going?" she asked awkwardly.

"Up to get the calf," he replied, averting his face.

"Arnold?"

At the door he paused reluctantly, his back to her, knowing that she was seeking him out, as his father was doing, and he called upon his pride to protect him from them.

"Was you knocking at my door last night?"

He looked over his shoulder at her, his eyes narrow and dry.

"What'd you want?" she asked humbly.

"I didn't want nothing," he said flatly.

Then he went out the door and down the back steps, his legs trembling from the fright his answer gave him.

KATHERINE DUNHAM   [1959]

Katherine Dunham's third-person autobiography recalls a father so violent that his daughter remembered him chiefly with fear. In spite of her difficult childhood, she has become an anthropologist, dancer, and choreographer, briefly attending the University of Chicago and in 1936 taking courses at Northwestern University as special field training for her research in the West Indies. In 1945 she founded the Katherine Dunham School of the Cultural Arts and the Katherine Dunham Dance Company, both in New York City, and for nearly twenty years she has toured this country, Europe, and South America with her own Bal Negre *and other revues.*

A Touch of Innocence

The summer was the hottest on record. The only relief came at night, when a slight breeze from the river wafted across the canal, bringing with it the familiar sewage odors intensified by the day's heat. The buildings on the west side of Bluff Street suffered most: backed up against the cliff, they received no crosscurrent of air. The father stood at the pressing machine bathed in sweat, his temper shortening with the rise in temperature. Each day the mother seemed more drawn and tired, and the unpleasantness between the parents was so marked that the girl sought any escape from the shop.

Though summer was normally an off season, business flourished at the West Side Cleaners and Dyers. A hired girl named Allegretta helped in the flat on Saturdays, and with her Katherine Dunham was almost entirely in charge of house cleaning and took more and more responsibility for the preparation of meals. Annette Dunham worked in the shop from early morning until late at night, as she reminded her husband when her refusal to let him invest in new machinery and real estate drove him to smoldering wrath and then open abuse.

The girl visited her Aunt Mayme and the doctor's wife as frequently as possible and took again her favorite walk to the locks; she felt too grown up to climb the cliff. Her brother went grimly about his work and studied between times for a special examination that might win him a scholarship to the University. But this was never mentioned.

Fear was familiar to the girl, but most of the time it had been fear of the unknown—the felt and sensed but not seen. This summer she entered into a new consideration of fear—the same kind that she had known once before when the man with his face cut open so that his teeth showed had stopped at the automobile in which she sat waiting on a hot Sunday afternoon in the City. But now this fear was of violence that stemmed from the very roots of her being, from the very core of her own family.

She lay sleepless at night, straining to hear sounds from behind the closed door across the living room, but also afraid to hear them because of what she would learn. On the hottest nights the door would be left open; and still, relentlessly, with no consideration for the boy on the couch in the dining room or the girl in her alcove, her parents would turn against each other, accusing, reproaching, vilifying, disparaging, one vituperation mounting upon another until they ended in stifling sobs from the mother or in the flight of Albert Dunham: half-dressed, he would fling doors open and slam them behind him and finish the night in the delivery truck or stretched out on a table in the back of the shop. Once the girl was certain that she heard blows struck and was afraid to look at her mother in the morning.

The climax of these arguments came on a night when she had fallen into a restless sleep of exhaustion. She awoke with a premonition of more serious trouble than usual and turned and twisted on the narrow bed, trying not to hear the voices and the more ominous sounds from the room facing her. After listening to an unmistakable struggle in which her father seemed to be attempting to eject his wife forcibly from the bedroom, the girl slipped out of bed and went to stand in the center of the living room. The only light was from the dim street lamp, but she could see her mother in her white nightgown, clinging to the frame of the door as her father pushed and dragged, striking her in his fury, cursing in his repeated threats to rid himself of her presence.

The girl heard the cries for help, but was unable to move. She began to think about Mrs. McGuire when her husband had come home drunk on Saturday nights and beaten her; she thought, too, that this must be what it was like to be dead, to have terrible things happening and not be able to move or do anything. Once she tried to reach out to her mother, but even her arm refused to obey her will. Then a light went on, and something changed in her mother. She looked wild with one kind of fear at one minute, then suddenly just as wild but with another kind of fear, this one more real. And the girl heard her brother's name and saw that he had stepped to her side.

"Stop it!" he said, but her mother kept calling her brother's name and saying, "Albert! Don't. Don't. He's your father!" The girl hardly had to turn at all to see her brother, and she looked with curiosity at the gun that he had pointed at his father, who stood with his mouth wide-open, that surprised, young-boy look on his face, which had been black and swollen with rage a second before.

"That isn't my BB gun," the girl thought. "He should be careful with that. It's his twenty-two."

"Stop it," her brother said again, and his voice was so quiet that it hung in the middle of the air between the four of them, not going anywhere, but hanging there like a sign that said just where to go— to turn right or left or stop.

"Put that gun down," her father said.

"I'll put it down all right," her brother said. "Oh, yes. I'll put it down. But if you touch her again, I'll kill you. I mean it." And he didn't put the gun down. He continued to look at his father, who still stood in the doorway of the bedroom.

Forgetting all of a sudden what had gone before and why the boy had come from the dining room in his wrinkled gray-and-blue-striped pajamas, pointing the rifle at his father, his face ash-colored and with dark circles under his eyes because he couldn't possibly sleep enough with so much hate and unrest all around—Annette Dunham tried ineffectually to shield her husband. Her hair had come unbraided during the struggle, and her eyes rolled wildly, and though she really was reacting in the only way she could, it seemed to the girl illogical after the soul-sickening cries for help and the obvious brutality of her mistreatment. After having dragged the boy into it by calling for him, she kept saying over and over in the tone of voice she always used when things happened that could never happen to her, "Albert, Albert, he's your *father!*"

The boy looked at her pityingly, wearily, as though to ask when she would ever understand, how it was that she refused to understand in spite of all their hours of confidences. He turned and went into the dining room, the gun at his side pointing downward, looking spent as though it had been used. The other three stood where they were; then the sister turned numbly to the room where her brother had gone.

"Which is the one?" she thought. "Which is the one with the bent knife, the razor in his hand? Who is doing this? Who is making everything full of fear and hate? Why did she have to holler? Doesn't she know that if she does it again, it will all be *her* fault? It nearly happened just now. It will happen. It's got to happen. It's been happening. Why is it so cold?"

But it shouldn't have been cold, because it was the next morning and she was in her mother's bed, well covered, and Dr. Williams was leaning over the thermometer trying to read it against the light, which was difficult because the green shade was drawn. Her mother stood next to him looking worried about the thermometer reading, but otherwise as though the night before had never been.

The doctor turned to the bed and smiled. "Well, young lady," he said, "where did you pick up that mosquito? Can't say as I expected to run into that around these parts. Malaria, of all things!"

"Why, that's impossible!" her mother said. "It just *couldn't* be malaria! That's only in Florida and Africa!"

"Well," the doctor said, a twinkle behind his thick glasses. "Guess we had to get to Africa *some* way, didn't we?"

Her father came in, and her heart began to pound the way it had the night before. She wanted to look away, but her head felt too heavy. He said something about playing around the canal, but Dr. Williams said No, it didn't have to be that way at all; there was a malaria belt in the Middle West, and no one seemed to be able to account for it or foretell just who would fall victim, but anyway mosquitoes can fly quite a distance, and maybe she didn't go to it, it probably came to her. Then he delved into his black case and took out capsules along with the ever-present white powders and wrote two prescriptions, an unusual procedure for him.

As he left, he told her mother that he thought the "young lady" was a little upset these days. It wouldn't hurt a bit to see that she was kept quiet and without excitement. She would be in bed for at least two weeks and ailing after that. When he repeated his instructions about no excitement, the girl thought she detected some special emphasis. She closed her eyes and turned to the wall, partly because she felt so ashamed that not only Bluff Street, but all of the Town, must by now be aware that the Dunhams were having a terrible time, and that Mr. Dunham beat his wife, and that his son was going to kill him with the rifle that they used to go rabbit hunting with a long time ago.

The malaria was persistent, alternately raging and subsiding for a month. The girl wearied of aching bones and stomach pains and chills and fever, but she was grateful for the comparative peace in the family. She moved again to her small room, and at night when it was too hot to sleep, she would search the heavens for her special Star. But the nights were murky, and most of the time she couldn't find it, and when she did, the Star seemed alien, embarrassed, like a host who wants to tell his guest that his welcome has run out but doesn't know how to say it. She prayed to it in spite of this, forcing herself to stay kneeling on the bed though her head felt dangerously heavy and her back ached and her knees trembled. Mostly she petitioned that everything be set right. And again she asked for strength and courage for herself, somehow sensing that little by little she would be pushed into some position for which she now felt woefully inadequate.

Her brother sat with her as much as he could, bringing her ice-cream cones or bottles of pink soda pop and one day a string of pearls. She recognized it immediately as one of a kind that hung in multiple ropes at the counter she had pored over with Dorothy Jackson. But he told her a long tale about where pearls come from and how these pearls had belonged to a princess in Hawaii. Then he told her such stories about the Hawaiians and what they looked like and what they did that she forgot to ask how he had managed to get the pearls, which by now were wrapped in so much romance that they had become priceless, because by now she believed him, because she wanted to enter into the spirit of things and be as entertained and entranced as he wanted her to be.

She was well again, but the fear stayed inside, settling into her stomach and rising into her chest, so that she felt herself holding her breath and then letting it out in long sighs and still not being able to take in enough air. Her first day up she looked for the rifle, but it was nowhere to be found. Her father's shotgun, which had stood in the corner of the bedroom on the side of the bed where he slept, was missing, too.

Her brother saw her looking under the couch where he slept in the dining room. "He took it," he said, smiling at her confusion. "Never mind. I'm going away pretty soon. I have a scholarship. But not until winter. Don't tell anybody." The bottom fell out of everything, and she sat on the couch and stared at him. "I'll come back," he said, "and then we'll all go away together." She knew what he meant by "all," but the thought of facing days and months and perhaps years without the presence of her brother, with only the terror of her father and what she now recognized to be the constant nagging of her mother, removed all hope of survival.

A spark had gone from her, and those who knew her best thought that it was the result of the malaria and that, as soon as cool weather came, she would recover her old restless energy. But at fourteen she felt old and tired and wasn't even much interested in Allegretta's confidences about how babies were born.

"Mens is terrible," Allegretta lectured, as they washed the white woodwork in the bathroom. "You jus' stay away fum um. Ain' Miz Dunnum tolt you yit?"

"Told me *what*, Allegretta?"

"Tolt you whar babies comes frum! Big girl like you ain't got no bu'ness so unknowin'."

The girl felt ashamed and backward at her ignorance. "They come out of inside," she said, feeling uncomfortable at such intimacy. "I saw a book where the calf was inside its mother. . . ."

"Hee hee!" Tears rolled down Allegretta's brown cheeks whenever she started to laugh. She was not long from Mississippi, and scrawny, and thought that she was eighteen but was not sure. Her hair stayed in tight knots until she prepared to leave on Saturday afternoon; then she undid it and heated an iron comb—which she always carried in her handbag along with a bottle of hot sauce, a can of Poro Hair Pressing Oil, and numerous other indispensable properties—and walked back and forth from the kitchen to the bathroom, where she stood before the mirror and pulled at the kinky knots with the hot iron until they sizzled out into flat, oily strands. At first, separate pieces stood up like the bristles on a hedgehog, but when she had smoothed the unruly ends into place and changed into a clean dress and screwed on pink earrings and put on lipstick and rouge and a little pink powder, she looked quite presentable.

"Ain' stiddyin' no cow!" she said. "Laws, whoever heerd tell talkin' 'bout cows stid of educatin' proper 'bout babies? Babies is *folks,* ain' no *cows.*" She emphatically "busted her suds," as she said of anything to do with washing, and began to fill in the gaps in the girl's neglected education.

"But how do you know when you're going to have a baby?" the girl asked, as they moved into the kitchen.

"*Know!* Lawd, chile, you *knows* all right." Allegretta had covered a good deal of ground during the washing of the bathroom woodwork and was now at what she considered the climax of her discourse. She stopped busting suds and looked at the girl as though to be sure that the impact of her words would receive full consideration.

"Den," she said in a voice husky with awe, "ya pee bags bus!"

"Your *what,* Allegretta?"

"*Pee bags,* girl, ya pee bags busses, 'en den's when ya *knows* hit done be time!" They stood over their bucket of Fels Naphtha soap powder and warm water turning tepid, each lost in her own thoughts. The girl was impressed by all that she had learned, chiefly because of the frankness of her narrator. She didn't want to show her own ignorance by asking more questions, but was unable to figure out a number of things in spite of her informant's meaty colloquialisms and graphic detail.

She always intended to ask Allegretta more, as casually as possible, because she felt that there were some things that by now she should know but that Annette Dunham would never in the world speak of. She didn't get around to it, though, and one day Allegretta didn't come to work. Then her mother told her that if they ever passed her on the street she wasn't to speak to her. The girl was astonished, considering Allegretta one of her best friends, until she overheard a telephone conversation.

"How *could* she?" her mother was saying, in her most "it-couldn't-have-possibly-happened-to-a-Poindexter" tone. "And me trusting her with Katherine and all the time her carrying on like that. I used to see her get all done up on Saturday afternoons." Whoever was on the other end of the line had some choice bits to add. Annette Dunham drew away from the telephone to look at it as though the very words had contaminated it. "Lord have mercy!" she said when she trusted the instrument again. "A *white* man! *Of all things!*" Then she drew upon her stock phrase for the worst that could possibly happen to anyone. "She ought to be run out of town!"

Katherine Dunham was deeply vexed with her mother for her rejection of the hired girl. If Allegretta approached all of life with the same innocent gusto as she had during their Saturday cleaning conferences, what she had done couldn't be so terrible. Allegretta was the only person who talked about such things who didn't make her feel uncomfortable or guilty or as if she were spying on something not quite clean.

She and her mother passed the girl once or twice downtown, and the daughter wondered if all of that under her smock was what they talked about, and what she would do if her pee bags busted while she was walking around window shopping. Her mother stared straight ahead without a sign of recognition, but the girl smiled at Allegretta in spite of what her mother had told her.

And to Annette Dunham's chagrin, she continued to do so on subsequent encounters.

There were many times as the summer drew to a close when the girl would willingly have suffered another attack of malaria if that could have insured against family strife.

Albert Dunham was not appeased by one victory, although to the girl it seemed monumental. He had cajoled and threatened and intimidated his wife all through the summer and finally, on the assurance that the venture was not speculation but a provision for the future, had persuaded her to sign the necessary papers for the purchase of a red brick house which had once occupied a position in the center of a modest estate, but which now encumbered the storage yard of an iron foundry. An elderly Frenchman owned a lot a block away, and by having the house moved to it on immense rollers, the father accomplished one of his lifelong dreams: to buy something considered useless or impractical and make it a profitable investment. It was a ten-room house with an attic and a gabled roof, and to transfer it from the foundry to the vacant lot was regarded as something of a feat. The curious drove to the spot from all parts of the Town to watch, and Albert Dunham absented himself from his business at every possible opportunity, not so much because he was needed to oversee the job as because he basked in the interest and admiration and sometimes the envy that he saw on the faces of spectators who were as driven as he to keep up with the times, but who hadn't been clever enough to think up such a move.

Once in place, the house was remodeled into two apartments. Years would pass before Annette Dunham and her husband occupied the downstairs flat, and by then the two children would have gone their separate ways. But at the time, just the talk of a house, a real place to call home with a room of her own, encouraged the girl. Then she would hear the nightly bickering again, and her enthusiasm would leave her, and she would wonder if people were ever satisfied or if something was wrong with all families. She began to take a great interest in imagining the inner lives of people, in projecting herself into their thinking and feeling, in wondering why they behaved as they did and if the other people around were concealing wounds and hurts and fears and bitterness behind their friendliness and smiles and the nice words that they said to each other. If she isolated her family from the others, she felt lost indeed. On the other hand, if all of life and all relationships were like the Dunhams', then she had been born into an ice age or into a black abyss with only more blackness beyond each door which was opened at so much effort and cost.

Shortly after the girl's recovery from malaria, her mother—as though her daughter's illness had suggested the idea—developed a Saturday-night practice of fainting on the doorstep of the shop, always when her husband was near by, so that he would have to stop whatever he was doing and carry her through the street and up the stairs to the flat. The first time this happened the girl was reading in bed and had just been wondering how late they intended to work. It was after eleven, and her brother was still on the delivery truck.

When her father passed through the living room with the inert figure, puffing and panting and dripping with sweat from the climb up the stairs, her blood stopped circulating and she thought, "Well, it's happened." She started across the room as she had on that other night, wondering why she couldn't move quickly or cry out or do something active or dynamic, as she imagined other people did at times like this. This time she kept walking until she stood in the doorway; she spoke above the pounding in her ears which came from her own heartbeat.

"What's the matter?" she managed to say.

Her father seemed upset, but not like someone who had just committed a murder. She stared at the figure on the bed, looking for blood or other signs of violence, and Annette Dunham began to groan, turning her head from side to side.

"Get some water," her father said.

At the kitchen sink she drank half a glass of water before she remembered what she was there for, and then hurried guiltily back into the bedroom, handing her father the glass from a distance, already condemning him as a criminal, already seeing him in jail.

Once in a long while Albert Dunham understood his daughter. "Your mother's fainted," he told her. "Get the smelling salts."

She fumbled in the drawer and found the bottle of lavender smelling salts that her mother sometimes carried to funerals. She couldn't look at her father because she knew he had read her thoughts, and she felt that from now on she would have nowhere to hide. She would have to let him see everything, how she was beginning to hate him, and how she was afraid of him and afraid for her brother even more than for her mother.

The fainting was presently supplemented by attacks of leg cramps, severe and without warning. They would occur in the middle of the night or when there was a guest for dinner or, worse still, in church. A series of low moans might announce their imminence, in which case the girl and her father would leave the dinner table or the church pew, half carrying and half dragging the mother to some sheltered spot. The girl would be the first to rush to the telephone to call the doctor, but he might be away from his office, and father and daughter would then become momentary allies in frantic efforts to calm the suffering woman. The girl went through an apprenticeship in applying hot fomentations and in massage and manipulation, and worked feverishly to straighten the leg that would have been drawn double by suddenly contracted tendons and muscles, strangulating the surrounding nerves, so that Annette Dunham would scream in a voice hardly recognizable as her own.

The girl learned to sleep lightly and to wake at the slightest unaccustomed sound, with her full faculties ready to go at once into action. Hardly were her mother's first cries uttered than she would light the fire under the teakettle, snatch the bottle of Sloan's Liniment and a towel from the bathroom, and take her place at the foot of the bed, where her father would already be at work over the twisted muscles. Her mother was usually so tidy that the girl hated seeing her with her hair in disorder, her eyes wild and rolling, and the corners of her mouth wetter than they should be.

Sometimes in her pain the mother turned accusingly on her two attendants, crying "Do something. Can't somebody *do* something? *Why* don't you help me? *Why* don't you *do* something!"

And all the while they would be pulling, massaging, perspiring, the father dutiful no matter how bitter, the girl numb and driven and guilty because of the revulsion she felt toward such nakedness.

She had had no experience with the leveling-down, the stripping of all pretenses, the ultimate groveling of the proudest, which pain achieves so effectively.

Annette Dunham lost no opportunity to blame her condition on overwork and the strain and abuse of her married life. Albert Dunham retorted that her troubles more than likely stemmed from her time of life, to which she rejoined that he should know all about this, having once been married to a woman far more senior to him than she herself was. The ugliness continued and grew until there was another physical struggle, this time while the brother was at a late rehearsal of the string quartet.

Bad became worse and still worse, until one day, having been told so many times to leave if she didn't like things the way they were, the mother called the girl into the bedroom, where preparations for departure were already apparent, and in the quavering voice she now used so frequently told her that she had been ejected bodily from the shop, that the joint bank account had been closed and a new one opened in the name of Albert M. Dunham alone, that her very life was in danger if she did not turn over to her husband each day whatever payments were made in the shop during his absence or had come in by way of the delivery wagon. When she had objected to expenditures she thought unnecessary, he had told her that her services were no longer needed and that she had tried her best to alienate his children from him. Then he struck her and said things that were the unkindest that could be said to a woman of her age, who had been as much a mother to the children as if she had borne them. The girl wept and clung to her as she never had done before, tired of being brave and stoical and indomitable like her brother, willing to be just for once, a frightened, lonely, sick child, tormented by too much awareness.

Her tears turned to hysteria, and her mother must have been moved, because she agreed to stay, no matter what.

"Take me away with you!" the girl pleaded. "Please, Mother, don't leave me with him. I hate him! I hate him! Please take me away!"

Annette Dunham, because she was a good mother and an upright wife and essentially moral in all of the ways set out by her Puritan forebears, was stabbed and shaken by her daughter's outburst.

"But, Katherine," she said, "he's your *father!* You mustn't say things like that!"

The girl turned hopelessly from her mother, defeated. Surely now it was only a matter of time. She sat in her own room until the sobs

had died and tried to stop thinking how near her own panic had
been to her mother's nakedness in pain. She set the table and began
to prepare for supper. Not a word was spoken during the entire meal.

School started, and each day she turned the corner from the Cass
Street bridge the girl had to hold herself back to keep from running
the long block to the shop. She felt that one day she would find her
mother dead or not there. When she saw her, her head bent over the
sewing machine as usual, she felt such relief that she could only
stand for the first few minutes and make nonsensical remarks.

That was the first week of school. The Sunday beginning the second week was exceptionally bad.

On Sunday, with rare exceptions, the father prepared the morning
meal, and his mood was reflected in his menu: pancakes or corncakes
or hoecake bread for average or sullen moods, sour-milk cornbread
or baking-powder biscuits when his mood was friendly or elated.
And on the friendly days he insisted on waiting on table, jumping up
to look into the oven, and returning with a plate of golden butter-
filled squares of cornbread or fluffy buttered biscuits.

His son had chosen this Sunday morning to announce his intention
of leaving junior college in midterm and accepting the scholarship
offered by the University. While the mother and daughter stared at
their plates and kept trying to swallow pancakes that didn't taste
good any more, the brother sat with his food untouched, presenting
his case as reasonably as possible.

He had managed to wrest from his father enough money during
the full-time summer work to pay for his cello lessons. Now school
had started, and he felt that he could no longer return to the old
routine of work before and after school, with only his food and the
bare necessities of clothing as grudging compensation. He was perfectly willing to forego lunch and carfare, but not his cello lessons.
The tips that he had carefully hoarded as a young boy had diminished to almost nothing, because he was now on more familiar terms
with the customers, and they respected him too much to offer tips.
Most important of all, he had to save toward the coming winter. The
scholarship, valuable as it was, would pay only tuition, leaving him
with no means of support unless he could find work that would not
interfere with his studies. Until now he had outwardly lived the life
set out for him, all of the time a different person inside. Now he
wanted to prepare for life as he saw it and felt that it should be; and
without his saying so, the others at the table knew that he meant a
life very different from the one he had so far led.

All of this seemed reasonable enough to the two holding their breaths over the already cold pancakes. But to the former German tailors' apprentice who, as he learned their trade, had listened to the saga of their Black Forest childhood—how they had been tied to the bedpost and thrashed for disobedience or gone without food or locked in a closet for days until chastened—it represented the final abnegation of "blood" and "descent" and "inheritance." It meant also the final break with his first-born, the last of the line, who should have dutifully learned more about solvents and tumblers and repairs and trading and business, in order to carry forward the Name and consequently the Race.

The father said to his son, "Eat your breakfast."

And the son said, "I'm not hungry." The father repeated, this time rising from his chair at the head of the table, "Don't talk back to me! I said eat your breakfast!"

"I don't want any breakfast," the boy repeated. "I was talking to you about what I intend to do, what I have to have, that's all."

The chair at the head of the table fell over backward as Albert Dunham reached across and struck his son. The girl sat with her mouth full of pancakes that refused to go down and stared into her plate, wanting badly to run from the table and out of the house and keep running.

Annette Dunham said, "Oh, Al, don't hit him! He was only *asking!*"

And the father, nostrils wide and voice thick, picked up the chair and said, "When I tell you to do something, you do it."

The son turned pale where he held his lips tightly together, but his cheek was dark red where his father's open hand had struck it. He ate the pancakes, and the only sound in the room was the scraping and clattering made by the man at the head of the table, who had expected further resistance or something else, but not just this.

When his plate was clean, the son excused himself from the table and went through the kitchen and into the bathroom. He closed the door, but it was easy, in the dead stillness not even disturbed now by Albert Dunham's knife and fork, to hear the sounds of retching. When the boy passed through the room again, he looked at his father triumphantly, even hesitating slightly as though to ask, "*Well, anything else?*"—and then went out of the room and down the stairs.

It was ill advised of the mother to pursue the subject further that day. The stormy discussion was carried from bedroom to kitchen to living room to dining room, until when time came for Brown's Chapel Christian Endeavor the girl was eager, instead of reluctant, to go, and even asked her mother if she might stay through for the evening service. But the two church services were only an interlude, and again in the flat above the shop the bitterness between husband and wife continued into the night.

The son returned home after everyone had gone to bed and began his habitual reading in the dining room. A moment later the father streaked through the living room and down the front stairs like a madman. Then the house was in total blackness, all electric current cut off from the main switch. The father found his way back to the bedroom by flashlight, gloating aloud over the victory. There was no sound from the dining room, but when the girl turned the corner at the Jefferson Street bridge the following day after school, she felt the emptiness and didn't bother to run the rest of the way home. The sewing machine was silent, her father sullenly worked over a skirt on her mother's pressing board, and upstairs the dishes were still in the sink from breakfast and the suitcases were gone from the bedroom closet.

She stood in the middle of the living room and wondered why everything seemed so empty, because her mother was almost always in the shop at this time anyway. Then she began mechanically to put things in order, noticing that the bed was still unmade and so guessing that she had left in the early morning.

Her brother came in while she was washing the dishes. "She must have left early," he said.

The girl agreed.

"Did she tell you anything yesterday?"

The girl shook her head.

"Did she leave you a letter?"

"No, did she leave you one?"

"No."

"Where do you suppose she went?"

"I don't know. She'll come back or let us know."

"Are you going away if she's still away by winter?"

"I have to. Don't worry. She'll come back before then. She said before that she was going, and didn't."

"I don't want to stay here alone. Suppose she never comes back!" The girl was crying, and he was drying the dishes without thinking about it or having to be asked to. Then he began to wash the dishes because she couldn't see what she was doing and just kept mopping helplessly at one plate that had some streaks of hardened egg left on it.

"Don't wash the dishes," she said. "It makes your fingers soft for the cello. You always said that."

"That doesn't matter. . . . Say, Kitty, wouldn't you like to go to the University, too? After junior college here?"

"Yes," she said, a little dubiously. "But it costs a lot, and I'd never get a scholarship."

"Never mind," he said, wringing out the dishcloth and handing it back to her. "By that time I'll be able to help you. Just keep going and don't pay any attention to him. You've got to think about getting away, that's all. Why, you could even go to Africa after you finish at the University!"

He smiled at her; now she had a secret to live by and for, and the flat didn't seem so empty, and instead of being cold and suffocated and without any hope at all, she felt strong and ready for anything. He was standing in the door, already too long away from the West Side Cleaners' truck.

"Don't give up Kitty!" he said. "Don't ever give up. You'll make it all right!" And by the way he said it she somehow felt that he meant she would make it whether he did or not, though he was so superior to her in every way that she could see no doubt anywhere as far as he was concerned—except for a smile that sometimes seemed to be hinting at a sweet and sad and wise farewell, as though actually making the farewell just wasn't worth the effort.

After a few days a letter arrived from Delavan. The girl had avoided her father as much as possible and had said nothing about her mother. Once she had to ask for lunch money, and her father told her then that it was time for her to begin learning how to work in the shop, how to remove the spots from dresses and answer the telephone and keep books and press knife pleats and lengthen or shorten pants cuffs and skirt hems.

The letter was from Annette Dunham and it said, "Dear Katherine, I couldn't stand it any longer. I was sorry not to tell you but I had to take the morning train to Delavan. I won't come back until your father can treat me decently. Be a good girl and take care of the house. Your Aunt Alice is very sick. It is a good thing that I came when I did. Tell Albert not to cause any trouble. It doesn't do any good to argue with your father. After all, he is your father. With love, Your mother."

The girl sat at the desk with the open account book before her, and read and reread the letter for some sign that life might again be resumed as it had been before, even with its troubles, but with her mother there. She tried to find the comfort and love and affection that she knew must be hidden somewhere between the lines, and felt that her own incapacity kept her from discovering them.

Her brother read the letter with no expression and said, "She'll be back. You just watch and see. She won't stay away." But he didn't seem too happy about the letter. The same day the father received a letter, and whatever was in it only added to his habitual sullenness.

The volume of business continued to increase; by the second week of his wife's absence the father, even after hiring a replacement and conscripting his daughter's help, found the efficiency of the shop deteriorating. The girl was beginning to feel the strain of added duties; she refrained with difficulty from showing her discontent at having to forego the late-afternoon dancing classes, and she had to beg a letter from the dean of girls to convince her father that two evenings a week were required in out-of-doors sports to fulfill the requirements of the curriculum. These he allowed her, with the understanding that she still put in a certain amount of daily time in the shop if she expected her school expenses.

Toward the end of the first month of the semester, she took stock of her clothes and found that, although she could manage well enough with dresses by lengthening skirts and switching combinations, her shoes presented a real problem. Last year's shoes were impossibly small; her good patent-leather slippers, saved especially for funerals and club meetings and church suppers, were hopelessly outgrown; and the shoes that she had used steadily during the last part of the summer were worn through on the soles, so that the shoemaker just looked at them and shook his head; besides, she would have had to stay home from school while they were in the shop, because she had absolutely nothing else to put on, not even bedroom slippers. So she put pieces of cardboard in the shoes every morning and wrote and asked her mother what to do. Her mother wrote back immediately that she should ask her father for the money to buy shoes, especially since she now worked in the shop and took care of the flat and cooked most of the meals. She would have sent the money, she said, but things were going very badly with Aunt Alice and Uncle Ed. She would explain later.

All at once the shoes went to pieces. First the cardboard fell out while the girl was walking along the corridor between classes, because the holes had grown much larger as she went to and from school. Then it began to rain every day, and the sodden cardboard would have disintegrated by the time she reached the school steps. She started carrying extra pieces and would go into the girls' washroom to make a replacement before the first class, flushing the bits down the toilet so that no one would suspect her dilemma. Then there was the embarrassment of taking her shoes off for gym class and having to hide them quickly away in the locker and spirit them as quickly out again when she dressed. And of course her stockings were abused because of the holes in the shoes and had to be darned nightly.

One day as she walked home in the rain, the squish of water between her toes and the roughness of the pavement where the cardboard had given way, roused her from apathy to anger. She hated her father for subjecting her to such discomfort and indignity, and her mother for having left her in such a position.

"She should have stayed!" she thought over and over, and then she said to herself, "He's got to. He's got to get me a pair of shoes. I'll stay home from school, and they'll put him in jail." Her anger gave her the courage to burst into the shop and rip both shoes off in front of Mr. Crusoe and the new sewing woman.

"I've got to have some shoes," she said. "Mother said to get them. She promised them before she went away. I can't go to school this way!"

"I have nothing to do with what your mother promises," her father answered, not looking at her or at the shoes, but going on with his pressing.

Her anger became hysteria. "I've got to have shoes!" she cried. "I won't work here any more if I can't have shoes!"

Mr. Crusoe put on his hat and went out the back door, as he often did when a crisis was in the air. He was a mild man by nature and disapproved of his employer's violent behavior. He was, however, well paid and knew that he would risk his job by taking a stand; and he had a family of his own to think about.

"You ran her away," the girl cried. "I want her back! You make her come back or I'll go away, too!"

The pressing iron stopped in mid-air, then slammed down onto its stand. She should have been afraid then and flinched or drawn back. But resentment had piled up and been held back until she had no control whatever; she was swept along in her assault on injustice.

Her father may not have intended to strike her, but she didn't wait to find out. She darted to one side and found the electric iron from the ladies' pressing board in her hand. Then she was calm.

"You touch me," she said, "just touch me. and I'll kill you. Maybe Albert didn't do it, but I will. I'll kill you, I tell you!"

And she almost hoped that he would make the move, so that it would all be over with. There was only the sound of the gas in the pressing iron and her own heart pounding out its triumph over fear. Her father reached for his battered felt hat and turned to the back door and went out. She realized that she was in her stocking feet and picked up the soaking shoes, from which wet gray wads of cardboard fell. As she passed the sewing woman, she could hardly walk straight because her head felt light and her throat felt as though someone with steel fingers had just squeezed it in both hands. She walked into the rain and up the stairway to the flat. She saw that her father had peeled potatoes and left two T-bone steaks on a platter to be cooked for dinner; he had also washed the break- fast dishes. She made his bed, set the table, and gathered enough courage to return to the shop for her evening duties.

Her father was alone at the pressing table. It seemed early for the others to have left, and she felt uneasy, wishing that her brother would happen in. Her father pressed for a while in silence, and she began marking bits of tape with the names of the owners of the last lot of clothing that had been put into the bin under Mr. Crusoe's pressing table. After a while her father spoke, and the quality of his voice disturbed her, because she couldn't believe it meant defeat, and she knew nothing about what might be buried far beneath the virulence that had effaced the father she remembered from Glen Ellyn or even from picnics and Bush Park and rabbit hunts and ice- cream freezing in years after that. She saw only one side of it; that her nights were fitful and her heartbeat unruly and her mother gone and her brother resented and beaten and herself unwanted and beaten, too, if she didn't behave exactly as she was supposed to; and her feet were wet and her shoes worn out, and even so she was not allowed to stay and learn more and play more after school like other girls of her age, but must spend the evening hours in a tight confinement filled with odors of gasoline and steam and pressed wool, or in the flat above, cleaning, cleaning, fighting a losing battle against the dust wheel.

"I wrote your mother today," he said, "asking her to come back.

I had already written her. I told your brother about it, but you didn't give me a chance."

The girl stood quietly at the basket of dirty, half-sorted clothes. She could hardly believe what she was hearing, but the warm flow in her veins and the glad thump of her heart were real.

"I'm glad," she said, after a moment of trying to keep the sound of tears out of her voice. "I'm glad you asked her." At that moment she didn't hate her father. She loved everyone, even people she didn't know.

"About the shoes," her father said. "Business is good, but there are a lot of payments to be met on the new house. Making it into two apartments takes more money than your mother realizes. That's why we have so much trouble."

The girl felt suddenly deflated. She would rather not hear anything at all like criticism of her mother or justification for her father's behavior. She would just like to think about her mother's return and perhaps about a family like other people's—and above all, she admitted to herself with a fleeting feeling of guilt, a new pair of shoes.

"How much would a new pair of shoes cost?" her father asked.

From long experience with her mother's efforts to extract money from her husband, the girl quoted an outside figure, the sound of which surprised even herself.

Her father looked up in astonishment. "Why, I could put another window in the attic for that!" he said. "You'd better wait till your mother gets here!"

The girl's heart dropped to the floor. "Oh, I *can't!*" she cried. "Can't you see what my shoes are like? And I'm so ashamed. Everybody looks at me now. They can see the cardboard."

"They can be half-soled," her father said.

"But they *can't!* The man won't do it! And, besides, what would I wear while he did it?"

"I saw some shoes of your mother's in the closet," her father said. "They should be just about right for you, and the soles are good and strong. I'll get them."

The girl wondered what shoes they could be. She went on wetting the strips of tape on a damp sponge and marking names with an indelible pencil. Then she sewed the names into the cloths and after that went through the pockets and seams for forgotten articles.

Her father returned with a pair of shoes. They had medium heels, higher than those girls of her age wore. They were narrow, as all of Annette Dunham's shoes were, and certainly long enough for the girl. The soles were strong, and they were tie pumps. But they were of white canvas. Shoes that the mother wore only on the hottest days of the summer, and then most of the time at picnics. The girl concentrated on a green stain on the toe of one of them and wondered what picnic it was a souvenir of. She felt sick with apprehension as she took off the wet shoes and tried on the white ones. Then she sighed with relief.

"They won't go on," she said. "See, just half my foot gets in."

Her father seemed pleased with himself. "Take your stockings off," he said, "and dry your feet and put a little powder on. Then they'll fit. They're good and strong and will do fine until your mother gets back."

Her brother entered in time to witness the triumph of the shoes. She stood stockingless, her instep and ankles covered with the powder used to whiten freshly cleaned kid gloves. Her feet had slid in with the greatest of ease, while she tried to make them expand and prayed that they would stick halfway. It was the end of October, and cold and rainy nearly every day, and in the Midwest the traditional day for taking off straw hats and white shoes was Labor Day. She would surely be the laughing stock of the whole school. What good had it done to make the hockey team and get ninety-nine in Latin and be asked into the Girls' Athletic Association? She bit her lips to keep tears back and refused to look at her brother.

He paid no attention to the shoes. "Did he tell you?" he asked, his voice light and gayer than she had heard it for a long time. "Did he tell you that Mother's coming back?"

She felt ungrateful to be near to tears about the shoes when her prayers had been answered and soon everything would be all right again. "Yes," she said, and managed to smile at her father.

"Now you'd better go and fix the steak," her father said. "Put the potatoes on, and I'll be up in a few minutes to mash them. Those are fine steaks. Henry Simon did all right this time!" And, as she went out the front door: "Don't cook mine too long. Nobody ought to eat steaks like you and your brother eat them. All of the taste is cooked away."

Dinner was almost friendly, and every time she remembered the white shoes, which were warm and comfortable until she realized that they were way out of season and for a grown woman, she thought instead of her mother's return, and the shoes didn't seem so bad.

But when she wore them the next day and the rain had soaked through to turn them a dirty gray, she wanted to turn and run away or take them off and go barefoot. She even wished for her old shoes, but her father had thrown them out, feeling actually pleased with himself for his brilliant solution of the problem.

All that she had feared became fact. She was looked at, and her shoes were pointed out, and she could hear snickers that in her misery were amplified to raucous laughter. When she was worn out with blushing and trying to look as though nothing were wrong and it was the most natural thing in the world to wear her mother's white shoes to school in late October, they developed a new way of embarrassing her. They now squeaked when they were dry, so that if the day was not rainy, she soaked them in water before leaving home, hoping to be spared at least a part of her suffering. To make matters worse her mother had written that Aunt Alice's condition was so grave that she was not expected to live, and that Ed Poindexter was taking it badly, and that she would have to stay until the crisis was over one way or another.

Two weeks passed in waiting, and one night as her brother helped her with the dishes, she burst again into anger.

"I don't think she's coming," she said. "I think he's lying anyway. I don't think he even asked her. I don't think she'd stay just because Aunt Alice is sick. I bet he didn't even ask her. He just wanted to make me stop asking for shoes and put these on me for good!"

"No," her brother said. "Don't forget he needs her every bit as much as we do. I think this has taught him a lesson. Nobody can do as much as she does, and, besides, he doesn't have to pay her." The logic of this quieted the girl, and she resigned herself again to the white shoes.

MAXINE W. KUMIN [1961]

Maxine W. Kumin, who has written poems for children as well as about children, has three of her own. In fact, she did not seriously begin to write poetry until after the arrival of her third child, her son. Born in

1925 in Philadelphia, she attended Radcliffe College, where she received
her B.A. in 1946 and her M.A. in 1948.

Poem for My Son

Where water laps my hips
it licks your chin. You stand
on tiptoe looking up
and swivel on my hands.
We play at this and laugh,
but understand you weigh
now almost less than life
and little more than sea.
So fine a line exists
between buoyance and stone
that, catching at my wrists,
I feel love notch the bone
to think you might have gone.

To think they smacked and pumped
to squall you into being
when you swam down, lungs limp
as a new balloon, and dying.
Six years today they bent
a black tube through your chest.
The tank hissed in the tent.
I leaned against the mast
outside the sterile nest.

And now inside the sea
You bump along my arm
learning the narrow way
you've come from that red worm.
I tell you, save your air
and let the least swell ease you.
Put down, you flail for shore.
I cannot bribe nor teach you
to know the wet will keep you.

And cannot tell myself
unfasten from the boy.

On the Atlantic shelf
I see you wash away
to war or love or luck,
prodigious king, a stranger.
Times I stepped on a crack
my mother was in danger,
and time will find the chinks
to work the same in me.
You bobbled in my flanks.
They cut you from my sea.
Now you must mind your way.

Once, after a long swim
come overhand and wheezy
across the dappled seam
of lake, I foundered, dizzy,
uncertain which was better:
to fall there and unwind
in thirty feet of water
or fight back for the land.
Life would not let me lose it.
It yanked me by the nose.
Blackfaced and thick with vomit
it thrashed me to my knees.
We only think we choose.

But say we choose. Pretend it.
My pulse knit in your wrist
expands. Go now and spend it.
The sea will take our kiss.
Now, boy, swim off for this.

ISABELLA GARDNER   [1961]

Isabella Gardner, who is a former associate editor of Poetry Magazine, *has published two volumes of poetry,* Birthdays from the Ocean *and* The

Looking Glass. *Like many contemporary mothers who are also poets, she can write an unsentimental but warm poem about her son.*

A Loud Song, Mother

My son is five years old and tonight he sang this song to me.
He said, it's a loud song, Mother, block up your ears a little, he
said wait I must get my voice ready first. Then tunelessly
but with a bursting beat he chanted from his room enormously,

        strangers in my name
        strangers all around me
        strangers running toward me
        strangers all over the world
        strangers running on stars

A deafening declaration this jubilant shout of grief
that trumpets final fellowship and flutes a whole belief.
Alone and in the dark he clears his throat to yawp his truth
that each living human creature's name is Ruth.
He sings a world of strangers running on the burning stars
a race on every-colored feet with freshly calloused scars.

Our stark still strangers waited back of doors and under beds
their socket eyes stared at us out of closets; in our heads.
We crawled on hob-nailed knees across our wasted starless land
each smugly thinking his the only face that wore a brand.

Sons, may you starve the maggot fears that ate our spirit's meat
and stride with brother strangers in your seven-league bare feet.

MARCELLINE HEMINGWAY SANFORD
[1962]

Ernest Hemingway's sister, Marcelline Hemingway Sanford, who is a distinguished writer and lecturer on the theater, attended Oberlin College, the University of Chicago, and the School of Speech at Northwestern University. Although she was nearly two years older than her brother, their mother brought them up as if they were twins, so that Mrs. Sanford's

memories are even more intimate and vivid than an older sister's usually
would be.

"Ernest Had Enough to Bear . . ."

For days Ernie had been watching the mails. He was irritable and
on edge with the waiting. Then the letter came. After he read it he
went to bed and was actually ill. We didn't know what was the
matter with Ernie at first. He did not respond to medical treatment,
and he ran a temperature. Dad was worried about him. I went up to
Ernie's room to see if I could be of any help to him. Ernie thrust the
letter toward me.

"Read it," he said from the depths of his grief. "No. I'll tell you."
Then he turned to the wall. He was physically sick for several days
but he did not mention the letter again.

Ag, Ernie told me, was not coming to America. She was going
to marry an Italian major instead.

In time Ernest felt better. He got out among his friends again. I
have thought many times since that day that the letter from Agnes
may have been the most valuable one my brother ever received.
Perhaps without that rankling memory, *A Farewell to Arms* might
never have been written.

As time went on, that spring of 1919, Ernest grew impatient at his
lack of physical activity. The silver knee cap the surgeons in Milan
had put in place bothered him less, he said. Although bits of shrap-
nel continued to hurt and annoy him as they worked toward the
surface of his legs and feet, he was determined to do something
more active than merely walking with his cane. Ernie found he
could dance almost as well as before he went to war. The sliding
steps seemed easier for him than the abruptness of walking. Mother
and Dad were worried about Ernest for several reasons. For one
thing they knew he could not be happy without some athletic
activity in his life. They were glad when Ernest decided to take up
swimming at the Y.M.C.A. tank.

One night there was a swimming meet at the "Y." Ernie had been
down to swim in the pool rather regularly, but we didn't see how he
could swim in fast competition with that bad knee of his. We didn't
mention our fears to him, of course.

The evening the swimming meet was held most of our family
was gathered in the dining room after dinner was over. The dining
room was smaller and cozier than the living room. The table had

been cleared and, as we often did, my sisters and I stood leaning our backs against the big green enameled hot water radiator on the north side of the room. Mother, I remember, was seated at the black upright practice piano on the opposite side. Daddy, his suit coat hung over the back of his chair, was looking over some papers as he sat in his shirt sleeves at the empty white-covered dining table.

I remember that Ernie came into the house the back way. He walked into the dining room through the swinging door from the kitchen. Daddy turned toward Ernest.

"How'd it go, boy?" Daddy asked kindly.

"Swell," Ernie said.

"Which race did you swim in?" one of the sisters inquired.

"Listen, kid, I'm a plunger now, see. I don't go in for any other events. I got third."

Mother and I sighed with relief.

There were loud congratulations from everybody. Ernie beamed.

Finally somebody asked innocently, "How many were entered in the plunges?" For a minute Ernie didn't answer. He just looked at us without an impression on his face. We waited.

"Three," Ernie said. He turned and went upstairs to bed.

We all knew the sister who asked that question could have bitten her tongue out.

All these months Ernie continued to wear his Red Cross uniform. It was very becoming and he looked extremely handsome in it, but the main reason he wore it was because the high boots, which were part of the uniform, gave needed support to his wounded legs. He told me he didn't know how he could walk without those high, firm boots. He polished them daily. They were the nicest footgear any of us had ever seen. Ernie said he couldn't wear these good boots with civilian clothes, so he continued to dress in his uniform.

One Saturday that spring of 1919, I went to a matinee in a Chicago theater. In the row behind me I could hear two women talking. They seemed to be discussing a returned soldier.

"Why does that boy have to flaunt that fancy uniform around the town all these months?" said a voice in my ear. "He's been home from war since last winter. Why doesn't he stop trying to be a hero and put on civilian clothes? I've got no patience with these kids that keep trying to show off."

"Maybe he hasn't got any civilian clothes left that fit him," said the other voice. "Don't be too hard on him."

"Oh, that's not it," the first voice went on. "He just likes to get the girls crazy about him. Have you noticed how he hangs around the high school all the time? Wouldn't you think he'd find something else to do? Why doesn't he get a job? He likes having the girls moon over him! You know as well as I do that's why Ernest Hemingway wears his uniform."

I sat perfectly still for a minute. I was so shocked and angry I could hardly breathe. The women went on talking. I had to reply. When I could control myself I turned around in my seat to see that they were teachers from Oak Park High School.

"I beg your pardon," I said. "I couldn't help overhearing your remarks about my brother. Maybe it would interest you to know why he *has* to wear that uniform all this time. Pieces of metal keep coming out of his legs. Sometimes he has to wear dressings over the places that are festered. Do you know that those high leather boots give his sore legs support? He doesn't wear those boots for fun, he wears them because he has to. Most people don't know it, but Ernie has a lot of pain. He can't get a job yet, as you suggested, because he isn't able to stand on his feet more than a few hours at a time. I don't blame him for hanging around the high school. He just gets darn lonesome, and so would you if you were home and all your friends were away in college or had jobs during the daytime. I should think teachers like you would be more understanding instead of talking so mean about a boy who's going through all that Ernest has to bear!"

I was so angry I could feel I was beginning to cry. I was also so embarrassed after I had dared to say all this that I climbed out of my seat and went to the rest room until I calmed down. When I finally came back, the curtain was up and I watched the play, though to this day I couldn't tell you what it was about. I ignored the teachers. But at the first intermission, when the lights went up, they asked me to go out into the hallway with them, and they both apologized profusely. I said I was sorry I had been rude to them, but they insisted they were glad I had spoken up. One of them said she was sure that few people in Oak Park had any idea of Ernest's real situation. Though I was still upset, we parted as friends, and I watched the rest of the play. I was surprised at myself. Though I had often criticized Ernie personally, I had no idea I could become so angry when I heard someone else criticize him, particularly when, as in the case of the teachers, the criticism was so unkindly worded and unfair.

I remember that I told Mother about the incident when I got home that evening. Mother's reaction was typical of her.

"Good for you, Marce!" said Mother. "I'm glad you gave it to them! They deserved it!" But Mother warned me not to let Ernest know what the teachers had said. Mother and I both knew how sensitive Ernest was. We knew he would be deeply hurt if he thought others felt unkindly toward him. Ernest had enough to bear without any of us adding anything more.

IV   ❦   LOVERS

Courting in the Nineties

It is a common feeling that young men are afraid to marry, and that the enthusiastic lover that we women so delight to read of, is rarely to be found in society; and is this not our fault in good measure?

Our sex demands too much and the bend of a girl's mind, as a rule, is for a style of living which few young men can support.

—FELICIA HOLT, in "Marriage and Money," 1889

It is often said that Romance is shocked at the idea of a mother finding a husband for her daughter. With equal truth it may be asserted that Delicacy is shocked at a young girl hunting a husband entirely by herself. Mother and home throw a charm and a refinement around such efforts, and no good young man will refuse to acknowledge the wisdom and respectability of the English custom that "a wife is to be courted on her father's hearthstone." Men all need the corrective influence of a noble social standard, and it is in the home women create that standard.

—AMELIA E. BARR, in the *Ladies' Home Journal,* 1891

You never allowed a man to give you a present except flowers or candy or possibly a book. To receive a piece of jewelry from a man to whom you were not engaged was a sign of being a fast woman, and the idea that you would permit any man to kiss you before you were engaged to him never even crossed my mind.

All these restrictions seem foolish nowadays, but I wonder if the girls weren't safer. It requires more character to be as free as youth is today.

—ELEANOR ROOSEVELT, in *This Is My Story,* 1937

SARAH ORNE JEWETT [1889]

Born in Maine, educated chiefly at home, and never married, Sarah Orne Jewett (1849-1909) was best at writing about celibate men and women. "The Taking of Captain Ball" depicts a lover who remained uncaught.

The Taking of Captain Ball

I

There was a natural disinclination to the cares of housekeeping in Captain Ball's mind, and he would have left the sea much earlier in life if he had not cared more for living on board ship. A man was his own master there, and meddlesome neighbors and parsons and tearful womenfolks could be made to keep their distance. But as years went on, and the extremes of weather produced much affliction in the shape of rheumatism, this, and the decline of the merchant-service, and the degeneracy of common seamen, forced Captain Ball to come ashore for good. He regretted that he could no longer follow the sea, and grumbled at his hard fate in spite of many alleviations. He might have been condemned to an inland town, but in reality his house was within sight of tide-water, and he found plenty of companionship in the decayed seaport where he had been born and bred. There were several retired ship-masters who closely approached his own rank and dignity. They all gave other excuses than that of age and infirmity for being out of business, took a sober satisfaction in their eleven o'clock bitters, and discussed the shipping list of the morning paper with far more interest than the political or general news of the other columns.

While Captain Asaph Ball was away on his long voyages he had left his house in charge of an elder sister, who was joint owner. She was a grim old person, very stern in matters of sectarian opinion, and the captain recognized in his heart of hearts that she alone was his superior officer. He endeavored to placate her with generous offerings of tea and camel's-hair scarfs and East Indian sweetmeats, not to speak of unnecessary and sometimes very beautiful china for the tea parties that she never gave, and handsome dress patterns with which she scorned to decorate her sinful shape of clay. She pinched herself to the verge of want in order to send large sums of money to the missionaries, but she saved the captain's money for him against the time when his willful lavishness and improvidence might find him a poor man. She was always looking forward to the days when he would be aged and forlorn, that burly seafaring brother of hers. She loved to remind him of his latter end, and in writing her long letters that were to reach him in foreign ports, she told little of the neighborhood news and results of voyages, but bewailed, in page after page, his sad condition of impenitence and the shortness of time. The captain would rather have faced a mutinous crew any day than his sister's solemn statements of this sort, but he loyally read them through, though with heavy sighs, and worked himself into his best broadcloth suit, at least once while he lay in port, to go to church on Sunday, out of good New England habit and respect to her opinions. It was not his sister's principles, but her phrases that the captain failed to comprehend. Sometimes when he returned to his ship he took pains to write a letter to dear sister Ann, and to casually mention the fact of his attendance upon public worship, and even to recall the text and purport of the sermon. He was apt to fall asleep in his humble place at the very back of the church, and his report of the services would have puzzled a far less keen theologian than Miss Ann Ball. In fact these poor makeshifts of religious interest did not deceive her, and the captain had an uneasy consciousness that, to use his own expression, the thicker he laid on the words, the quicker she saw through them. And somehow or other that manly straightforwardness and honesty of his, that free-handed generosity, that true unselfishness which made him stick by his ship when the crew had run away from a poor black cook who was taken down with the yellow fever, which made him nurse the frightened beggar as tenderly as a woman, and bring him back to life, and send him packing afterward with plenty of money in his pocket—all these fine traits that made Captain Ball respected in every port where his loud voice and clumsy figure and bronzed face were known, seemed to count for nothing with the stern sister. At least her younger brother thought so. But when, a few years after he came ashore for good, she died and left him alone in the neat old white house, which his instinctive good taste and his father's before him had made a museum of East Indian treasures, he found all his letters stored away with loving care after they had been read and reread into tatters, and among her own papers such touching expressions of love and pride and longing for his soul's good, that poor Captain Asaph broke down altogether and cried like a schoolboy. She had saved every line of newspaper which even mentioned his ships' names. She had loved him deeply in the repressed New England fashion, that under a gray and forbidding crust of manner, like a chilled lava bed, hides glowing fire of loyalty and devotion.

Sister Ann was a princess among housekeepers, and for some time after her death the captain was a piteous mourner indeed. No growing schoolboy could be more shy and miserable in the presence of women than he, though nobody had a readier friendliness or more offhand sailor ways among men. The few intimate family friends who came to his assistance at the time of his sister's illness and death added untold misery to the gloomy situation. Yet he received the minister with outspoken gratitude in spite of that worthy man's trepidation. Everybody said that poor Captain Ball looked as if his heart was broken. "I tell ye I feel as if I was tied in a bag of fleas," said the distressed mariner, and his pastor turned away to cough, and so hide the smile that would come. "Widders an' old maids, they're busier than the devil in a gale o'wind," grumbled the captain. "Poor Ann, she was worth every one of 'em lashed together, and here you find me with a head-wind every way I try to steer." The minister was a man, at any rate; his very presence was a protection.

Some wretched days went by while Captain Ball tried to keep his lonely house with the assistance of one Silas Jenkins, who had made several voyages with him as cook, but they soon proved that the best of sailors may make the worst of housekeepers. Life looked darker and darker, and when, one morning, Silas inadvertently overheated and warped the new cooking stove, which had been the pride of Miss Ball's heart, the breakfastless captain dismissed him in a fit of blind rage. The captain was first cross and then abject when he went hungry, and in this latter stage was ready to abase himself enough to recall Widow Sparks, his sister's lieutenant, who lived close by in Ropewalk Lane, forgetting that he had driven her into calling him an old hog two days after the funeral. He groaned aloud as he thought of her, but reached for his hat and cane, when there came a gentle, feminine rap at the door.

"Let 'em knock!" grumbled the captain, angrily, but after a moment's reflection he scowled and went to lift the latch.

There stood upon the doorstep a middle-aged-looking woman, with a pleasant though determined face. The captain scowled again, but involuntarily opened his foredoor a little wider.

"Capt'in Asaph Ball, I presume?"

"The same," answered the captain.

"I have been told, sir, that you need a housekeeper, owing to recent affliction."

There was a squally moment of resistance in the old sailor's breast, but circumstances seemed to be wrecking him on a lee shore. Down came his flag on the run.

"I can't say but what I do, ma'am," and with lofty courtesy, such as an admiral might use to his foe of equal rank, the master of the house signified that his guest could enter. When they were seated opposite each other in the desolate sitting room he felt himself the weaker human being of the two. Five years earlier, and he would have put to sea before the week's end, if only to gain the poor freedom of a coastwise line schooner.

"Well, speak up, can't ye?" he said, trying to laugh. "Tell me what's the tax, and how much you can take hold and do, without coming to me for orders every hand's turn o' the day. I've had Silas Jinkens here, one o' my old ship's cooks; he served well at sea, and I thought he had some head; but we've been beat, I tell ye, and you'll find some work to put things shipshape. He's gitting in years, that's the trouble; I oughtn't to have called on him," said Captain Ball, anxious to maintain even so poorly the dignity of his sex.

"I like your looks; you seem a good steady hand, with no nonsense about ye." He cast a shy glance at his companion, and would not have believed that any woman could have come to the house a stranger, and have given him such an immediate feeling of confidence and relief.

"I'll tell ye what's about the worst of the matter," and the captain pulled a letter out of his deep coat pocket. His feelings had been pent up too long. At the sight of the pretty handwriting and aggravatingly soft-spoken sentences, Asaph Ball was forced to inconsiderate speech. The would-be housekeeper pushed back her rocking chair as he began, and tucked her feet under, setting her bonnet a little beside, as if she were close-reefed and anchored to ride out the gale.

"I'm in most need of an able person," he roared, "on account of this letter's settin' me adrift about knowing what to do. 'Tis from a gal that wants to come and make her home here. Land sakes alive, puts herself right forrard! I don't want her, *an' I won't have her*. She may be a great-niece; I don't say she ain't; but what should I do with one o' them jiggetin' gals about? In the name o' reason, why should

I be set out o' my course? I'm left at the mercy o' you womenfolks," and the captain got stiffly to his feet. "If you've had experience, an' think you can do for me, why, stop an' try, an' I'll be much obleeged to ye. You'll find me a good provider, and we'll let one another alone, and get along some way or 'nother."

The captain's voice fairly broke; he had been speaking as if to a brother man; he was tired out and perplexed. Ann had saved him so many petty trials, and now she was gone. The poor man had watched her suffer and seen her die, and he was as tenderhearted and as lonely as a child, however he might bluster. Even such infrequent matters as family letters had been left to his busy sister. It happened that they had inherited a feud with an elder half-brother's family in the West, though the captain was aware of the existence of this forth-putting great-niece, who had been craftily named for Miss Ann Ball, and so gained a precarious hold on her affections; but to harbor one of the race was to consent to the whole. Captain Ball was not a man to bring down upon himself an army of interferers and plunderers, and he now threw down the poor girl's well-meant letter with an outrageous expression of his feelings. Then he felt a silly weakness, and hastened to wipe his eyes with his pocket handkerchief.

"I've been beat, I tell ye," he said, brokenly.

There was a look of apparent sympathy, mingled with victory, on the housekeeper's face. Perhaps she had known some other old sailor of the same make, for she rose and turned her face aside to look out of the window until the captain's long upper lip had time to draw itself straight and stern again. Plainly she was a woman of experience and discretion.

"I'll take my shawl and bunnit right off, sir," she said, in a considerate little voice. "I see a-plenty to do; there'll be time enough after I get you your dinner to see to havin' my trunk here; but it needn't stay a day longer than you give the word."

"That's clever," said the captain. "I'll step right down street and get us a good fish, an' you can fry it or make a chowder, just which you see fit. It now wants a little of eleven—" and an air of pleased anticipation lighted his face—"I must be on my way."

"If it's all the same to you, I guess we don't want no company till we get to rights a little. You're kind of tired out, sir," said the housekeeper, feelingly. "By-and-by you can have the young girl come an' make you a visit, and either let her go or keep her, 'cordin' as seems fit. I may not turn out to suit."

"What may I call you, ma'am?" inquired Captain Ball. "Mis'

French? Not one o' them Fleet Street Frenches?" (suspiciously). "Oh, come from Massachusetts way!" (with relief).

"I was stopping with some friends that had a letter from some o' the minister's folks here, and they told how bad off you was," said Mrs. French, modestly. "I was out of employment, an' I said to myself that I should feel real happy to go and do for that Captain Ball. He knows what he wants, and I know what I want, and no flummery."

"You know somethin' o' life, I do declare," and the captain fairly beamed. "I never was called a hard man at sea, but I like to give my orders, and have folks foller 'em. If it was womenfolks that wrote, they may have set me forth more'n ordinary. I had every widder and single woman in town here while Ann lay dead, and my natural feelin's war all worked up. I see 'em dressed up and smirkin' and settin' their nets to ketch me when I was in an extremity. I wouldn't give a kentle o' sp'iled fish for the whole on 'em. I ain't a marryin' man, there's once for all for ye," and the old sailor stepped toward the door with some temper.

"Ef you'll write to the young woman, sir, just to put off comin' for a couple or three weeks," suggested Mrs. French.

"*This afternoon, ma'am,*" said the captain, as if it were the ay, ay, sir, of an able seaman who sprang to his duty of reefing the main-topsail.

Captain Ball walked down to the fish shop with stately steps and measured taps of his heavy cane. He stopped on the way, a little belated, and assured two or three retired ship-masters that he had manned the old brig complete at last; he even gave a handsome wink of his left eye over the edge of a glass, and pronounced his morning grog to be A No. 1, prime.

Mrs. French picked up her gown at each side with thumb and finger, and swept the captain a low courtesy behind his back as he went away; then she turned up the aforesaid gown and sought for one of the lamented Miss Ann Ball's calico aprons, and if ever a New England woman did a morning's work in an hour, it was this same Mrs. French.

" 'Tain't everyone knows how to make what *I* call a chowder," said the captain, pleased and replete, as he leaned back in his chair after dinner. "Mis' French, you shall have everything to do with, an' I ain't no kitchen colonel myself to bother ye."

There was a new subject for gossip in that seaport town. More than one woman had felt herself to be a fitting helpmate for the captain, and was confident that if time had been allowed, she could have made sure of even such wary game as he. When a stranger stepped in and occupied the ground at once, it gave nobody a fair chance, and Mrs. French was recognized as a presuming adventuress by all disappointed aspirants for the captain's hand. The captain was afraid at times that Mrs. French carried almost too many guns, but she made him so comfortable that she had the upper hand, and at last he was conscious of little objection to whatever this able housekeeper proposed. Her only intimate friends were the minister and his wife, and the captain himself was so won over to familiarity by the kindness of his pastor in the time of affliction that when after some weeks Mrs. French invited the good people to tea, Captain Ball sat manfully at the foot of his table, and listened with no small pleasure to the delighted exclamations of the parson's wife over his store of china and glass. There was a little feeling of guilt when he remembered how many times in his sister's day he had evaded such occasions by complaint of inward malady, or staying boldly along the wharves until long past suppertime, and forcing good Miss Ann to as many anxious excuses as if her brother's cranky ways were not as well known to the guests as to herself.

II

Mrs. Captain Topliff and Miss Miranda Hull were sitting together one late summer afternoon in Mrs. Topliff's south chamber. They were at work upon a black dress which was to be made over, and each sat by a front window with the blinds carefully set ajar.

"This is a real handy room to sew in," said Miranda, who had come early after dinner for a good long afternoon. "You git the light as long as there is any; and I do like a straw carpet; I don't feel 's if I made so much work scatterin' pieces."

"Don't you have no concern about pieces," answered Mrs. Topliff, amiably. "I was precious glad to get you right on the sudden so. You see, I counted on my other dress lasting me till winter, and sort of put this by to do at a leisure time. I knew 'twa'n't fit to wear as 'twas. Anyway, I've done dealin' with Stover; he told me, lookin' me right in the eye, that was as good wearin' a piece o' goods as he had in the store. 'Twas a real cheat; you can put your finger right through it."

"You've got some wear out of it," ventured Miranda, meekly, bending over her work. "I made it up quite a spell ago, I know. Six or seven years, ain't it, Mis' Topliff?"

"Yes, to be sure," replied Mrs. Topliff, with suppressed indignation; "but this we're to work on I had before the Centennial. I know I wouldn't take it to Philadelphy that time I went because 'twas too good. An' the first two or three years of a dress don't count. You know how 'tis; you just wear 'em to meetin' a pleasant Sunday, or to a funeral, p'r'aps, an' keep 'em in a safe cluset meanwhiles."

"Goods don't wear as 't used to," agreed Miranda; "but 'tis all the better for my trade. Land! there's some dresses in this town I'm sick o' bein' called on to make good 's new. Now I call you reasonable about such things, but there's some I could name—" Miss Hull at this point put several pins into her mouth, as if to guard a secret.

Mrs. Topliff looked up with interest. "I always thought Ann Ball was the meanest woman about expense. She looked respectable too, and I s'pose she'd said the heathen was gittin' the good o' what she saved. She must have given away hundreds o' dollars in that way."

"She left plenty too, and I s'pose Cap'n Asaph's Mis' French will get the good of it now," said Miranda through the pins. "Seems to me he's gittin' caught in spite of himself. Old vain creatur', he seemed to think all the womenfolks in town was in love with him."

"Some was," answered Mrs. Topliff. "I think any woman that needed a home would naturally think 'twas a good chance." Miranda had indulged high hopes, but wished to ignore them now.

"Some that had a home seemed inclined to bestow their affections, I observed," retorted the dressmaker, who had lost her little property by unfortunate investment, but would not be called homeless by Mrs. Topliff. Everybody knew that the widow had set herself down valiantly to besiege the enemy; but after this passage at arms between the friends they went on amiably with their conversation.

"Seems to me the minister and Mis' Calvinn are dreadful intimate at the cap'n's. I wonder if the cap'n 's goin' to give as much to the heathen as his sister did?" said Mrs. Topliff, presently.

"I understood he told the minister that none o' the heathen was wuth it that ever he see," replied Miranda in a pinless voice at last. "Mr. Calvinn only laughed; he knows the cap'n's ways. But I shouldn't thought Asaph Ball would have let his hired help set out and ask company to tea just four weeks from the day his only sister was laid away. 'Twa'n't feelin'."

"That Mis' French wanted to get the minister's folks to back her up, don't you understand?" was Mrs. Topliff's comment. "I should think the Calvinns wouldn't want to be so free and easy with a woman from nobody knows where. She runs in and out o' the parsonage any time o' day as Ann Ball never took it upon her to do. Ann liked Mis' Calvinn, but she always had to go through with just so much, and be formal with everybody."

"I'll tell you something that exasperated *me*," confided the disappointed Miranda. "That night they was there to tea Mis' Calvinn was praising up a handsome flowered china bowl that was on the table, with some kind of a fancy custard in it, and the cap'n told her to take it along when she went home, if she wanted it, speakin' right out thoughtless, as men do; and that Mis' French chirped up, 'Yes, I'm glad; you ought to have somethin' to remember the cap'n's sister by,' says she. Can't you hear just how up an' comin' it was?"

"I can so," said Mrs. Topliff. "I see that bowl myself on Miss Calvinn's card table when I was makin' a call there day before yesterday. I wondered how she come by it. 'Tis an elegant bowl. Ann must have set the world by it, poor thing. Wonder if he ain't goin' to give remembrances to those that knew his sister ever since they can remember? Mirandy Hull, that Mis' French is a fox!"

" 'Twas Widow Sparks gave me the particulars," continued Mrs. Topliff. "She declared at first that never would she step foot inside his doors again, but I always thought the cap'n put up with a good deal. Her husband's havin' been killed in one o' his ships by a fall when he was full o' liquor, and her bein' there so much to help Ann, and their havin' provided for her all these years one way an' another, didn't give her the right to undertake the housekeepin' and direction o' everything soon as Ann died. She dressed up as if 'twas for meetin', and 'tended the front door, and saw the folks that came. You'd thought she was ma'am of everything; and to hear her talk up to the cap'n! I thought I should die o' laughing when he blowed out at her. You know how he gives them great whoos when he's put about. 'Go below, can't ye, till your watch 's called,' says he, same's 'twas aboard ship; but there! everybody knew he was all broke down, and everything tried him. But to see her flounce out o' that back door!"

" 'Twas the evenin' after the funeral," Miranda said, presently. "I was there, too, you may rec'lect, seeing what I could do. The cap'n thought I was the proper one to look after her things, and guard against moths. He said there wa'n't no haste, but I knew better, an' told him I'd brought some camphire right with me. Well, did you git anything further out o' Mis' Sparks?"

"That French woman made all up with her, and Mis' Sparks swallowed her resentment. She's a good-feelin', ignorant kind o' woman, an' she needed the money bad," answered Mrs. Topliff. "If you'll never repeat, I'll tell you somethin' that'll make your eyes stick out, Miranda."

Miranda promised, and filled her mouth with pins preparatory to proper silence.

"You know the Balls had a half-brother that went off out West somewhere in New York State years ago. I don't remember him, but he brought up a family, and some of 'em came here years ago. Ann used to get letters from 'em sometimes, she's told me, and I dare say used to do for 'em. Well, Mis' Sparks says that there was a smart young girl, niece or great-niece o' the cap'n, wrote on and wanted to come an' live with him for the sake o' the home—his own blood and kin, you see, and very needy—and Mis' Sparks heard 'em talk about her, and that wicked, low, offscourin' has got round Asaph Ball till he's consented to put the pore girl off. You see, she wants to contrive time to make him marry her, and then she'll do as she pleases about his folks. Now ain't it a shame? When I see her parade up the broad aisle, I want to stick out my tongue at her—I do so, right in meetin'. If the cap'n's goin' to have a shock within a year, I could wish it might be soon, to disappoint such a woman. Who is she, anyway? She makes me think o' some carr'on bird pouncin' down on us right out o' the air." Mrs. Topliff sniffed and jerked about in her chair, having worked herself into a fine fit of temper.

"There ain't no up nor down to this material, is there?" inquired Miranda, meekly. She was thinking that if she were as well off as Mrs. Topliff, and toward seventy years of age, she would never show a matrimonial disappointment in this open way. It was ridiculous for a woman who had any respect for herself and for the opinion of society. Miranda had much more dignity, and tried to cool off Mrs. Topliff's warmth by discussion of the black gown.

" 'Tain't pleasant to have such a character among us. Do you think it is, Mirandy?" asked Mrs. Topliff, after a few minutes of silence. "She's a good-looking person, but with something sly about her. I don't mean to call on her again until she accounts for herself. Livin' nearer than any of Ann's friends, I thought there would be a good many ways I could oblige the cap'n if he'd grant the opportunity, but 'tain't so to be. Now Mr. Topliff was such an easygoin', pleasant-tempered man that I take time to remember others is made different."

Miranda smiled. Her companion had suffered many things from a most trying husband: it was difficult to see why she was willing to risk her peace of mind again.

"Cap'n Asaph looks now as meek as Moses," she suggested, as she pared a newly basted seam with her creaking scissors. "Mis' French, whoever she may be, has got him right under her thumb. I, for one, believe she'll never get him, for all her pains. He's as sharp as she is any day, when it comes to that; but he's made comfortable, and she starches his shirt bosoms so's you can hear 'em creak 'way across the meeting-house. I was in there the other night—she wanted to see me about some work—and 'twas neat as wax, and an awful good scent o' somethin' they'd had for supper."

"That kind's always smart enough," granted the widow Topliff. "I want to know if she cooks him a hot supper every night? Well, she'll catch him if anybody can. Why don't you get a look in some o' the clusets, if you go there to work? Ann was so formal I never spoke up as I wanted to about seeing her things. They must have an awful sight of china, and as for the linen and so on that the cap'n and his father before him fetched home from sea, you couldn't find an end to it. Ann never made 'way with much. I hope the mice ain't bang-ing into it and makin' their nests. Ann was very particular, but I dare say it wore her out tryin' to take care o' such a houseful."

"I'm going there Wednesday," said Miranda. "I'll spy round all I can, but I don't like to carry from one house to another. I never was one to make trouble; 'twould make my business more difficult than 'tis a'ready."

"I'd trust you," responded Mrs. Topliff, emphatically. "But there, Mirandy, you know you can trust me too, and anything you say goes no further."

"Yes'm," returned Miranda, somewhat absently. "To cut this the way you want it is going to give the folds a ter'ble skimpy look."

"I thought it would from the first," was Mrs. Topliff's obliging answer.

III

The captain could not believe that two months had passed since his sister's death, but Mrs. French assured him one evening that it was so. He had troubled himself very little about public opinion, though hints of his housekeeper's suspicious character and abom-inable intentions had reached his ears through more than one disin-terested tale-bearer. Indeed, the minister and his wife were the only persons among the old family friends who kept up any sort of inter-course with Mrs. French. The ladies of the parish had not dared to asperse her character themselves to the gruff captain, but were contented with ignoring her existence and setting their husbands to the fray. "Why don't you tell him what folks think?" was a frequent question; but after a first venture even the most intimate and valiant friends were sure to mind their own business, as the indignant captain bade them. Two of them had been partially won over to Mrs. French's side by a taste of her good cooking. In fact, these were Captain Dunn and Captain Alister, who, at the eleven-o'clock rendezvous, reported their wives as absent at the County Conference, and were promptly bidden to a chowder dinner by the independent Captain Ball, who gloried in the fact that neither of his companions would dare to ask a friend home unexpectedly. Our hero promised his guests that what they didn't find in eatables they would make up in drinkables, and actually produced a glistening decanter of Madeira that had made several voyages in his father's ships while he himself was a boy. There were several casks and long rows of cob-webby bottles in the cellar, which had been provided against possible use in case of illness, but the captain rarely touched them, though he went regularly every morning for the social glass of what he frankly persisted in calling his grog. The dinner party proved to be a noble occasion, and Mrs. French won the esteem of the three elderly seamen by her discreet behavior as well as by the flavor of the chowder.

They walked out into the old garden when the feast was over, and continued their somewhat excited discussion of the decline of shipping on the seats of the ancient latticed summerhouse. There Mrs. French surprised them by bringing out a tray of coffee, served in the handsome old cups which the captain's father had brought home from France. She was certainly a good-looking woman, and stepped modestly and soberly along the walk between the mallows and marigolds. Her feminine rivals insisted that she looked both bold and sly, but she minded her work like a steam-tug, as the captain whispered admiringly to his friends.

" 'Ain't never ascertained where she came from last, have ye?" inquired Captain Alister, emboldened by the best Madeira and the good fellowship of the occasion.

"I'm acquainted with all I need to know," answered Captain Ball, shortly; but his face darkened, and when his guests finished their coffee they thought it was high time to go away.

Everybody was sorry that a jarring note had been struck on so delightful an occasion, but it couldn't be undone. On the whole, the dinner was an uncommon pleasure, and the host walked back into the house to compliment his housekeeper, though the sting of his friend's untimely question expressed itself by a remark that they had made most too much of an everyday matter by having the coffee in those best cups.

Mrs. French laughed. "'Twill give 'em something to talk about; 'twas good coffee, this last you got, anyway," and Captain Asaph walked away, restored to a pleased and cheerful frame of mind. When he waked up after a solid after-dinner nap, Mrs. French, in her decent afternoon gown, as calm as if there had been no company to dinner, was just coming down the front stairs.

She seated herself by the window, and pretended to look in the street. The captain shook his newspaper at an invading fly. It was early September, and flies were cruelly persistent. Somehow his nap had not entirely refreshed him, and he watched his housekeeper with something like disapproval.

"I want to talk with you about something, sir," said Mrs. French.

"She's going to raise her pay," the captain grumbled to himself. "Well, speak out, can't ye, ma'am?" he said.

"You know I've ben sayin' all along that you ought to get your niece—"

"She's my *great*-niece," blew the captain, "an' I don't know as I want her." The awful certainty came upon him that those hints were well-founded about Mrs. French's determination to marry him, and his stormy nature rose in wild revolt. "Can't you keep your place, ma'am?" and he gave a great *whoo!* as if he were letting off superabundant steam. She might prove to carry too many guns for him, and he grew very red in the face. It was a much worse moment than when a ship comes driving at you amidships out of the fog.

"Why, yes, sir, I should be glad to keep my place," said Mrs. French, taking the less grave meaning of his remark by instinct, if not by preference; "only it seems your duty to let your great-niece come some time or other, and I can go off. Perhaps it is an untimely season to speak about it, but, you see, I have had it in mind, and now I've got through with my jelly, and there's a space between now and housecleaning, I guess you'd better let the young woman come. Folks have got wind about your refusing her earlier, and think hard of me: my position isn't altogether pleasant," and she changed color a little, and looked him full in the face.

The captain's eyes fell. He did owe her something. He never had been so comfortable in his life, on shore, as she had made him. She had heard some cursed ill-natured speeches, and he very well knew that a more self-respecting woman never lived. But now her moment of self-assertion seemed to have come, and, to use his own words, she had him fast. Stop! there was a way of escape.

"Then I *will* send for the gal. Perhaps you're right, ma'am. I've slept myself into the doldrums. *Whoo! whoo!*" he said, loudly—anything to gain a little time. "Anything you say, ma'am," he protested. "I've got to step downtown on some business," and the captain fled with ponderous footsteps out through the dining room to the little side entry where he hung his hat; then a moment later he went away, clicking his cane along the narrow sidewalk. He had escaped that time, and wrote a brief note to his great-niece, Ann Ball—how familiar the name looked!—with a sense of victory.

He dreaded the next interview with his housekeeper, but she was business-like and self-possessed, and seemed to be giving him plenty of time. The captain regretted his letter, and felt as if he were going to be broken up once more in his home comfort. He spoke only when it was absolutely necessary, and simply nodded his head when Mrs. French said that she was ready to start as soon as she showed the young woman about the house. But what favorite dishes were served the captain in those intervening days! and there was one cool evening when the housekeeper had the social assistance of a fire in the Franklin stove. The captain thought that his only safety lay in sleep, and promptly took that means of saving himself from a dangerous conversation. He even went to a panorama on Friday night, a diversion that would usually be quite beneath his dignity. It was difficult to avoid asking Mrs. French to accompany him, she helped him on with his coat so pleasantly, but "she'd git her claws on me comin' home perhaps," mused the self-distrustful mariner, and stoutly went his way to the panorama alone. It was a very dull show indeed, and he bravely confessed it, and then was angry at a twinkle in Mrs. French's eyes. Yet he should miss the good creature, and for the life of him he could not think lightly of her. "She knows well how able she is to do for me. Womenfolks is cap'ns ashore," sighed the captain as he went upstairs to bed.

"Womenfolks is cap'ns ashore," he repeated, in solemn confidence to one of his intimate friends, as they stood next day on one of the deserted wharves, looking out across the empty harbor roads. There was nothing coming in. How they had watched the deep-laden ships enter between the outer points and drop their great sails in home waters! How they had ruled those ships themselves, and been the ablest ship-masters of their day, with nobody to question their decisions! There's no such absolute monarchy as a sea captain's. He is a petty king, indeed, as he sails the high seas from port to port.

There was a fine easterly breeze and a bright sun that day, but Captain Ball came toiling up the cobble-stoned street toward his house as if he were vexed by a head-wind. He carried a post-card between his thumb and finger, and grumbled aloud as he stumped along. "Mis' French!" he called, loudly, as he opened the door, and that worthy woman appeared with a floured apron, and a mind divided between her employer's special business and her own affairs of pie-making.

"She's coming this same day," roared the captain. "Might have given some notice, I'm sure. 'Be with you Saturday afternoon,' and her name 'Ann.' That's all she's written. Whoo! whoo! 'tis a dreadful close day," and the poor old fellow fumbled for his big silk handkerchief. "I don't know what train she'll take. I ain't going to hang round up at the depot; my rheumatism troubles me."

"I wouldn't, if I was you," answered Mrs. French, shortly, and left him with a pettish movement to open the oven door.

The captain passed into the sitting room, and sat down heavily in his large chair. On the wall facing him was a picture of his old ship the *Ocean Rover* leaving the harbor of Bristol. It was not valuable as a marine painting, but the sea was blue in that picture, and the canvas was all spread, to the very skyscrapers; it was an emblem of that freedom which Captain Asaph Ball had once enjoyed. Dinner that day was a melancholy meal, and after it was cleared away the master of the house forlornly watched Mrs. French gather her armful of her own belongings, and mount the stairs as if she were going to pack her box that very afternoon. It did not seem possible that she meant to leave before Monday, but the captain could not bring himself to ask any questions. He was at the mercy of womankind. "A jiggeting girl. I don't know how to act with her. She sha'n't rule me," he muttered to himself. "She and Mis' French may think they've got things right to their hands, but I'll stand my ground—I'll stand my ground," and the captain gently slid into the calmer waters of his afternoon nap.

When he waked the house was still, and with sudden consciousness of approaching danger, and a fear lest Mrs. French might have some last words to say if she found him awake, he stole out of his house as softly as possible and went downtown, hiding his secret woes and joining in the long seafaring reminiscences with which he and his friends usually diverted themselves. As he came up the street again toward suppertime, he saw that the blinds were thrown open in the parlor windows, and his heart began to beat loudly. He could hear women's voices, and he went in by a side gate and sought the quiet garden. It had suffered from a touch of frost; so had the captain.

Mrs. French heard the gate creak, and presently she came to the garden door at the end of the front entry. "Come in, won't ye, cap'n?" she called, persuasively, and with a mighty sea oath the captain rose and obeyed.

The house was still. He strode along the entry like a brave man: there was nothing of the coward about Asaph Ball when he made up his mind to a thing. There was nobody in the best parlor, and he turned toward the sitting room, but there sat smiling Mrs. French.

"Where is the gal?" blew the captain.

"Here I be, sir," said Mrs. French, with a flushed and beaming face. "I thought 'twas full time to put you out of your misery."

"What's all this mean? *Whoo! whoo!*"

"Here I be; take me or leave me, uncle," answered the housekeeper: she began to be anxious, the captain looked so bewildered and irate. "Folks seemed to think that you was peculiar, and I was impressed that it would be better to just come first without a word's bein' said, and find out how you an' me got on; then, if we didn't make out, nobody'd be bound. I'm sure *I* didn't want to be."

"Who was that I heard talking with ye as I come by?" blew the captain very loud.

"That was Mis' Cap'n Topliff; an' an old cat she is," calmly replied Mrs. French. "She hasn't been near me before this three months, but plenty of stories she's set goin' about us, and plenty of spyin' she's done. I thought I'd tell you who I was within a week after I come, but I found out how things was goin', and I had to spite 'em well before I got through. I expected that something would turn up, an' the whole story get out. But we've been middlin' comfortable, haven't we, sir? an' I thought 'twas 'bout time to give you a little surprise. Mis' Calvinn and the minister knows the whole story," she concluded: "I wouldn't have kep' it from them. Mis' Calvinn said all along 'twould be a good lesson—"

"Who wrote that post-card from the office?" demanded the captain, apparently but half persuaded.

"I did," said Mrs. French.

"Good Hector, you womenfolks!" and Captain Ball ventured to cross the room and establish himself in his chair. Then, being a man of humor, he saw that he had a round turn on those who had spite-fully sought to question him.

"You needn't let on that you haven't known me all along," suggested Mrs. French. "I should be pleased if you would call me by my Christian name, sir. I was married to Mr. French only a short time; he was taken away very sudden. The letter that came after aunt's death was directed to my maiden name, but aunt knew well about me. I've got some means, an' I ain't distressed but what I can earn my living."

"They don't call me such an old Turk, I hope!" exclaimed the ex-cited captain, deprecating the underrated estimate of himself which was suddenly presented. "I aint' a bad man at sea, now I tell ye," and he turned away, much moved at the injustice of society. "I've got no head for genealogy. Ann usually set in to give me the family particulars when I was logy with sleep a Sunday night. I thought you was a French from Massachusetts way."

"I had to say somethin'," responded the housekeeper, promptly.

"Well, well!" and a suppressed laugh shook the captain like an earthquake. He was suddenly set free from his enemies, while an hour before he had felt hemmed in on every side.

They had a cheerful supper, and Ann French cut a pie, and said, as she passed him more than a quarter part of it, that she thought she should give up when she was baking that morning, and saw the look on his face as he handed her the post-card.

"You're fit to be captain of a privateer," acknowledged Captain Asaph, handsomely. The complications of shore life were very astonishing to this seafaring man of the old school.

On Monday morning early he had a delightful sense of triumph. Captain Alister, who was the chief gossip of the waterside club, took it upon himself—a cheap thing to do, as everybody said afterward—to ask many questions about those unvalued relatives of the Balls, who had settled long ago in New York State. Were there any left of the captain's half-brother's family?

"I've got a niece living—a great-niece she is," answered Captain Ball, with a broad smile—"makes me feel old. You see, my half-brother was a grown man when I was born. I never saw him scarcely; there was some misunderstandin', an' he always lived with his own mother's folks; and father, he married again, and had me and Ann thirty year after. Why, my half-brother 'd been 'most a hundred; I don't know but more."

Captain Asaph spoke in a cheerful tone; the audience meditated, and Captain Alister mentioned meekly that time did slip away.

"Ever see any of 'em?" he inquired. In some way public interest was aroused in the niece.

"Ever see any of 'em?" repeated the captain, in a loud tone. "You fool, Alister, who's keepin' my house this minute? Why, Ann French; Ann Ball that was, and a smart, likely woman she is. I ain't a marryin' man: there's been plenty o' fools to try me. I've been picked over well by you and others, and I thought if it pleased you, you could take your own time."

The honest captain for once lent himself to deception. You would have thought that he had planned the siege himself. He took his stick from where it leaned against a decaying piece of ship timber and went clicking away. The explanation of his housekeeping arrangements was not long in flying about the town, and Mrs. Captain Topliff made an early call to say that she had always suspected it from the first, from the family likeness.

From this time Captain Ball submitted to the rule of Mrs. French, and under her sensible and fearless sway became, as everybody said, more like other people than ever before. As he grew older it was more and more convenient to have a superior officer to save him from petty responsibilities. But now and then, after the first relief at finding that Mrs. French was not seeking his hand in marriage, and that the jiggeting girl was a mere fabrication, Captain Ball was both surprised and a little ashamed to discover that something in his heart had suffered disappointment in the matter of the great-niece. Those who knew him well would have as soon expected to see a flower grow out of a cobble-stone as that Captain Asaph Ball should hide such a sentiment in his honest breast. He had fancied her a pretty girl in a pink dress, who would make some life in the quiet house, and sit and sing at her sewing, in all her foolish furbelows, by the front window as he came up the street.

SARA TEASDALE   *[1911]*

Sara Teasdale (1889-1933) herself practiced the cruelty she preaches below, particularly in the case of Vachel Lindsay, whose hopes for years she alternately raised and dashed. Like many of the women represented in this anthology, she was educated largely at home.

Four Winds

"Four winds blowing through the sky,
You have seen poor maidens die,
Tell me then what I shall do
That my lover may be true."
Said the wind from out the south,
"Lay no kiss upon his mouth,"
And the wind from out the west,
"Wound the heart within his breast,"
And the wind from out the east,
"Sent him empty from the feast,"
And the wind from out the north,
"In the tempest thrust him forth;
When thou art more cruel than he,
Then will love be kind to thee."

EDNA ST. VINCENT MILLAY   [1917, 1931]

Edna St. Vincent Millay, who began her college career at Barnard and finished at Vassar in 1917, is perhaps best known for her love sonnets. These two poems present opposite points of view about love and time. In the first the speaker is a woman; in the second, a man.

Two Sonnets

Time does not bring relief; you all have lied
Who told me time would ease me of my pain!
I miss him in the weeping of the rain;
I want him at the shrinking of the tide;
The old snows melt from every mountain-side,
And last year's leaves are smoke in every lane;
But last year's bitter loving must remain
Heaped on my heart, and my old thoughts abide.

There are a hundred places where I fear
To go,—so with his memory they brim.
And entering with relief some quiet place
Where never fell his foot or shone his face
I say, "There is no memory of him here!"
And so stand stricken, so remembering him.

Well, I have lost you; and I lost you fairly;
In my own way, and with my full consent.
Say what you will, kings in a tumbrel rarely
Went to their deaths more proud than this one went.
Some nights of apprehension and hot weeping
I will confess; but that's permitted me;
Day dried my eyes; I was not one for keeping
Rubbed in a cage a wing that would be free.
If I had loved you less or played you slyly
I might have held you for a summer more,
But at the cost of words I value highly,
And no such summer as the one before.
Should I outlive this anguish—and men do—
I shall have only good to say of you.

AMY LOWELL   [1927]

*In spite of—or perhaps because of—the grotesque plumpness which
discouraged admirers, Amy Lowell (1874-1925) vividly imagined the man
who would love and abandon her. Although she received honorary de-
grees, she never attended college.*

A Communication

You deceived me handsomely
With your inconsolable grief at parting.
I really believed in your crocodile tears
And suffered at the exhibition of your suffering;
A little for myself also at the breaking of an old tie,

A habit grown as comfortably pleasant
As the wearing of a friendly dressing-gown.
For we had passed the stage of exhilaration
And reached the solace of a quiet domesticity.
I was prepared to linger over it in retrospect,
Not too unhappily, for had we not agreed a thousand times
That this sundering was merely geographical.
And now a month has passed and not a word have I had from you,
Not so much as a scrawl to say you could not write!

Fate lays innumerable springes for persons of imagination.
Because I wished to believe,
I saw in your Byronic gesture of woe,
Not what it purported to be, certainly,
But something not too different.
You cast a larger shadow than yourself, that I realized,
But even I, who should have known better,
Believed it was your shadow.
I crave your pardon for my blunder.
The mask was well assumed,
I should have been critical enough to understand it was an artistic
    production.
I congratulate you on the verisimilitude of it,
But I shall not be fooled again, be sure of that.
In future I shall see you as you are:
A plaster figure of a man that's grown a little dusty.
We all have knick-knacks round which once meant something.
It is rather a wrench to take them from their niches,
But life goes on, imperious, and bric-à-brac accumulates.
Still, because I cherished you once, I will not throw you away just
    yet.
I will put you on an upper shelf in the pantry of my mind,
Among old flower-vases I no longer use, being of a bygone fashion.
It may interest you to know that the place you occupied
Looks a little strange to me without you,
But that, of course, will pass.

ELINOR WYLIE [1928]

Elinor Wylie's three husbands and innumerable admirers attest to her familiarity with the subject of what women think of men, although she died in 1928 at the early age of forty-three. "The Puritan's Ballad" represents the demon lover, a phenomenon which often intrigues women, although this is its sole representative in the present collection.

The Puritan's Ballad

My love came up from Barnegat,
  The sea was in his eyes;
He trod as softly as a cat
  And told me terrible lies.

His hair was yellow as new-cut pine
  In shavings curled and feathered;
I thought how silver it would shine
  By cruel winters weathered.

But he was in his twentieth year,
  This time I'm speaking of;
We were head over heels in love with fear
  And half a-feared of love.

My hair was piled in a copper crown—
  A devilish living thing,
And tortoise-shell pins fell down, fell down,
  When that snake uncoiled to spring.

His feet were used to treading a gale
  And balancing thereon;
His face was brown as a foreign sail
  Threadbare against the sun.

His arms were thick as hickory logs
  Whittled to little wrists;
Strong as the teeth of terrier dogs
  Were the fingers of his fists.

Within his arms I feared to sink
  Where lions shook their manes,
And dragons drawn in azure ink
  Leapt quickened by his veins.

Dreadful his strength and length of limb
  As the sea to foundering ships;
I dipped my hands in love for him
  No deeper than their tips.

But our palms were welded by a flame
  The moment we came to part,
And on his knuckles I read my name
  Enscrolled within a heart.

And something made our wills to bend
  As wild as trees blown over;
We were no longer friend and friend,
  But only lover and lover.

"In seven weeks or seventy years—
  God grant it may be sooner!—
I'll make a handkerchief for your tears
  From the sails of my captain's schooner.

"We'll wear our loves like wedding rings
  Long polished to our touch;
We shall be busy with other things
  And they cannot bother us much.

"When you are skimming the wrinkled cream
  And your ring clinks on the pan,
You'll say to yourself in a pensive dream,
  'How wonderful a man!'

"When I am slitting a fish's head
  And my ring clanks on the knife,
I'll say with thanks, as a prayer is said,
  'How beautiful a wife!'

"And I shall fold my decorous paws
  In velvet smooth and deep,

Like a kitten that covers up its claws
 To sleep and sleep and sleep.

"Like a little blue pigeon you shall bow
 Your bright alarming crest;
In the crook of my arm you'll lay your brow
 To rest and rest and rest."

Will he never come back from Barnegat
 With thunder in his eyes,
Treading as soft as a tiger cat,
 To tell me terrible lies?

GERTRUDE ATHERTON   [1932]

Gertrude Atherton (1857-1948), who received her smattering of education at various private schools, resolved never to marry again after her husband died because "husbands are a great responsibility." In 1932, looking back on her adventures before the turn of the century, she recalled one instance in which she gave a would-be lover his come-uppance.

Man of the World

I accumulated four devoted admirers, and, taking a firm stand with my husband, permitted them to call in the afternoon and evening. I was determined to study such material as came to hand, to say nothing of gratifying my vanity, and desire to have an amusing winter. But I paid the price! Whenever they were there George stalked up and down the hall, looking coal black, or hung over the banisters muttering. For the sake of peace I returned to the country before the winter was over.

One of my quartet had afforded a certain excitement, however. He was a New Yorker visiting in San Francisco, and being an eligible bachelor, was much sought after. It amused me to worry match-making mothers and anxious daughters, and it is to be confessed that I gave him a good deal of encouragement. At first he really interested me, for he had lived in Paris for the greater part of his life, and been a friend of the Prince Imperial and the Empress Eugénie, whom he claimed to have assisted in her flight to England. A man of the world at last!

But if the native product was easy to manage even by a tyro like myself he was not. When George was far enough removed—at the head of the stairs for instance—he made as violent love to me as a man may when he is unable to lift his voice, the door is wide open, and the object of his passion seated quite three feet away. He was a small dark man approaching forty, who always looked on these occasions as if he were about to explode. I thought him rather funny, but was deeply interested in what he would say next. I knew he wouldn't do anything, with George in the offing, likely to swoop down at any moment. Really, George displayed more self-control at this time than I would have given him credit for.

But finally I realized that the man was dangerous. He began to talk wildly about challenging George to a duel and killing him; he "had fought innumerable duels and was a dead shot." One evening he came, looking white and desperate, and in a febrile hissing whisper implored me to elope with him, threatening to kill himself if I did not. I was really frightened, but hastily decided there was only one way to get rid of him and that was by lacerating his vanity so deeply that his passion would sputter out.

"Listen!" I said. "I am going to tell you something and I want you to understand that every word of it is true. I intend to be a novelist and I've only been making a study of you. You are not interesting in yourself, but through you I have learned something of the world outside of California and of men of your type. But even from the writer's point of view you don't interest me any longer. You've become a bore. I think you'd better go now. If you don't, I'll call my husband and he's very dangerous when roused. He'd merely laugh if you challenged him to a duel, laugh, and put a bullet in you without any ceremony. Then there would be a scandal. I don't want any scandals. You're not worth it. So be kind enough to go."

He had stared at me incredulously during the greater part of this harangue, for he had thought me a simple unsophisticated young creature who must succumb to his blandishments in due course. When he realized the awful truth: that he had been disporting himself under a microscope for the education of an embryonic novelist, he turned as black as George, and for a moment I thought he would assault me. I was about to call for lawful protection when he seized his hat and rushed from the house.

He did not kill himself. He got very drunk. For three days he was quite happy in imagining himself the Prince Imperial redivivus. And then his host, one of my quartet (he never spoke to me again), packed his clothes, and put him, still drunk, on a train for New York. So ended my first experience with a man of the world.

BABETTE DEUTSCH *[1939]*

Babette Deutsch was born in New York City in 1895, graduated from Barnard College in 1917, and has taught at Columbia since 1944. Coming of Age, her new and selected poems, published in 1959, is only one of a long list of publications, creative and discursive. As John Kouwenhoven notes in his Preface, "The Dispassionate Shepherdess" represents an attitude strikingly prevalent among modern women.

The Dispassionate Shepherdess

Do not live with me, do not be my love.
And yet I think we may some pleasures prove
That who enjoy each other, in the haste
Of their most inward kissing, seldom taste.

Being absent from me, you shall still delay
To come to me, and if another day,
No matter, so your greeting burn as though
The words had all the while been packed in snow.

No other gift you'll offer me but such
As I can neither wear, nor smell, nor touch—
No flowers breathing of evening, and no stones
Whose chilly fire outlasts our skeletons.

You'll give me once a thought that stings, and once
A look to make my blood doubt that it runs.
You'll give me rough and sharp perplexities,
And never, never will you give me ease.

For one another's blessing not designed,
Marked for possession only of the mind,
And soon, because such cherishing is brief,
To ask whereon was founded the belief

That there was anything at all uncommon
In what each felt for each as man and woman—
If this then be our case, if this our story,
Shall we rail at heaven? Shall we, at worst, be sorry?

Heaven's too deaf, we should grow hoarse with railing,
And sorrow never quickened what was failing.
But if you think we thus may pleasures prove,
Do not live with me, do not be my love.

SAMPLER: Men As Apes

It is no exaggeration to say that among all living creatures, only man, because of his prehensile appendages, is capable of rape in the full meaning of this term—that is, sexual possession of the female against her will. Every time I see one of the numerous pictures in popular movies or magazines showing an anthropomorphous ape or a powerful, bearlike masculine creature with a completely helpless female in his arms, I am reminded of my old favorite speculation: thus it was that primitive man took possession of woman and subjected her to sexual desire. Interestingly enough, in many myths and fantasy formations, brutal possession is interpreted as a kindly act of rescue. Thus the ape with his powerful arms, or the bear, saves the girl from a threatening disaster that is mostly of a sexual nature—and the threat comes from someone else, not from the rescuer. In young girls' dreams the mighty hairy human-animal figure often appears not as a seducer, but as a savior from sexual dangers. This metamorphosis of the seducer into a savior reveals the wish-fulfilling character of the girl's dreams and her masochistic longings, which reproduce the situation of the primitive conquered woman.
—HELENE DEUTSCH, M.D., in *The Psychology of Women*, 1944

Lonely men, unrequited men, men who find love and sex difficult turn to the myth of rape in the belief that love, if it cannot be evoked, can at least be bullied into putting in an appearance. But force and aggression drive love away as often as they serve to capture it. The tough men of the movies win their loves less by a brandishing of fists than by a restraint so marked as to approach indifference.

—RUTH HERSCHBERGER, in *Adam's Rib*, 1948

HORTENSE CALISHER   [1950]

Hortense Calisher, who graduated from Barnard College in 1932 and taught a short story course there from 1956 to 1958, has published two volumes of short stories and two novels, False Entry *and* Textures of Life. *She is married to the writer and teacher Curtis Harnack and lives in New York City.*

In Greenwich There Are Many Graveled Walks

On an afternoon in early August, Peter Birge, just returned from driving his mother to the Greenwich sanitarium she had to frequent at intervals, sat down heavily on a furbelowed sofa in the small apartment he and she had shared ever since his return from the Army a year ago. He was thinking that his usually competent solitude had become more than he could bear. He was a tall, well-built young man of about twenty-three, with a pleasant face whose even, standardized look was the effect of proper food, a good dentist, the best schools, and a brush haircut. The heat, which bored steadily into the room through a Venetian blind lowered over a half-open window, made his white T-shirt cling to his chest and arms, which were still brown from a week's sailing in July at a cousin's place on the Sound. The family of cousins, one cut according to the pattern of a two-car-and-country-club suburbia, had always looked with distaste on his precocious childhood with his mother in the Village and, the few times he had been farmed out to them during those early years, had received his healthy normality with ill-concealed surprise, as if they had clearly expected to have to fatten up what they undoubtedly referred to in private as "poor Anne's boy." He had only gone there at all, this time, when it became certain that the money saved up for a summer abroad, where his Army stint had not sent him, would have to be spent on one of his mother's trips to Greenwich, leaving barely enough, as it was, for his next, and final, year at the School of Journalism. Half out of disheartenment over his collapsed summer, half to provide himself with a credible "out" for the too jovially pressing cousins at Rye, he had registered for some courses at the Columbia summer session. Now these were almost over, too, leaving a gap before the fall semester began. He had cut this morning's classes in order to drive his mother up to the place in Connecticut.

He stepped to the window and looked through the blind at the convertible parked below, on West Tenth Street. He ought to call the garage for the pickup man, or else, until he thought of someplace to go, he ought to hop down and put up the top. Otherwise, baking there in the hot sun, the car would be like a griddle when he went to use it, and the leather seats were cracking badly anyway.

It had been cool when he and his mother started, just after dawn that morning, and the air of the well-ordered countryside had had that almost speaking freshness of early day. With her head bound in a silk scarf and her chubby little chin tucked into the cardigan which he had buttoned on her without forcing her arms into the sleeves, his mother, peering up at him with the near-gaiety born of relief, had had the exhausted charm of a child who has just been promised the thing for which it has nagged. Anyone looking at the shingled hair, the feet in small brogues—anyone not close enough to see how drawn and beakish her nose looked in the middle of her little round face, which never reddened much with drink but at the worst times took on a sagging, quilted whiteness—might have thought the two of them were a couple, any couple, just off for a day in the country. No one would have thought that only a few hours before, some time after two, he had been awakened, pounded straight up on his feet, by the sharp, familiar cry and then the agonized susurrus of prattling that went on and on and on, that was different from her everyday, artlessly confidential prattle only in that now she could not stop, she could not stop, *she could not stop,* and above the small, working mouth with its eliding, spinning voice, the glazed button eyes opened wider and wider, as if she were trying to breathe through them. Later, after the triple bromide, the warm bath, and the crooning, practiced soothing he administered so well, she had hiccuped into crying, then into stillness at last, and had fallen asleep on his breast. Later still, she had awakened him, for he must have fallen asleep there in the big chair with her, and with the weak, humiliated goodness which always followed these times she had even tried to help him with the preparations for the journey—preparations which, without a word between them, they had set about at once. There'd been no doubt, of course, that she would have to go. There never was.

He left the window and sat down again in the big chair, and smoked one cigarette after another. Actually, for a drunkard—or an alcoholic, as people preferred to say these days—his mother was the least troublesome of any. He had thought of it while he packed the pairs of daintily kept shoes, the sweet-smelling blouses and froufrou underwear, the tiny, perfect dresses—of what comfort it was that she had never grown raddled or blowzy. Years ago, she had perfected the routine within which she could feel safe for months at a time. It had gone on for longer than he could remember: from before the death of his father, a Swedish engineer, on the income of whose patents they had always been able to live fairly comfortably; probably even during her life with that other long-dead man, the painter whose model and mistress she had been in the years before she married his father. There would be the long, drugged sleep of the morning, then the unsteady hours when she manicured herself back into cleanliness and reality. Then, at about four or five in the afternoon, she and the dog (for there was always a dog) would make their short pilgrimage to the clubby, cozy little hangout where she would be a fixture until far into the morning, where she had been a fixture for the last twenty years.

Once, while he was at boarding school, she had made a supreme effort to get herself out of the routine—for his sake, no doubt—and he had returned at Easter to a new apartment, uptown, on Central Park West. All that this had resulted in was inordinate taxi fares and the repetitious nightmare evenings which she had gotten lost and he had found her, a small, untidy heap, in front of their old place. After a few months, they had moved back to the Village, to those few important blocks where she felt safe and known and loved. For they all knew her there, or got to know her—the aging painters, the newcomer poets, the omniscient news hacks, the military spinsters who bred dogs, the anomalous, sandaled young men. And they accepted her, this dainty hanger-on who neither painted nor wrote but hung their paintings on her walls, faithfully read their particolored magazines, and knew them all—their shibboleths, their feuds, the whole vocabulary of their disintegration, and, in a mild, occasional manner, their beds.

Even this, he could not remember not knowing. At ten, he had been an expert compounder of remedies for hang-over, and of an evening, standing sleepily in his pajamas to be admired by the friends his mother sometimes brought home, he could have predicted accurately whether the party would end in a brawl or in a murmurous coupling in the dark.

It was curious, he supposed now, stubbing out a final cigarette, that he had never judged resentfully either his mother or her world. By the accepted standards, his mother had done her best; he had been well housed, well schooled, even better loved than some of the familied boys he had known. Wisely, too, she had kept out of his other life, so that he had never had to be embarrassed there except once, and this when he was grown, when she had visited his Army camp. Watching her at a post party for visitors, poised there, so chic, so distinctive, he had suddenly seen it begin: the fear, the scare, then the compulsive talking, which always started so innocently that only he would have noticed at first—that warm, excited, buttery flow of harmless little lies and pretensions which gathered its dreadful speed and content and ended then, after he had whipped her away, just as it had ended this morning.

On the way up this morning, he had been too clever to subject her to a restaurant, but at a drive-in place he was able to get her to take some coffee. How grateful they had both been for the coffee, she looking up at him, tremulous, her lips pecking at the cup, he blessing the coffee as it went down her! And afterward, as they flew onward he could feel her straining like a homing pigeon toward their destination, toward the place where she felt safest of all, where she would gladly have stayed forever if she had just had enough money for it, if they would only let her stay. For there the pretty little woman and her dog—a poodle, this time—would be received like the honored guest that she was, so trusted and docile a guest, who asked only to hide there during the season of her discomfort, who was surely the least troublesome of them all.

He had no complaints, then, he assured himself as he sat on the burning front seat of the convertible trying to think of somewhere to go. It was just that while others of his age still shared a communal wonder at what life might hold, he had long since been solitary in his knowledge of what life was.

Up in a sky as honestly blue as a flag, an airplane droned smartly toward Jersey. Out at Rye, the younger crowd at the club would be commandeering the hot blue day, the sand, and the water, as if these were all extensions of themselves. They would use the evening this way, too, disappearing from the veranda after a dance, exploring each other's rhythm-and-whisky-whetted appetites in the backs of cars. They all thought themselves a pretty sophisticated bunch, the young men who had graduated not into a war but into its hung-over peace, the young girls attending junior colleges so modern that the deans had to spend all their time declaring that their girls were being trained for the family and the community. But when Peter looked close and saw how academic their sophistication was, how their undamaged eyes were still starry with expectancy, their lips still avidly open for what life would surely bring, then he became envious and awkward with them, like a guest at a party to whose members he carried bad news he had no right to know, no right to tell.

He turned on the ignition and let the humming motor prod him into a decision. He would drop in at Robert Vielum's, where he had dropped in quite often until recently, for the same reason that others stopped by at Vielum's—because there was always likely to be somebody there. The door of Robert's old-fashioned apartment, on Claremont Avenue, almost always opened on a heartening jangle of conversation and music, which meant that others had gathered there, too, to help themselves over the pauses so endemic to university life—the life of the mind—and there were usually several members of Robert's large acquaintance among the subliterary, quasi-artistic, who had strayed in, ostensibly en route somewhere, and who lingered on hopefully on the chance that in each other's company they might find out what that somewhere was.

Robert was a perennial taker of courses—one of those nonmatriculated students of indefinable age and income, some of whom pursued, with monkish zeal and no apparent regard for time, this or that freakishly peripheral research project of their own conception, and others of whom, like Robert, seemed to derive a Ponce de Léon sustenance from the young. Robert himself, a large man of between forty and fifty, whose small features were somewhat cramped together in a wide face, never seemed bothered by his own lack of direction, implying rather that this was really the catholic approach of the "whole man," alongside of which the serious pursuit of a degree was somehow foolish, possibly vulgar. Rumor connected him with a rich Boston family that had remittanced him at least as far as New

York, but he never spoke about himself, although he was extraordinarily alert to gossip. Whatever income he had he supplemented by renting his extra room to a series of young men students. The one opulence among his dun-colored, perhaps consciously Spartan effects was a really fine record-player, which he kept going at all hours with selections from his massive collection. Occasionally he annotated the music, or the advance-copy novel that lay on his table, with foreign-language tags drawn from the wide, if obscure, latitudes of his travels, and it was his magic talent for assuming that his young friends, too, had known, had experienced, that, more than anything, kept them enthralled.

"*Fabelhaft!* Isn't it?" he would say of the Mozart. "Remember how they did it that last time at Salzburg!" and they would all sit there, included, belonging, headily remembering the Salzburg to which they had never been. Or he would pick up the novel and lay it down again. "*La plume de mon oncle,* I'm afraid. *La plume de mon oncle Gide. Eheu,* poor Gide!"—and they would each make note of the fact that one need not read that particular book, that even, possibly, it was no longer necessary to read Gide.

Peter parked the car and walked into the entrance of Robert's apartment house, smiling to himself, lightened by the prospect of company. After all, he had been weaned on the salon talk of such circles; these self-fancying little bohemias at least made him feel at home. And Robert was cleverer than most—it was amusing to watch him. For just as soon as his satellites thought themselves secure on the promontory of some "trend" he had pointed out to them, they would find that he had deserted them, had gone on to another trend, another eminence, from which he beckoned, cocksure and just faintly malicious. He harmed no one permanently. And if he concealed some skeleton of a weakness, some closeted Difference with the Authorities, he kept it decently interred.

As Peter stood in the dark, soiled hallway and rang the bell of Robert's apartment, he found himself as suddenly depressed again, unaccountably reminded of his mother. There were so many of them, and they affected you so, these charmers who, if they could not offer you the large strength, could still atone for the lack with so many small decencies. It was admirable, surely, the way they managed this. And surely, after all, they harmed no one.

Robert opened the door. "Why, hello, Peter!" He seemed surprised, almost relieved. "Greetings!" he added, in a voice whose boom was more in the manner than the substance. "Come in, Pietro, come in!" He wore white linen shorts, a zebra-striped beach shirt, and huaraches, in which he moved easily, leading the way down the dark hall of the apartment, past the two bedrooms, into the living room. All of the apartment was on a court, but on the top floor, so it received a medium, dingy light from above. The living room, long and pleasant, with an old white mantel, a gas log, and many books, always came as a surprise after the rest of the place, and at any time of day Robert kept a few lamps lit, which rouged the room with an evening excitement.

As they entered, Robert reached over in passing and turned on the record-player. Music filled the room, muted but insistent, as if he wanted it to patch up some lull he had left behind. Two young men sat in front of the dead gas log. Between them was a table littered with maps, an open atlas, travel folders, glass beer steins. Vince, the current roomer, had his head on his clenched fists. The other man, a stranger, indolently raised a dark, handsome head as they entered.

"Vince!" Robert spoke sharply. "You know Peter Birge. And this is Mario Osti. Peter Birge."

The dark young man nodded and smiled, lounging in his chair. Vince nodded. His red-rimmed eyes looked beyond Peter into some distance he seemed to prefer.

"God, isn't it but hot!" Robert said. "I'll get you a beer." He bent over Mario with an inquiring look, a caressing hand on the empty glass in front of him.

Mario stretched back on the chair, smiled upward at Robert, and shook his head sleepily. "Only makes me hotter." He yawned, spread his arms languorously, and let them fall. He had the animal self-possession of the very handsome; it was almost a shock to hear him speak.

Robert bustled off to the kitchen.

"Robert!" Vince called, in his light, pouting voice. "Get me a drink. Not a beer. A drink." He scratched at the blond stubble on his cheek with a nervous, pointed nail. On his round head and retroussé face, the stubble produced the illusion of a desiccated baby, until, looking closer, one imagined that he might never have been one, but might have been spawned at the age he was, to mummify perhaps but not to grow. He wore white shorts exactly like Robert's, and his blue-and-white striped shirt was a smaller version of Robert's brown-and-white, so that the two of them made an ensemble, like the twin outfits the children wore on the beach at Rye.

"You know I don't keep whisky here." Robert held three steins deftly balanced, his heavy hips neatly avoiding the small tables which scattered the room. "You've had enough, wherever you got it." It was true, Peter remembered, that Robert was fonder of drinks with a flutter of ceremony about them—*café brulé* perhaps, or, in the spring, a *Maibowle*, over which he could chant the triumphant details of his pursuit of the necessary woodruff. But actually one tippled here on the exhilarating effect of wearing one's newest façade, in the fit company of others similarly attired.

Peter picked up his stein. "You and Vince all set for Morocco, I gather."

"Morocco?" Robert took a long pull at his beer. "No. No, that's been changed. I forgot you hadn't been around. Mario's been brushing up my Italian. He and I are off for Rome the day after tomorrow."

The last record on the changer ended in an archaic battery of horns. In the silence while Robert slid on a new batch of records, Peter heard Vince's nail scrape, scrape along his cheek. Still leaning back, Mario shaped smoke with his lips. Large and facilely drawn, they looked, more than anything, accessible—to a stream of smoke, of food, to another mouth, to any plum that might drop.

"You going to study over there?" Peter said to him.

"Paint." Mario shaped and let drift another corolla of smoke.

"No," Robert said, clicking on the record arm. "I'm afraid Africa's démodé." A harpsichord began to play, its dwarf notes hollow and perfect. Robert raised his voice a shade above the music. "Full of fashion photographers. And little come-lately writers." He sucked in his cheeks and made a face. "Trying out their passions under the beeg, bad sun."

"*Eheu,* poor Africa?" said Peter.

Robert laughed. Vince stared at him out of wizened eyes. Not drink, so much, after all, Peter decided, looking professionally at the mottled cherub face before he realized that he was comparing it with another face, but lately left. He looked away.

"Weren't you going over, Peter?" Robert leaned against the machine.

"Not this year." Carefully Peter kept out of his voice the knell the words made in his mind. In Greenwich, there were many graveled walks, unshrubbed except for the nurses who dotted them, silent and attitudinized as trees. "Isn't that Landowska playing?"

"Hmm. Nice and cooling on a hot day. Or a fevered brow." Robert fiddled with the volume control. The music became louder, then lowered. "Vince wrote a poem about that once. About the Mozart, really, wasn't it, Vince? 'A lovely clock between ourselves and time.'" He enunciated daintily, pushing the words away from him with his tongue.

"Turn it off!" Vince stood up, his small fists clenched, hanging at his sides.

"No, let her finish," Robert turned deliberately and closed the lid of the machine, so that the faint hiss of the needle vanished from the frail, metronomic notes. He smiled. "What a time-obsessed crowd writers are. Now Mario doesn't have to bother with that dimension."

"Not unless I paint portraits," Mario said. His parted lips exposed his teeth, like some white, unexpected flint of intelligence.

"*Dolce far niente,*" Robert said softly. He repeated the phrase dreamily, so that half-known Italian words—"*loggia,*" the "Ponte Vecchio," the "Lungarno"—imprinted themselves one by one on Peter's mind, and he saw the two of them, Mario and Roberto now, already in the frayed-gold light of Florence, in the umber dusk of half-imagined towns.

A word, muffled, came out of Vince's throat. He lunged for the record-player. Robert seized his wrist and held it down on the lid. They were locked that way, staring at each other, when the doorbell rang.

"That must be Susan," Robert said. He released Vince and looked down, watching the blood return to his fingers, flexing his palm.

With a second choked sound, Vince flung out his fist in an awkward attempt at a punch. It grazed Robert's cheek, clawing downward. A thin line of red appeared on Robert's cheek. Fist to mouth. Vince stood a moment; then he rushed from the room. They heard the nearer bedroom door slam and the lock click. The bell rang again, a short, hesitant burr.

Robert clapped his hand to his cheek, shrugged, and left the room.

Mario got up out of his chair for the first time. "Aren't you going to ask who Susan is?"

"Should I?" Peter leaned away from the face bent confidentially near, curly with glee.

"His daughter," Mario whispered. "He said he was expecting his *daughter*. Can you imagine? *Robert!*"

Peter moved farther away from the mobile, pressing face and, standing at the window, studied the gritty details of the courtyard. A vertical line of lighted windows, each with a glimpse of stair,

marked the hallways on each of the five floors. Most of the other
windows were dim and closed, or opened just a few inches above
their white ledges, and the yard was quiet. People would be away or
out in the sun, or in their brighter front rooms dressing for dinner,
all of them avoiding this dark shaft that connected the backs of their
lives. Or, here and there, was there someone sitting in the fading
light, someone lying on a bed with his face pressed to a pillow? The
window a few feet to the right, around the corner of the court, must
be the window of the room into which Vince had gone. There was
no light in it.

Robert returned, a Kleenex held against his cheek. With him was
a pretty, ruffle-headed girl in a navy-blue dress with a red arrow at
each shoulder. He switched on another lamp. For the next arrival,
Peter thought, surely he will tug back a velvet curtain or break out
with a heraldic flourish of drums, recorded by Red Seal. Or perhaps
the musty wardrobe was opening at last and this was the skeleton—
this girl who had just shaken hands with Mario, and now extended
her hand toward Peter, tentatively, timidly, as if she did not habitually shake hands but today would observe every custom she could.

"How do you do?"

"How do you do?" Peter said. The hand he held for a moment was
small and childish, the nails unpainted, but the rest of her was very
correct for the eye of the beholder, like the young models one sees
in magazines, sitting or standing against a column, always in three-
quarter view, so that the picture, the ensemble, will not be marred
by the human glance. Mario took from her a red dressing case that
she held in her free hand, bent to pick up a pair of white gloves that
she had dropped, and returned them with an avid interest which
overbalanced, like a waiter's gallantry. She sat down, brushing at
the gloves.

"The train was awfully dusty—and crowded." She smiled tightly
at Robert, looked hastily and obliquely at each of the other two, and
bent over the gloves, brushing earnestly, stopping as if someone had
said something, and, when no one did, brushing again.

"Well, well, well," Robert said. His manners, always good, were
never so to the point of clichés, which would be for him what nervous *gaffes* were for other people. He coughed, rubbed his cheek with
the back of his hand, looked at the hand, and stuffed the Kleenex
into the pocket of his shorts. "How was camp?"

Mario's eyebrows went up. The girl was twenty, surely, Peter
thought.

"All right," she said. She gave Robert the stiff smile again and looked down into her lap. "I like helping children. They can use it." Her hands folded on top of the gloves, then inched under and hid beneath them.

"Susan's been counseling at a camp which broke up early because of a polio scare," Robert said as he sat down. "She's going to use Vince's room while I'm away, until college opens."

"Oh—" She looked up at Peter. "Then you aren't Vince?"

"No. I just dropped in. I'm Peter Birge."

She gave him a neat nod of acknowledgment. "I'm glad, because I certainly wouldn't want to inconvenience—"

"Did you get hold of your mother in Reno?" Robert asked quickly.

"Not yet. But she couldn't break up her residence term anyway. And Arthur must have closed up the house here. The phone was disconnected."

"Arthur's Susan's stepfather," Robert explained with a little laugh. "Number three, I think. Or is it *four,* Sue?"

Without moving, she seemed to retreat, so that again there was nothing left for the observer except the girl against the column, any one of a dozen with the short, anonymous nose, the capped hair, the foot arched in the trim shoe, and half an iris glossed with an expertly aimed photoflood. "Three," she said. Then one of the hidden hands stole out from under the gloves, and she began to munch evenly on a fingernail.

"Heavens, you haven't still got that *habit!*" Robert said.

"What a heavy papa you make, Roberto," Mario said.

She flushed, and put the hand back in her lap, tucking the fingers under. She looked from Peter to Mario and back again. "Then you're not Vince," she said. "I didn't think you were."

The darkness increased around the lamps. Behind Peter, the court had become brisk with lights, windows sliding up, and the taps running.

"Guess Vince fell asleep. I'd better get him up and send him on his way." Robert shrugged, and rose.

"Oh, don't! I wouldn't want to be an inconvenience," the girl said, with a polite terror which suggested she might often have been one.

"On the contrary." Robert spread his palms, with a smile, and walked down the hall. They heard him knocking on a door, then his indistinct voice.

In the triangular silence, Mario stepped past Peter and slid the window up softly. He leaned out to listen, peering sidewise at the window to the right. As he was pulling himself back in, he looked down. His hands stiffened on the ledge. Very slowly he pulled himself all the way in and stood up. Behind him a tin ventilator clattered inward and fell to the floor. In the shadowy lamplight his too classic face was like marble which moved numbly. He swayed a little, as if with vertigo.

"I'd better get out of here!"

They heard his heavy breath as he dashed from the room. The slam of the outer door blended with Robert's battering, louder now, on the door down the hall.

"What's down there?" She was beside Peter, otherwise he could not have heard her. They took hands, like strangers met on a narrow footbridge or on one of those steep places where people cling together more for anchorage against their own impulse than for balance. Carefully they leaned out over the sill. Yes—it was down there, the shirt, zebra-striped, just decipherable on the merged shadow of the courtyard below.

Carefully, as if they were made of eggshell, as if by some guarded movement they could still rescue themselves from disaster, they drew back and straightened up. Robert, his face askew with the impossible question, was behind them.

After this, there was the hubbub—the ambulance from St. Luke's, the prowl car, the two detectives from the precinct station house, and finally the "super," a vague man with the grub pallor and shamble of those who live in basements. He pawed over the keys on the thong around his wrist and, after several tries, opened the bedroom door. It was a quiet, unviolent room with a tossed bed and an open window, with a stagy significance acquired only momentarily in the minds of those who gathered in a group at its door.

Much later, after midnight, Peter and Susan sat in the bald glare of an all-night restaurant. With hysterical eagerness, Robert had gone on to the station house with the two detectives to register the salient facts, to help ferret out the relatives in Ohio, to arrange, in fact, anything that might still be arrangeable about Vince. Almost without noticing, he had acquiesced in Peter's proposal to look after Susan. Susan herself, after silently watching the gratuitous burbling of her father, as if it were a phenomenon she could neither believe nor leave, had followed Peter without comment. At his suggestion, they had stopped off at the restaurant on their way to her stepfather's house, for which she had a key.

"Thanks. I was starved." She leaned back and pushed at the short bang of hair on her forehead.

"Hadn't you eaten at all?"

"Just those pasty sandwiches they sell on the train. There wasn't any diner."

"Smoke?"

"I do, but I'm just too tired. I can get into a hotel all right, don't you think? If I can't get in at Arthur's?"

"I know the manager of a small one near us," Peter said. "But if you don't mind coming to my place, you can use my mother's room for tonight. Or for as long as you need, probably."

"What about your mother?"

"She's away. She'll be away for quite a while."

"Not in Reno, by any chance?" There was a roughness, almost a coarseness, in her tone, like that in the overdone camaraderie of the shy.

"No. My father died when I was eight. Why?"

"Oh, something in the way you spoke. And then you're so competent. Does she work?"

"No. My father left something. Does yours?"

She stood up and picked up her bedraggled gloves. "No," she said, and her voice was suddenly distant and delicate again. "She marries." She turned and walked out ahead of him.

He paid, rushed out of the restaurant, and caught up with her.

"Thought maybe you'd run out on me," he said.

She got in the car without answering.

They drove through the Park, toward the address in the East Seventies that she had given him. A weak smell of grass underlay the gas-blended air, but the Park seemed limp and worn, as if the strain of the day's effluvia had been too much for it. At the Seventy-second Street stop signal, the blank light of a street lamp invaded the car.

"Thought you might be feeling Mrs. Grundyish at my suggesting the apartment," Peter said.

"Mrs. Grundy wasn't around much when I grew up." The signal changed and they moved ahead.

They stopped in a street which had almost no lights along its smartly converted house fronts. This was one of the streets, still sequestered by money, whose houses came alive only under the accelerated, febrile glitter of winter and would dream through the gross summer days, their interiors deadened with muslin or stirred faintly with the subterranean clinkings of caretakers. No. 4 was dark.

"I would rather stay over at your place, if I have to," the girl said. Her voice was offhand and prim. "I hate hotels. We always stopped at them in between."

"Let's get out and see."

They stepped down into the areaway in front of the entrance, the car door banging hollowly behind them. She fumbled in her purse and took out a key, although it was already obvious that it would not be usable. In his childhood, he had often hung around in the areaways of old brownstones such as this had been. In the corners there had always been a soft, decaying smell, and the ironwork, bent and smeared, always hung loose and broken-toothed. The areaway of this house had been repaved with slippery flag; even in the humid night there was no smell. Black-tongued grillwork, with an oily shine and padlocked, secured the windows and the smooth door. Fastened on the grillwork in front of the door was the neat, square proclamation of a protection agency.

"You don't have a key for the padlocks, do you?"

"No." She stood on the curb, looking up at the house. "It was a nice room I had there. Nicest one I ever did have, really." She crossed to the car and got in.

He followed her over to the car and got in beside her. She had her head in her hands.

"I don't. I don't care about any of it, really." She sat up, her face averted. "My parents, or any of the people they tangle with." She wound the lever on the door slowly, then reversed it. "Robert, or my mother, or Arthur," she said, "although he was always pleasant enough. Even Vince—even if I'd known him."

"He was just a screwed-up kid. It could have been anybody's window."

"No." Suddenly she turned and faced him. "I should think it would be the best privilege there is, though. To care, I mean."

When he did not immediately reply, she gave him a little pat on the arm and sat back. "Excuse it, please. I guess I'm groggy." She turned around and put her head on the crook of her arm. Her words came faintly through it. "Wake me when we get there."

She was asleep by the time they reached his street. He parked the car as quietly as possible beneath his own windows. He himself had never felt more awake in his life. He could have sat there until morning with her sleep-secured beside him. He sat thinking of how different it would be at Rye, or anywhere, with her along, with someone along who was the same age. For they were the same age, whatever that was, whatever the age was of people like them. There was nothing he would be unable to tell her.

To the north, above the rooftops, the electric mauve of midtown blanked out any auguries in the sky, but he wasn't looking for anything like that. Tomorrow he would take her for a drive—whatever the weather. There were a lot of good roads around Greenwich.

CARSON MCCULLERS [1951]

Born in Georgia in 1917, Carson McCullers came to New York for her college education, studying at Columbia and New York Universities. In her novels and stories men and women in love figure largely, although "A Tree, a Rock, a Cloud" is not so much about a lover as about a man in love.

A Tree, a Rock, a Cloud

It was raining that morning, and still very dark. When the boy reached the streetcar café he had almost finished his route and he went in for a cup of coffee. The place was an all-night café owned by a bitter and stingy man called Leo. After the raw, empty street, the café seemed friendly and bright: along the counter there were a couple of soldiers, three spinners from the cotton mill, and in a corner a man who sat hunched over with his nose and half his face down in a beer mug. The boy wore a helmet such as aviators wear. When he went into the café he unbuckled the chin strap and raised the right flap up over his pink little ear; often as he drank his coffee someone would speak to him in a friendly way. But this morning Leo did not look into his face and none of the men were talking. He paid and was leaving the café when a voice called out to him:

"Son! Hey Son!"

He turned back and the man in the corner was crooking his finger and nodding to him. He had brought his face out of the beer mug and he seemed suddenly very happy. The man was long and pale, with a big nose and faded orange hair.

"Hey Son!"

The boy went toward him. He was an undersized boy of about

twelve, with one shoulder drawn higher than the other because of
the weight of the paper sack. His face was shallow, freckled, and
his eyes were round child eyes.

"Yeah, Mister?"

The man laid one hand on the paper boy's shoulders, then grasped
the boy's chin and turned his face slowly from one side to the other.
The boy shrank back uneasily.

"Say! What's the big idea?"

The boy's voice was shrill; inside the café it was suddenly very
quiet.

The man said slowly. "I love you."

All along the counter the men laughed. The boy, who had scowled
and sidled away, did not know what to do. He looked over the
counter at Leo, and Leo watched him with a weary, brittle jeer. The
boy tried to laugh also. But the man was serious and sad.

"I did not mean to tease you, Son," he said. "Sit down and have a
beer with me. There is something I have to explain."

Cautiously, out of the corner of his eye, the paper boy questioned
the men along the counter to see what he should do. But they had
gone back to their beer or their breakfast and did not notice him.
Leo put a cup of coffee on the counter and a little jug of cream.

"He is a minor," Leo said.

The paper boy slid himself up onto the stool. His ear beneath the
upturned flap of the helmet was very small and red. The man was
nodding at him soberly. "It is important," he said. Then he reached
in his hip pocket and brought out something which he held up in
the palm of his hand for the boy to see.

"Look very carefully," he said.

The boy stared, but there was nothing to look at very carefully.
The man held in his big, grimy palm a photograph. It was the face
of a woman, but blurred, so that only the hat and the dress she was
wearing stood out clearly.

"See?" the man asked.

The boy nodded and the man placed another picture in his palm.
The woman was standing on a beach in a bathing suit. The suit
made her stomach very big, and that was the main thing you noticed.

"Got a good look?" He leaned over closer and finally asked: "You
ever seen her before?"

The boy sat motionless, staring slantwise at the man. "Not so I
know of."

"Very well." The man blew on the photographs and put them back into his pocket. "That was my wife."

"Dead?" the boy asked.

Slowly the man shook his head. He pursed his lips as though about to whistle and answered in a long-drawn way: "Nuuu—" he said. "I will explain."

The beer on the counter before the man was in a large brown mug. He did not pick it up to drink. Instead he bent down and, putting his face over the rim, he rested there for a moment. Then with both hands he tilted the mug and sipped.

"Some night you'll go to sleep with your big nose in a mug and drown," said Leo. "Prominent transient drowns in beer. That would be a cute death."

The paper boy tried to signal to Leo. While the man was not looking he screwed up his face and worked his mouth to question soundlessly: "Drunk?" But Leo only raised his eyebrows and turned away to put some pink strips of bacon on the grill. The man pushed the mug away from him, straightened himself, and folded his loose crooked hands on the counter. His face was sad as he looked at the paper boy. He did not blink, but from time to time the lids closed down with delicate gravity over his pale green eyes. It was nearing dawn and the boy shifted the weight of the paper sack.

"I am talking about love," the man said. "With me it is a science."

The boy half slid down from the stool. But the man raised his forefinger, and there was something about him that held the boy and would not let him go away.

"Twelve years ago I married the woman in the photograph. She was my wife for one year, nine months, three days, and two nights. I loved her. Yes . . ." He tightened his blurred, rambling voice and said again: "I loved her. I thought also that she loved me. I was a railroad engineer. She had all home comforts and luxuries. It never crept into my brain that she was not satisfied. But do you know what happened?"

"Mgneeow!" said Leo.

The man did not take his eyes from the boy's face. "She left me. I came in one night and the house was empty and she was gone. She left me."

"With a fellow?" the boy asked.

Gently the man placed his palm down on the counter. "Why naturally, Son. A woman does not run off like that alone."

The café was quiet, the soft rain black and endless in the street outside. Leo pressed down the frying bacon with the prongs of his long fork. "So you have been chasing the floozie for eleven years. You frazzled old rascal!"

For the first time the man glanced at Leo. "Please don't be vulgar. Besides, I was not speaking to you." He turned back to the boy and said in a trusting and secretive undertone. "Let's not pay any attention to him. O.K.?"

The paper boy nodded doubtfully.

"It was like this," the man continued. "I am a person who feels many things. All my life one thing after another has impressed me. Moonlight. The leg of a pretty girl. One thing after another. But the point is that when I had enjoyed anything there was a peculiar sensation as though it was laying around loose in me. Nothing seemed to finish itself up or fit in with the other things. Women? I had my portion of them. The same. Afterwards laying around loose in me. I was a man who had never loved."

Very slowly he closed his eyelids, and the gesture was like a curtain drawn at the end of a scene in a play. When he spoke again his voice was excited and the words came fast—the lobes of his large, loose ears seemed to tremble.

"Then I met this woman. I was fifty-one years old and she always said she was thirty. I met her at a filling station and we were married within three days. And do you know what it was like? I just can't tell you. All I had ever felt was gathered together around this woman. Nothing lay around loose in me any more but was finished up by her."

The man stopped suddenly and stroked his long nose. His voice sank down to a steady and reproachful undertone: "I'm not explaining this right. What happened was this. There were these beautiful feelings and loose little pleasures inside me. And this woman was something like an assembly line for my soul. I run these little pieces of myself through her and I come out complete. Now do you follow me?"

"What was her name?" the boy asked.

"Oh," he said. "I called her Dodo. But that is immaterial."

"Did you try to make her come back?"

The man did not seem to hear. "Under the circumstances you can imagine how I felt when she left me."

Leo took the bacon from the grill and folded two strips of it between a bun. He had a gray face, with slitted eyes, and a pinched

nose saddled by faint blue shadows. One of the mill workers signaled for more coffee and Leo poured it. He did not give refills on
coffee free. The spinner ate breakfast there every morning, but the
better Leo knew his customers the stingier he treated them. He
nibbled his own bun as though he grudged it to himself.

"And you never got hold of her again?"

The boy did not know what to think of the man, and his child's
face was uncertain with mingled curiosity and doubt. He was new
on the paper route; it was still strange to him to be out in the town
in the black, queer early morning.

"Yes," the man said. "I took a number of steps to get her back. I
went around trying to locate her. I went to Tulsa where she had
folks. And to Mobile. I went to every town she had ever mentioned
to me, and I hunted down every man she had formerly been connected with. Tulsa, Atlanta, Chicago, Cheehaw, Memphis . . . For
the better part of two years I chased around the country trying to
lay hold of her."

"But the pair of them had vanished from the face of the earth!"
said Leo.

"Don't listen to him," the man said confidentially. "And also just
forget those two years. They are not important. What matters is
that around the third year a curious thing begun to happen to me."

"What?" the boy asked.

The man leaned down and tilted his mug to take a sip of beer.
But as he hovered over the mug his nostrils fluttered slightly; he
sniffed the staleness of the beer and did not drink. "Love is a curious
thing to begin with. At first I thought only of getting her back. It
was a kind of mania. But then as time went on I tried to remember
her. But do you know what happened?"

"No," the boy said.

"When I laid myself down on a bed and tried to think about her
my mind became a blank. I couldn't see her. I would take out her
pictures and look. No good. Nothing doing. A blank. Can you imagine it?"

"Say, Mac!" Leo called down the counter. "Can you imagine this
bozo's mind a blank!"

Slowly, as though fanning away flies, the man waved his hand.
His green eyes were concentrated and fixed on the shallow little
face of the paper boy.

"But a sudden piece of glass on a sidewalk. Or a nickel tune in a
music box. A shadow on a wall at night. And I would remember. It

might happen in a street and I would cry or bang my head against a lamp post. You follow me?"

"A piece of glass . . ." the boy said.

"Anything. I would walk around and I had no power of how and when to remember her. You think you can put up a kind of shield. But remembering don't come to a man face forward—it corners around sideways. I was at the mercy of everything I saw and heard. Suddenly instead of me combing the countryside to find her she begun to chase me around in my very soul. *She* chasing *me*, mind you! And in my soul."

The boy asked finally: "What part of the country were you in then?"

"Ooh," the man groaned. "I was a sick mortal. It was like small-pox. I confess, Son, that I boozed. I fornicated. I committed any sin that suddenly appealed to me. I am loath to confess it but I will do so. When I recall that period it is all curdled in my mind, it was so terrible."

The man leaned his head down and tapped his forehead on the counter. For a few seconds he stayed bowed over in this position, the back of his stringy neck covered with orange furze, his hands with their long warped fingers held palm to palm in an attitude of prayer. Then the man straightened himself; he was smiling and suddenly his face was bright and tremulous and old.

"It was in the fifth year that it happened," he said. "And with it I started my science."

Leo's mouth jerked with a pale, quick grin. "Well, none of we boys are getting any younger," he said. Then with sudden anger he balled up a dishcloth he was holding and threw it down hard on the floor. "You draggle-tailed old Romeo!"

"What happened?" the boy asked.

The old man's voice was high and clear: "Peace," he answered.

"Huh?"

"It is hard to explain scientifically, Son," he said. "I guess the logical explanation is that she and I had fleed around from each other for so long that finally we just got tangled up together and lay down and quit. Peace. A queer and beautiful blankness. It was spring in Portland and the rain came every afternoon. All evening I just stayed there on my bed in the dark. And that is how the science come to me."

The windows in the streetcar were pale blue with light. The two soldiers paid for their beers and opened the door—one of the soldiers combed his hair and wiped off his muddy puttees before they went outside. The three mill workers bent silently over their breakfasts. Leo's clock was ticking on the wall.

"It is this. And listen carefully. I meditated on love and reasoned it out. I realized what is wrong with us. Men fall in love for the first time. And what do they fall in love with?"

The boy's soft mouth was partly open and he did not answer.

"A woman," the old man said. "Without science, with nothing to go by, they undertake the most dangerous and sacred experience in God's earth. They fall in love with a woman. Is that correct, Son?"

"Yeah," the boy said faintly.

"They start at the wrong end of love. They begin at the climax. Can you wonder it is so miserable? Do you know how men should love?"

The old man reached over and grasped the boy by the collar of his leather jacket. He gave him a gentle little shake and his green eyes gazed down unblinking and grave.

"Son, do you know how love should be begun?"

The boy sat small and listening and still. Slowly he shook his head. The old man leaned closer and whispered:

"A tree. A rock. A cloud."

It was still raining outside in the street: a mild, gray, endless rain. The mill whistle blew for the six o'clock shift and the three spinners paid and went away. There was no one in the café but Leo, the old man, and the little paper boy.

"The weather was like this in Portland," he said. "At the time my science was begun. I meditated and I started very cautious. I would pick up something from the street and take it home with me. I bought a goldfish and I concentrated on the goldfish and I loved it. I graduated from one thing to another. Day by day I was getting this technique. On the road from Portland to San Diego—"

"Aw shut up!" screamed Leo suddenly. "Shut up! Shut up!"

The old man still held the collar of the boy's jacket; he was trembling and his face was earnest and bright and wild. "For six years now I have gone around by myself and built up my science. And now I am a master. Son. I can love anything. No longer do I have to think about it even. I see a street full of people and a beautiful light comes in me. I watch a bird in the sky. Or I meet a traveler on the road. Everything, Son. And anybody. All stranger and all loved! Do you realize what a science like mine can mean?"

The boy held himself stiffly, his hands curled tight around the counter edge. Finally he asked: "Did you ever really find that lady?"

"What? What say, Son?"

"I mean," the boy asked timidly. "Have you fallen in love with a woman again?"

The old man loosened his grasp on the boy's collar. He turned away and for the first time his green eyes had a vague and scattered look. He lifted the mug from the counter, drank down the yellow beer. His head was shaking slowly from side to side. Then finally he answered: "No, Son. You see that is the last step in my science. I go cautious. And I am not quite ready yet."

"Well!" said Leo. "Well well well!"

The old man stood in the open doorway. "Remember," he said. Framed there in the gray damp light of the early morning he looked shrunken and seedy and frail. But his smile was bright. "Remember I love you," he said with a last nod. And the door closed quietly behind him.

The boy did not speak for a long time. He pulled down the bangs on his forehead and slid his grimy little forefinger around the rim of his empty cup. Then without looking at Leo he finally asked:

"Was he drunk?"

"No," said Leo shortly.

The boy raised his clear voice higher. "Then was he a dope fiend?"

"No."

The boy looked up at Leo, and his flat little face was desperate, his voice urgent and shrill. "Was he crazy? Do you think he was a lunatic?" The paper boy's voice dropped suddenly with doubt. "Leo? Or not?"

But Leo would not answer him. Leo had run a night café for fourteen years, and he held himself to be a critic of craziness. There were the town characters and also the transients who roamed in from the night. He knew the manias of all of them. But he did not want to satisfy the questions of the waiting child. He tightened his pale face and was silent.

So the boy pulled down the right flap of his helmet and as he turned to leave he made the only comment that seemed safe to him, the only remark that could not be laughed down and despised:

"He sure has done a lot of traveling."

LOUISE BOGAN   [1957]

Louise Bogan, who published her collected poems in 1954, was born in Maine in 1897 and spent one year at Boston University.

The Meeting

For years I thought I knew, at the bottom of the dream,
Who spoke but to say farewell,
Whose smile dissolved, after his first words
Gentle and plausible.

Each time I found him, it was always the same:
Recognition and surprise,
And then the silence, after the first words,
And the shifting of the eyes.

Then the moment when he had nothing to say
And only smiled again,
But this time toward a place beyond me, where I
    could not stay—
No world of men.

Now I am not sure. Who are you? Who have you been?
Why do our paths cross?
At the deepest bottom of the dream you are let in,
A symbol of loss.

Eye to eye we look, and we greet each other
Like friends from the same land.
Bitter compliance! Like a faithless brother
You take and drop my hand.

MARYA MANNES [1958]

Marya Mannes, who was born in New York City in 1904, has worked on Vogue *and is now a writer for* The Reporter. *She writes often about men, attacking and admiring them by turns.*

If I Were a Man

If I were a man, I'd be a rake until I married; and that, with any luck, would not be till my late twenties. I cannot imagine a better occupation of spare time than the seduction of a number of different women—unless, if you are a woman, it is seduction by a number of different men. It depends on what you are. It depends on how much vitality you have. It depends, certainly, on how fond you are of the opposite sex. And I find the theory—propounded daily and lengthily by the ladies who write columns of advice in the papers—that this kind of sport is a sign of immaturity in men and disturbance in women rather preposterous. It may comfort women by diminishing men and elevating themselves, but it is not very convincing. A great many mature, productive and distinguished men have trod the primrose path and a great many wise and productive women have, in their time, tasted the delights of compliance. And how, indeed, is one equipped to recognize and practice virtue if one has not experienced its absence? Of what good is control if one has not endured the consequences of its lack?

But the Church and psychiatry have done their best to discredit dilatory passions, with the result that most American men have a very limited understanding of the nature of women, and most American women have suffered from this ignorance. The domesticated male may be safe, but he is not exciting. Nor is a society in which amorous exchanges (usually between persons long married to others) can be initiated only through the release of drink and pursued only behind the country-club hedge. Ten to one that the men and women involved married the girl and boy next door in their teens. This is hardly an education.

For I think this education of men by women and women by men is an essential one. It can happen best through a fortunate marriage, but then again a marriage can be fortunate because both husband and wife have been thus educated and know the nature of love fully. There is nothing more complicated than the long-term relationship between a man and woman, and if I were a man I'd want to look around pretty extensively before I tackled one.

For it is ignorance as well as drink that makes Bill H. think that Susie Q. is a dream-girl and a volcano, while Mary H., pressed close to Harry Q. on the dance floor, imagines him, deliriously, as a satyr. They are, simply, other people's wives and husbands, usually no better and no worse, no hotter or colder, than the original partner. But the Q.'s and the H.'s had no chance to find this out in their youth. What they are doing now is merely delayed exploration at a time when discovery could be destructive.

That is why I would explore the infinite variety of women before my marriage, rather than after. And I would prefer as my life partner a woman who knew almost as much as I did. I say almost, because I imagine it is in the nature of man to enjoy teaching.

Being a woman, and like all women responding strongly to words, I am continually amazed that so many men do not know the power they can exert through words alone. The attraction of the strong silent lover is a myth, propagated, one might suppose, by inarticulate men. But all really great lovers are articulate, and verbal seduction is the surest road to actual seduction. The man who knows this can be ugly as sin and still prevail over a handsomer tongue-tied rival. Young men can afford to be speechless blunderers, but if they want to exert attraction in later years, they had better learn to talk.

And I do not mean garrulity. I mean talk directly addressed to the woman *about* the woman. Verbal attention is as important as sexual attention. It is the knowledge of what to say, when.

It is also the knowledge of every facet of the woman herself, which must be reflected back to her in words. For the woman—to love a man—must be in love with herself as *he* sees her. This is, of course, a matter of mutual narcissism, but I think it is stronger in women than in men, and more demanding. In any case, I would take great pleasure in presenting this image as accurately to her as I could. General compliments are pleasing to hear, but the specific compliment bears far greater fruit. For the man who remarks on the line of her chin or the shape of her thigh, a woman will do anything.

Having won a woman, I think I would be tough with her; making my dominance of her in the sexual realm quite clear, exacting deference to my masculinity and rebuffing aggressive inroads of all kinds. I would not tolerate the loud or derisive voice or any efforts, private or public, to diminish my stature as a man. I would exert this dominance because women expect and want it; and when they don't get it, they are left with contempt for the man. If American men realized this, they would no longer endure their submissive state, and American women would at least be permitted to enjoy what a wise old artist once called "the voluptuousness of obedience."

If I were a man, I would be a hellion, I would; the kind of man a woman like myself would fall in love with—and probably live to regret it!

ELIZABETH JANEWAY   [1959]

In Elizabeth Janeway's The Third Choice, *Diana Belchamber describes herself as an "addict of hysteria." This excerpt from Diana's memoirs, written when she is a widow and a cripple, recalls the way she flung herself from lover to husband. Mrs. Janeway, who graduated from Barnard College in 1935, has achieved distinction both as a novelist and as a critic. She has been especially generous in encouraging young writers of talent.*

The Third Choice

A thousand years ago, then, on a summer day, being demanding, greedy, insensitive and headlong, I left my husband in London and went with my lover to France. It was a bright day, warm for England. We had a smooth crossing.

I can see us still. Two minute figures stand at the rail watching France approach. Gerald and I. I am very smartly dressed in a taupe suit and a small feather toque with a veil. Gerald looks tired. This has been a strain for him. He has never run away with anyone in quite my circumstances, with a husband so rich, that is, so everywhere acquainted with the powerful and the established, the people who do not forget. Or rather, whose servants—the police, the bureaucrats—do not forget. He is putting himself in great jeopardy for me, being very rash. This is out of character for Gerald. It is I who am headlong, not he. He is worried. I am a great gamble. I may very well ruin him. And I don't seem to understand this, quite, being conventionally more attentive to my own chances of ruin.

Yes, 1919 is really that long ago. There had certainly been non-ruinous elopements before, but the one I was undertaking was the kind that asks for ruin.

It is, in fact, a considerable tribute to what I was in 1919 that Gerald ran off with me. All his experience and reason must have argued against it. But he came.

And I—I was frightened not to go. Because of James. I had seen, the night before, that he was about to believe the stories about Gerald and me that people must have been telling him for weeks. He was watching me in a kind of open, astonished wonder which of course could only change to conviction the minute he began to doubt me. And therefore I did not wait.

We got away all right, no scene with James because we went so quickly. And we had shared enough time already to manage ourselves quite decently in public. We could travel alone or together and no one looking at us would have guessed anything. But the war had unfortunately left behind several light-years of red tape which kept curling up around the feet of travelers crossing frontiers or registering in hotels. And we had passports with different names, and we had to keep showing them.

In other words, no privacy. We could not disappear and turn up somewhere else as a honeymoon couple named Smith. I don't mean that the French were censorious to us, just that room clerks and chiefs of police and customs officials and conductors knew all about us. There is, I suppose, a special temperament that enjoys sinning in public, making an exhibition of oneself, startling the bourgeois—I don't share it.

We tried Spain where there hadn't been any war. Things seemed easier. Then I decided to rent a house and I had to get out my passport and it wasn't made out in the name I had been using—Well, it's a detail. We had apparently picked a village with a rabidly anti-Protestant priest and—and so we left, after the children spat at us.

And, you might say, gave up and went to the obvious place, Capri. Where naturally they knew all about us too, but didn't care. Capri was riddled with people that other people knew all about. I daresay it still is. We took a house with a view and a patio and a grapevine. That is, I did. It was my money.

Is that one reason Gerald came with me? I suppose it had some influence, though he must have known that the real money was all James's. He told me quite frankly that he didn't have any himself. There'd been a small income out of Ireland before the war, but

Irish rents didn't get paid to absentee owners in 1919. And yet—he didn't come with me for money. It was my money that made it possible for us to go, that's all. I mean the three thousand or so in my personal bank account, and my jewelry. It was Gerald's idea, or so he said at any rate, that he would set up an agency somewhere, in Rome perhaps, to sell British motorcars. Every now and then he would go off to Rome for several days to talk about this to people and to sell some more of my jewelry. That is what we lived on through the winter and into the spring of 1920.

It was that February that my father died, but of course I didn't know it. I must have got pregnant about the same time, but I didn't know that either. You see, I never had before and it didn't occur to me to worry about it.

Would you believe it? It's true. What did I call myself—greedy, demanding, headlong, insensitive? Insensitive is hardly the word. I must add stupid. It was as if my brain were waterlogged and my reasoning power simply cut off at the source. My passion for Gerald and the life of the flesh occupied all my time and energy and attention. This was where my greed sucked its fill, where my demands beat and were answered. It was a revelation. I had never lost myself before, I had always been conscious, alert, present. Even the time in Paris was not like this. *There* our passion had seemed a part of the bloody climax of the war, there was something outside, bigger, containing it, of which it was a reflection. But in Capri that winter and spring, it was everything, all experience, and I was unfolded like a napkin and laid out on its surface, absorbed into it, I *was* my experience—sun in the morning, light on the sea, bougainvillea and lilies, a cart creaking by on the road to Anacapri—I was completely passive at the heart of action. It moved through me, and I lived it.

Every now and then before I realize what I'm doing and stop, I find that I have read a bit of an argument that seems to be bothering people today about women's role in the world: one side of it says that everyone would be happier and better off if women became totally passive, members of a harem without walls who left initiating action to men. I always think of Capri when I read that—or to be explicit, I feel a sensation at the back of my head that *means* Capri. It's a sort of numb tingling, and it's enough to stop me reading or thinking along the lines that awaken it.

Well. As I say, I hadn't bothered to think about becoming pregnant. It was Gerald who figured it out one morning. He waked me to make love and afterward must have lain beside me counting. I wanted to sleep a little again, but he was restless, I could feel it. Finally he asked me.

I said it was nonsense, stretching and yawning luxuriously.

He got up out of bed and went and looked out the window. There was a view down to the sea there. He must have been thinking about getting away already. Then he came back to bed and caressed me and asked me to see a doctor.

I said again that it was nonsense.

Do I have to put all this down? I can't, really. It is *only* nauseating. If it were more, if there were a lesson or a moral— But surely the moral is already clear. If you are stupid, you do stupid things.

Very quickly, then, this is what happened. I refused to see any doctor on the island, so Gerald took me up to Rome. The doctor there told me I was three months pregnant. Gerald's face became very smooth, smooth all over. I was stunned, I remember that. Then I was simply ablaze with joy. This reaction came so quickly and was so triumphant that Gerald never even had a chance to ask me whether I would have an abortion. Before he could begin to hint that a child might be a slight inconvenience, I had started a speech about the miracles performed by love, about the child who would be both of us, and was not that in all truth a miracle even though it happened every day, and about how I had been afraid of time but now we had set our mark upon it, Life did conquer Death, and Order Chaos—I really talked like that.

What could he do but take me back to the island, settle me down, cosset me and plan his escape? Nothing at all. So that is what he did.

He stayed two months. I thought he loved me more than ever. It's possible I was right, as one can love the last gleam of light before the sun sets, knowing that it must set. He knew he must leave me. I don't doubt that he regretted it. If he had wanted to, he could have gone any time, any time at all, but he stayed two months. For those two months we loved each other with a passion that devoured time. Summer came on. I was not able to generalize enough to notice it. I lived in Gerald, in his looks and presence and touch. It seemed to me that we two were as much one as the child and I. We did not have to speak to each other, even.

Though we did speak. He said to me once, "You are me and I am you, now. Nothing can ever change it. It's like a dye that won't ever come out. There are old dyes like that, that people now have forgotten how to make. All except us."

And he said, "You have given me an American accent, do you

know that? All the rest of my life, people will think I am lying when I say I have never seen America."

That was a mistake on his part. It put America in my mind.

I can't say that I thought about going home, because I wasn't yet able to think. I was still toxic with love—or lust—or passion—or whatever name you prefer. They are all the same thing, all. But the child within me was beginning to stir and at the same time—because of it, maybe—I myself began to stir a little. My brain cells experienced a first faint revival. The child was becoming real as it moved within me, instead of just a symbol of the union between Gerald and me. It was going to exist. I was going to have to be responsible for it. The maternal instinct, wakening, brought with it dim stirrings of rationality.

I "thought," then, in the preposterous, dreamlike fashion that I thought in those days, that I would like to have the child born at home, in clean, antiseptic America.

The moment I thought anything, I said it—to Gerald.

This was the signal to him that time had run out and he must leave me. Naturally he was not going to go to America with me, and get himself a job, and meet James to arrange a divorce, and take me to an American hospital for the birth of the child, and wait in humiliating anguish while I was in labor. It was just as likely that the Apollo Belvedere would do these things.

But he was not going to *not* do them, either—lie about it, I mean, or argue with me, or persuade me to stay in Italy through the summer. He was going to leave me. I was in for a tragedy—through my fault, through my fault, through my most grievous fault: my own stupidity. Gerald was completely aware that I was in for tragedy. He was sorry, but he did not intend to take part in it. He did not want to, he did not have to, he did not intend to. Yes, he was sorry. If an animal is hurt and must be killed, its owner is sorry. But the owner does not stay to watch the veterinary perform the foreknown act of death. That is the way Gerald felt.

My pregnancy was beginning to show, too. I expect it embarrassed him. No, that sounds too bitter. After almost forty years, what is there to be bitter about? It made him uncomfortable and unhappy, that is closer to the truth. He had found an extraordinary pleasure in my body, my ease of movement. I was very strong and lithe and able to run and swim well at a time when most women who did these things were hairy amazons. It was hard for him to see me clumsy, or wait with me while I paused on a flight of steps which I had always flown up in an instant. He winced.

Everything, everything, said that he should go.

I did too. I gave him all the jewelry I had left—my pearls were there—and sent him to Rome with it. We would have to have money to travel home. I was beginning to notice things, to plan. I got hold of a paper that listed some sailings for America and instructed him about taking passage. I reminded him to see about a visa. I was becoming myself again, headlong and demanding, in touch with the real world, the woman who had picked him up one morning a year before and dumped him in France before night fell. That must be the ultimate reason why Gerald came away with me, after all. I took him. Now I seemed to be about to do it again.

But he wasn't going to let me. He had seen me open my hands and drop all my power, all my command, hand over all my strength. And now, without so much as a "Please," I was taking it back. He couldn't have liked that a bit.

You must see this: he was afraid of me. He knew that I loved him more than he loved me, in spite of the fact that—I believe now and have always believed—that he loved me with every possible bit of himself that was capable of love, to the fullest extent of his power. Since I loved him more, my power was greater.

The thing about Gerald was this: he was afraid of power, disinclined for it. He was perfectly honest about it. It meant responsibility. Responsibility meant that you had to act. If you acted you did not know what would come of it, you could never see the end, and thus you put yourself in jeopardy. I had forced him to it once, and now his fears were proven right. Over and over and over again his actions had made this clear, but I did not see it.

For I enjoyed—enjoy—power and responsibility, I have never been in the least afraid to act, and so though I thought I knew all about Gerald, I didn't.

You see what I am doing, all these years later? I am excusing him. In fairness, I must say this too: when he left me, taking my pearls, vanishing into Rome, he honestly and truly did not think that any harm would come to me. Any physical harm, I mean. My strength and power and the fact that he associated me with the world of the rich persuaded him that materially I could look after myself. I don't know what he thought I would do. I do know he thought I would do something.

As for the rest of it—you know the kind of person who says, "I couldn't stand to see her suffer"? He couldn't. He left.

He didn't leave me a note; I suppose because he wanted time to vanish. He didn't write me from Naples or Rome; I suppose because then I would have known at least one place he had stopped at. But I got the news about his going a couple of days after he'd left, long before I'd begun to expect him back from all the errands I'd given him to do in Rome. It was really very simple. He took a little English girl with him, a sweet, round, cozy little thing, like a kitten. She and her family were staying in a ramshackle villa that an aunt had left them. Her father, God help us, was a clergyman. *She* wrote, once they were on the mainland, that she had eloped with him and that they would marry as soon as they got out of Italy, because she naturally could not marry in a Roman Catholic church, they would go to France and be married in a civil ceremony there.

Her father came up to see me. He was speechless. He held the letter out to me. Tears ran down his cheeks—

I was sitting in the patio under the grapevine. What I could not understand was how Gerald had got to know her at all, for it seemed to me we had not been apart for a minute, for months. I found myself saying, "She must be mad. She has made this up. I'm so terribly sorry for you. My husband has an attraction for young girls, I'm afraid. There is an age, you know, where they imagine things—"

He had found two photographs of them together. He showed them to me.

I got rid of him somehow. I suppose it was easy because he could see my condition, and he was a kind man, even in his distress. And I left. At once. In a complete daze. I shook, I couldn't pack. I dropped things. Julia, the Italian maid we'd had, packed for me; and robbed me, I found out later. *She* didn't seem very surprised at Gerald's defection. It came to me sometime, I don't really remember when, that he must have made love to her too.

I didn't know where I was going. I hadn't money to get home—to get to America, that is, where my father was dead and my mother had been told that I was ill, recovering in a nursing home from a breakdown brought on by too much war work. I had to get out of Italy, that was all I knew. I went north, traveling "hard" to save money. People could see I was pregnant and were kind. I had one nightmare fear—that somewhere along the way I would overtake Gerald and the little girl he had brought along in his pocket to comfort him for the hurt of having to leave his love. When we stopped at a station, I cowered. I always got out last, after peering around. Everyone thought I was hiding from some man's pursuit, instead of desperately attempting not to overtake him. He must be a beast, they felt, seeing me pregnant. So they helped me and hid me and I vanished.

I mention this because it turned out to be why I ended starving and stealing. James had known where I was. In a sense, Gerald was right in thinking that, because I had been rich, I could not come to physical harm after he left me. James had had a detective agency track me. It couldn't have been simpler, as I say everyone knew we were sinning, and who we were, though at Capri they were polite enough to call me by Gerald's name. But at any rate, James knew I had gone, alone, within a week after I left. He even knew the name of the girl Gerald went with. Only he couldn't find me.

I wanted to die, I guess. Not that I tried. It didn't seem necessary. It was painful to breathe. It was painful to have anything touch my skin. Light hurt my eyes. Noise hurt my ears. I wanted to go somewhere dark and not be bothered, nor touched, nor spoken to.

I went right through Paris. I had met Gerald in Paris. I couldn't stop there. I went to the Gare du Nord, planning—if a lemming plans—to go on to England. But I saw two people I knew, the Maudsleys. They didn't see me, they were quarreling with a porter, for they were always stingy, but the sight of someone I knew was like a blow in the face and I walked past them trembling and found a place to sit and thought, Where can I go? Where does no one know me? Where have I never been? And I realized that Belgium, in another world during the war, was now quite close, and that my French would do there as well as here, and so I went to Brussels. I found a hotel near the station that advertised rooms for twenty francs—it was called The Splendid and Swiss and wasn't either—and for as long as I had any money I didn't go out of my room but lay in bed, hurting.

James looked all over France for me and northern Italy and Switzerland, but he didn't think of Belgium. I don't know why. Probably because we'd never been there. I don't know whether he ever would have found me but, as it happened, the police found him. I wasn't arrested for stealing, though I'd been living on what I could pick up for over three weeks. I don't know that I was technically arrested at all. But I tried to spend the night in one of the parks, and I was found and escorted to a police station. I'd been locked out of my room, my bill unpaid, and I had no money. No money at all—not a centime. I didn't make any trouble. It was September by then and the nights were growing chilly. The police were quite polite. I was seven months pregnant now, and my clothes were the clothes of a rich person, though wrinkled and stretched out of shape by my pregnancy, and I had an American passport. There hadn't been enough crazy American tourists around, in 1920, drunk and penniless, for the police to have become hardened to them. They were very kind to me, very correct, though I didn't give them a bit of help. They kept asking me where my husband was. I said I didn't know. Finally I turned my head away and said I definitely had no idea, and began to cry. I could see them all thinking, like the people I'd traveled with, He must be a beast!

"Do you think he is in Belgium, madame?" one of them asked me.

I just shook my head.

"In France, perhaps? Where—where were you with him last, madame?"

I was so beaten and tired and sick and hungry that I sobbed out "London!" though I had not meant to say a word. Then I started to say that that was over a year ago, and then I didn't say it because I was distinctly too tired to explain how the devil I was, in that case, seven months pregnant.

"In London," they said thoughtfully, repeating it to each other until it sounded like a long roll of drums, "A *Londres, Londres, Londres*," and I fainted while I listened.

That simplified everything. They put me right in the hospital. The roll of drums reached across the Channel and of course the American Embassy had James's address, and of course the hotel knew where he was—looking for me in Lausanne.

I knew he was coming even before he got to Brussels because in the afternoon two nurses came into the ward where I was lying. They had a wheelchair and instructions to move me into the most comfortable private room in the hospital. I laughed so hard I lost my breath and they gave me a sedative because they thought I was hysterical. I think it was the wheelchair that set me off. I had been so tired, so horribly tired, the day before, dragging myself through that park. I didn't dare sit too long anywhere and each time I got up the muscles of my poor big swollen self hurt more. It came to me that I could sit quietly in a church and so I went out of the park and found one and sat in front of a statue of the Virgin and had all kinds of blasphemous sleepy troubled thoughts about whether she, on the road to Bethlehem, had got as tired as I was now. Then a priest came in to hear confession and I got up and went back to the park—and the whirligig began, the police, the police station, my fainting, the half-dreamlike trip to the hospital and the bed in the ward which had been heaven enough for me all night long, but where I could not be allowed to stay because my rich husband was coming, and then I laughed some more—Oh, I suppose I was hysterical. When they got me into the big sunny private room and put me to bed there they shot me full of something that knocked me right out. So James saw me before I saw him. He hadn't known I was pregnant. Don't ask me why. Maybe the detectives were too delicate to tell him.

I suppose most men would have walked right out and never come back. James walked out. He walked around Brussels all night, but he came back in the morning.

He looked like death. He looked as if he were the one who'd fled across half Europe, who'd starved and slept in his clothes. I, on the contrary, had slept about twenty hours out of the last thirty-six. I said, "Well, James. I'm sorry they bothered you."

He stood looking down at me and I looked back, but I couldn't see into him any more. It reminded me of the time when I was a girl and he was Mr. Green, all-powerful. "You're alone," he said.

"Yes." It was ungracious of me, that monosyllabic reply, but I had gone back to being a pauper before him, and it exacerbated my pride. I hadn't put myself in the best room at the hospital at his expense, he had. Very well, then. Let him arrange our relationship! I wasn't asking for anything.

"I shan't ask you any questions," he said.

I almost said I wouldn't answer them if he did, but it seemed really *too* rude, so I said, "Thank you," in a rather sullen tone.

He said, "They say the—birth—" he brought it out finally, and I realized he couldn't say "child"—"will be in two months or so. Where—what are your plans?"

Fortunately seeing him had got me over my silly hysterics or I'd have laughed again at the idea of having plans. "I haven't any," I said.

He went over to the window and looked out at the tower of the Hôtel de Ville, where St. Michael floated in the morning sky. St. Michael is engaged in killing a dragon. I thought, looking at James's back, that he was trying to do the same thing: Gerald; Gerald and I; Gerald and I and the child. This idea seemed to me like a very real dragon for James. Looking at his back I began to realize what I had done to him.

I said, "I had a funny idea I'd like to have the baby at home. That is, I mean, in America. If—you could possibly help me to do that, I would appreciate it. If you would lend me the money to do that, I'd —pay you back afterwards. After I got a job."

He didn't turn around. He just hunched up a little. "A job," he said after a while.

I didn't say anything. What could I say? We both knew the only job I'd ever held was the war work I'd done. Alone in Paris, doing it, I'd met Gerald. Finally I said, "Maybe I couldn't pay you back. I don't know. I'd try."

"You can't go back to America," he said. His shoulders were still hunched up, his hands in his pockets. I realized he was telling me, by this negative, that he would be responsible for me. It should have been a great relief. It would have, I'm sure, if I'd ever thought ahead. I thought it would be polite of me to make some demonstration of gratitude, cry perhaps, but I couldn't.

So I just said, "Thank you very much." I was sorry for him, in a remote kind of way. There he was, in agony, and I had done it. What a sad, sad story, I thought. How tragic life is. Poor James.

Poor James said thoughtfully, "I don't need to be thanked."

"James," I said, "you don't *need* anything. You don't *need* to help me. There isn't any obligation from you to me."

"I wish I could believe that," he said. "I think there is. I married you. I knew it was wrong but I did it anyway. I've been telling myself that it was your fault, you could have stopped me. But it wasn't. You were a child. I knew you were a child."

"I wanted to marry you!"

"You don't give a child what it wants just because it wants it. A child can be greedy. Or misled. Older people owe it an obligation. I did you a bad turn."

Well, now I wasn't remote at all. I stared, appalled, at those hunched shoulders. Greedy! Misled! A child!

I choked out, "You—I did it—"

"Yes, you did, Diana. But I let you. What do you think I was afraid of? This. This. When I saw you with him—" He stopped. He turned around, he said, looking at me, "When I saw you with that vulgar cheap male whore I could have killed you. I saw it, I foresaw it. I warned you. I warned myself. None of it did any good. You insisted on humiliation—mine, yours. You wanted your roll in the dirt with him just the way you wanted me and money and position. You had to have it. Do you think you're a mystery to me? Do you think I don't know greed and desire and obsession when I see them? I know all about you. I've always known."

I was a long way beyond crying then.

He said, "I hope you're taking this all in. I hope what you learned in Capri will not go entirely over your head. I had him detained, by the way, and got the pearls back. The girl's gone home to her family."

I said, "Perhaps I can do that too."

His face changed. Of course I did not know my father had died. James stood looking at me and I looked back at him. We were both seeing each other without any deceptions—maybe for the first time. I found myself thinking, How interesting that he should have cared about the pearls and got them back! That is what being born rich does for you, you are trained to think of such things. It seemed to me quite admirable, more sensible and realistic than I would have expected of James.

He said, "Naturally you don't have to go anywhere now. Until this is over. That is—do you want to stay in Brussels? Did you come here for some reason?"

"Only because it wasn't England. I wanted to go where no one knew me."

He winced a little at that.

I saw it. It cheered me. I said, "I appreciate your helping me, James. If there were any way on earth I could manage without it, I would."

"Ah," he said, and smiled. "I hurt you then, didn't I, Diana? Good. Good. Bite on the bullet, my dear. You have a long life ahead of you in which to realize the value of stoicism." He came over to the bed looking down at me and almost laughing. He was not like himself at all. But then, he'd had a year to think of things he wanted to say to me.

I looked up at him as expressionlessly as I could and said, "Whatever I am, it isn't a coward."

"Quite right. I know that too. Well, now you will have a chance to prove your courage. I have been proving mine for a year. Goodbye. I'll be back this evening and we can decide where you will spend the next two months." He nodded and started to go.

I let him get to the door before I said, "Oh, James."

"Yes?"

"If Gerald is still in jail, could you arrange to have him let out? Now that you have the pearls back?" I lifted my head and met his eyes with an expression of bright interest as I asked this. He had hurt me, had he! I thought. Well, we would see who bit on the bullet!

It hit him. He had to bow before he could speak. "I'll wire at once," he said, and went.

I spent the weeks until my child was born in Bruges, a town with an imposing past and a nonexistent present. How appropriate to my state! I thought the moment I saw it. James had taken a small, solid old house for me, and hired the woman who owned it to stay and look after me. She was a widow who claimed that her husband had died defending his homeland from the Boche, but a neighbor kindly intimated that he had really met his end falling drunk into one of Bruges's numerous canals. Living with his widow, I found this quite possible to believe. She was as mean, grasping and hard as any Balzacian bourgeoise. It was a good thing. I don't know how I'd have passed the time there without our daily battle, she to cheat me and I to prevent it. It gave me a good healthy interest in life, and I got my exercise walking out every day to check on prices at the markets.

Otherwise I was alone. Bruges is full of tourists in the season, but October and November are not the season. The wind comes off the North Sea like a handmaiden of the Goddess Pneumonia and when the Goddess is really feeling at the top of her form she sends a fine drenching rain too. In between, Bruges enjoys fog. James drove me there, and established me, and introduced me to my land-lady, a doctor, and the gentleman who would handle my account at the bank. It was a lovely fall day—the Goddess Pneumonia had not yet waked from her estivation—and I stood by the door of my house and watched him get into the car he had hired and reverse it to drive off. He stopped by me and said, "Good-bye, Diana."

"Good-bye," I said politely.

"You can let me know at Claridges if you need anything. They'll know where I am."

"I shan't need anything."

"Dr. Frenet will arrange everything at the hospital."

"And nature no doubt will arrange everything else."

He looked at me thoughtfully. I couldn't have said anything nice or sweet or kind to him, in gratitude for what he was doing for me, if I'd been threatened with the rack. Well, I suppose I could under those circumstances, but under no others. "Would you like some books?" he asked.

"Thank you, I would," I said. "I've been planning to learn to make lace, but reading will give me a pleasant variety."

"I'll send you some from London."

"You're very kind."

He knew all about me, James. He'd told me so himself. He sat looking at me, held up by pride and pride alone. I knew he knew why I couldn't really thank him. You can't humble yourself if there's nothing left to hold you together but pride. He said, "You'll be all right, you know."

I was completely astonished. "What did you say?" I asked.

"You," he said. "You'll manage." And he drove off. It broke me up. I went into the house sobbing. James had tried to give me back to myself and comfort me and I couldn't stand it.

For two months I saw no one but my horrible landlady, Mme. Jordaens, and the doctor, and M. van Balen at the bank. James sent me a huge case of books, but no letters. I didn't know where he was. I read some, but mostly I thought.

What, I tried to find out, were the lessons to be learned from my life? I sat beside the fire in that overstuffed, poky, Flemish house, a house that breathed every maxim of prudence and greed, and tried to reconcile the two. God knows the latter came easily to me, but now I must practice the former. Mme. Jordaens and the house managed both attributes. Why shouldn't I? Indeed, I must. For now I was to have a child for whom I would be responsible, solely responsible. A child without a father. What kind of a raft of beliefs could I weave together beneath the child's feet and mine? Or were beliefs, like generosity, a luxury? Be practical, be prudent, I told myself, and I would sit reading, and whenever I came to a general principle, or an allusion to an ideal, I would put the book down and think off into the past, testing the point I had come on, and trying to decide whether it could have any use for me at all. We couldn't carry much on that raft, my child and I. We had no room for luxuries. Honor and honesty and kindness and care; loyalty; independence; what were these things worth to me? Had I not left James, the repository of so many of these virtues, for Gerald who had none, only charm? And I had been quite wrong. Now charm made me sick at my stomach. Stony, grasping, Mme. Jordaens and I judged it more or less the same: when we saw anyone charming coming, we were inclined to cross the street. I didn't think about Gerald at all—as a person, that is, or wonder where he was, or what had happened to him—any more than someone getting over the measles thinks about the character of his disease. I thought about the child, trying to penetrate the future. But not trying too hard, because that would invite bad luck. And I thought about James.

Because James was not who I had thought he was. He claimed to have been the one who supervised and controlled our relationship when I had been quite, quite sure it was I who did this. Perhaps he was wrong. Still—the James I had imagined myself living with would never even have made the claim. He would never have believed there was such a claim to be made. If the new James were real—then I had lived for five years with a man who deceived me about himself every minute. He was a man who saw much more than I had thought possible; but even more upsetting was the fact that he could see and judge and—not act. Hold himself in control. Let me run about his feet like a puppy, yapping and playing, and never knowing it was on a lead. There were people who saw and did not act because they were afraid. But the more I thought, the more I knew that James was not like that. If I wasn't a coward, neither was he. It was strength, not weakness, which made him hold his hand, not jerk the lead, let me run and play. For someone like me who acted instinctively, the stoic strength of refraining seemed—still seems—much greater, frighteningly greater, than my own impulsive energy.

So I thought about James. Without having to force myself to, either, for he had become more interesting than ever he'd been before—except, perhaps, for the time before he'd noticed me, when I made up stories about him and the great world. Now I'd had both. And though I'm sure I'd have bitterly regretted the great world if I'd had to settle down in a small American town and live without it, what I regretted, in Bruges, was James. It became clear to me that he was really a more interesting man than Gerald. More decisive. More able. Except for the one thing, more virile. In a way—intellectually—he was actually more attractive than Gerald. That is, he gave you something to chew on, whereas Gerald just appeared and disappeared like Jove in a shower of gold.

Did I think about winning James back? Yes, I certainly did. I acted out the scene where he asked me to return to him over and over again, whenever I needed to comfort myself. I always refused him. Disdainfully. My God, how I wanted to beat him, and hurt him! For the letters that never came, and the fog and rain and wind that did, and the things he'd said to me, and the answers I'd thought of later! For helping me when I needed it and going off and leaving me alone— It used to be a standard, if unscientific, theory that pregnant women were a little crazy, and from my own experience I think it's so.

Then I reached my time, one afternoon in early December. It was a sunny day, and Mme. Jordaens went and got the doctor and he came in a horse-drawn vehicle of a shape strange to me and took me to a hospital run by a nursing order of nuns. My room was small and whitewashed and bare, like a cell, and there was a crucifix on the wall.

I had a hard labor. It was the evening of the next day before the child was delivered.

On the morning after that they brought James in. My throat was very sore from the anesthetic they'd given me and I didn't speak, just licked my dry lips as he came toward me. He didn't say anything either. I was glad he had come. I hadn't expected it. He took my hand and I—I don't know why—I pulled his hand to my face and rested it against my cheek. I think I must have been lonely, very lonely. We stayed that way for a moment and then he said to the nun at the door, "I would like to see my wife alone." She told him it was against the rules, but he said he would make it all right and finally, unwillingly, she went off.

He's come, he's come, he's come—was all I could think. After all the daydreams and the long imaginary conversations, he is really here. Instead of the angry joy I had expected, I felt tears run out of my eyes and over my temples—I was lying flat on my back. They wet James's hand. This is reality, I was discovering—yourself torn and aching and crying and vulnerable, not yourself witty and disdainful and furious. This is what the world is like. The pain had revealed it to me. I had never felt pain before. I knew now I could be a coward.

"Was it so bad?" asked James in a strained voice.

"No," I said with a gasp. "It wasn't really. It wasn't bad at all. They've all been good to me."

"I would have been here last night except for the snow."

"Is it snowing?" I asked.

"Yes. Quite a lot."

"How funny. It was sunny yesterday—day before—whenever I came here." Here, since we'd finished with the weather, the conversation ran down.

But at this point the nun came back, with the Mother Superior in tow, and James had to go out in the hall and have a good thorough argument about being left alone with me. They went off finally, he must have promised to buy the hospital something, I wonder what. Anyway he came back and pulled a chair out and sat down facing me. I turned my head and managed a smile.

He said, "Di, I had a story all fixed up for you. I thought I'd tell it to you until the minute I walked in here. Dr. Frenet would have backed me up. So would the old girls. I had it all taken care of. You'd have believed it, too."

I must still have been misty from dope because I just blinked at him.

"A story," he said, and nodded his head. "A lie."

"What for?" I asked.

"To get rid of the baby. You had a little girl, Di. I was going to tell you it was dead. Frenet has a family that will adopt it—for a certain amount, of course. Enough to pay its keep."

I was still staring. "But why?"

"Because I can't—have the child. I'm sorry. It can't be done."

"Why should you?" I said. "I don't see—" Then I stopped. He was sitting and looking at me and waiting for me to understand. He was strong and patient and he didn't move at all. Not even to blink. I turned my head on the pillow. The window was small and the wall was thick, I could barely see that it was indeed snowing hard. He was asking me now if I wanted to come back, and I didn't have any answer.

I could go back to James, or I could keep my child.

"A girl," I said. "I was going to call a girl Claire."

"She's quite healthy," said James. He cleared his throat. "The doctor says she's—you know—fine. Nothing to worry about. She's perfect."

The tears began to run out of my eyes again.

"What would you do with her, Di?" said James. "How would you live? This is a good solid family, cousins of Frenet's, not here but south, he's a Walloon, not a Fleming. I didn't ask him where, even. He comes from Liége, some place around there. They want the money to buy another farm. They'd get enough income out of it to raise her decently and then give her the farm as her dowry. She'd—have a family, and roots, and all that. Wouldn't she be better off than—the way you'd have to live?"

I remembered then how he'd left me in the fall, by my door. "You said I could manage," I whispered.

"And you did. You managed all this without—without any fuss or trouble or being sorry for yourself. You did fine."

"Why shouldn't I—go on, then?"

James said, "Because I won't give you a penny, Di. Not a penny."

I turned back and looked at him instead of the snow.

"Oh, hell, I don't mean I won't pay Frenet and the nuns and everything till you're well and out of here. I'll give you enough to get home, too. After that—not a penny."

I stared at him.

"Look, Di," he said, "I can't. Not because I'm a monster, not because of anything I feel or don't feel, for you or anyone else. The law says that any child born to my wife while I still acknowledge her as my wife is legally my child and the heir to my property."

"But I don't—" I began. "But I would never—"

"I don't think you would. On the other hand, I didn't think you'd —leave me as you did in London. I had thought of the possibility, I had seen there was a danger, but I didn't honestly think you would. So I can't take a chance. Besides, whatever *you* might swear you would never do, you can't tell what she might do."

"She?"

"The child."

"The child! But—"

"Look, Diana, have you never heard of a contested will? Nothing you say or swear to now could take from her the right to contest any will of mine if you are my wife and acknowledged by me to be so when she's born."

"But—but I am! You're here! I mean—"

"No, dear, it's no good. I have divorce papers drawn, Di. I don't acknowledge you if you keep the child. I can't. I'm sorry."

After a while I asked, "And if I don't keep her?"

"Why, then it's up to you. There's no obligation."

"But you'd take me back."

"I'd be willing to try." He was sitting on that hard little nun's chair—neat, spare, wiry, his eyes alert and alive. In that bare room, that house of women all dressed alike, soft-footed, indistinguishable, his personality reached me like a strong, sharp odor. How long it was since I had seen anyone so intelligent, curious and aware as James was. So extremely, humanly, civilizedly able! So different, I'm afraid, from **Gerald**.

"And the divorce?" I asked.

"It could be stopped. I'd be taking a chance, of course. If I take you back I can't sue you again over—" He jerked his head to indicate Gerald.

"Oh, couldn't you?"

"No. If I take you back I condone it."

"I see."

"You'll have to think about it pretty carefully. I'll take the risk, but not unless you feel fairly sure you want to."

I was beginning to get misty again, and James's preposterous calm gave the scene a dreamlike quality. I felt as if I were negotiating, in a nightmare, some very complicated contract, on which the fate of heaven and earth hinged, with some powerful supernatural figure. I opened my eyes wide, but James's dark figure against the white wall seemed to float, ominous, portentous, not larger but more intense than life. "It isn't right," I said.

He blinked. "What isn't?" he asked warily.

"To sacrifice the baby. You're trying to make me forget it. You have everything on your side, but it wouldn't be right."

He sat taking in, I suppose, that I was tiring and not in control, for he spoke quite gently. "I won't press you, Di. I told you how things are and have to be with me. Keep her if you can manage. But consider whether *you* wouldn't be sacrificing her, in that case, sacrificing her to your pride. I think my plan is best. But rest a bit, and think, and I'll come back tomorrow." He stood up and came over to the bed and touched my hair. I watched his face dumbly. There was kindness in it, and tolerance, and patience, but no hope. I watched him out and I knew I would have to give her up. A nun came in to me, after a while, but she didn't bring the baby and I didn't ask for her.

Later—oh, later I got so I could forget all about that time, for months and months. It was because the whole thing was so far outside the rest of my life that it was like a tuck in time—eighteen months stitched up out of the way, and the fabric stretching strong, in the same pattern, on both sides of the seam. For years the only thing that reminded me that the tuck was there at all was when Mary or my mother spoke of my father's death. And they didn't do that often because they believed that I didn't like to be reminded of a time when I had been suffering from a nervous breakdown.

And yet underneath I never forgot. I went back to James and was his wife and two years after Claire was born we had a son. But if you've been at the end of your rope, you never forget it. That room in the hospital is as clear before my eyes today as if I'd been in it ten minutes ago, and James sitting there invested with my guilt until his quiet neat human person grew numinous and frightening with it. I gave up my child. No doubt I had no real choice and James was right. To keep her with me would have meant that he had to ruin me, and what could a ruined woman do for her daughter? And no doubt I brought it on myself, and Gerald was right about risks and jeopardy. That day in the hospital in Bruges was the necessary end of the action that began in Paris the day Gerald and I met. No choice. So I gave her up. But part of me went numb then, and wooden—crippled, I suppose. And crippled now, nodding across the years, I realize that ever since I have dragged a foot, needed a crutch, covered a deformity.

V   HUSBANDS

Hindrances

Here's me—married a man to reform him. I done it. And now I've got him on my hands.

—Mis' Bates, in *Mister Pitt*, a play
by ZONA GALE, 1925

I think today every intelligent woman will agree with me that the ethics of the marriage code are an impossible proposition for a free-spirited woman to accede to. If, in spite of this, intelligent women continue to marry, it is simply because they have not the courage to stand up for their convictions, and if you will read through a list of the divorces of the last ten years you will realize that what I say is true. Many women to whom I have preached the doctrine of freedom have weakly replied, "But who is to support the children?" It seems to me that if the marriage ceremony is needed as a protection to insure the enforced support of children, then you are marrying a man who, you suspect, would under certain conditions refuse to support his children, and it is a pretty low-down proposition. For you are marrying a man whom you already suspect of being a villain. But I have not so poor an opinion of men that I believe the greater percentage of them to be such low specimens of humanity.

—ISADORA DUNCAN, in *My Life*, 1927

My father unfortunately balked at beating me. My husbands did not. I have always been terrorized by physical violence. The indignity of it humiliates me. This was their ammunition. And I evidently drove them to use it.

Their inadequacies, their feeling of secondary position in the household, always led to resentment, bitterness and jealousy. When they yelled for Daddy and I answered, they lashed out at me in fury.

Why did they always stay to the bitter end? Why didn't they leave as they so often threatened to? I suppose, like children, they were afraid to leave home.

—BETTE DAVIS, in *The Lonely Life*, 1962

ELLEN GLASGOW [1932]

Ellen Glasgow (1874-1945), who was born in Richmond, Virginia, educated herself for the most part because of her delicate health. Though she never married, she was a master at portraying men, whether they were weak, like Jayson Greylock in Barren Ground, *or incurably romantic, like Judge Gamaliel Bland Honeywell in* The Romantic Comedians. *General Archbald is an interesting third variation.*

General Archbald

"The room is too close," General Archbald said, while he stooped to receive the embraces of his daughter and his daughter-in-law.

At seventy-five, he was a tall, spare, very erect old man, with features carved into nobility by tragic experience. Beneath the thick silver-gray hair, the eyebrows were still dark and beetling; the eagle nose was still betrayed by the sensitive mouth under the short gray mustache. Only his eyes, with their far inward gaze, were the eyes of a man who had been born out of his time. In his early years, before the War Between the States, he had lived much abroad; yet everywhere, even in his native Virginia, he had known that he was not a part of his age. The clock was set too far back, or, perhaps, too far ahead. But he could not make himself feel as the people about him felt; he could not bring himself to believe the things they believed.

For thirty years he had been a good husband to a woman he had married by accident, because, after a country dance from which they had stolen away alone, they had been caught out in a sleigh until the end of a snowstorm. . . . To save appearances (what had his whole life been but saving his own or some other person's appearance?), he had proposed the next morning to a comparative stranger; and to save appearances (though she had been in love with another man), she had accepted him. To save appearances, they had lived amicably together, and more in duty than in passion, they had brought three well-appearing children into the world.

The son, a handsome and engaging fellow, had been killed in a fox-hunt; but his widow, a woman with a genuine gift for managing people and events, occupied Richard's room in his father's house and Richard's chair at the table. Though she had been as good as a right hand to him, the General was fond of saying, she was the only person left in the world, since God had removed his wife, whom the old man not only respected but feared. For the last two years, while her presence brightened his home, the hardest battle of his life had been fought to a finish between them. With all his frustrated youth and his aging rebellious soul, he had longed to marry again. He had longed to seek and find his one brief hour of delight, and she had stood in his way. Mild, charming, implacable, with all the secret malice of destiny, she had stood in his way. Even when he had found the love he desired in his age—a slim, nunlike woman, young but not too young to be companionable, smiling up over her Prayer-Book in Saint Luke's Church—he had felt that his longing was hopeless because his daughter-in-law was the stronger.

After a heartbroken youth (for he had known tragic passion), after thirty years of heroic fidelity in an age when marriage was an invisible prison, he had been obliged to sacrifice that fading glimmer of happiness. Supported by his daughters, who demanded that he should be faithful to a wife he had never loved, supported by public opinion, which exacted that he should remain inconsolable for the loss of a woman he had married by accident, his son's widow had stood, small, plump, immovable as the rock of ages, between him and his desire. Thirty years, and God alone would ever know what those years had meant to him! Not that he had wished for his wife's death. Not that he had failed in the obligations of marriage. But in that shared confinement of thirty years, in that lifelong penalty he had paid for an accident, for a broken sleigh, for being caught out in a snowstorm, there had been flashes of impulse in which he had asked himself, "How long shall I be able to live like this?"

Yet he had endured it. For thirty years, day and night, waking, sleeping, in sickness and in health, having children, as married persons are expected to do—for thirty years he had sacrificed his youth, his middle age, his dreams, his imagination, all the vital instincts that make a man, to the moral earnestness of tradition. Well, he had lived through it. He had lived through it until, at seventy-one, just as he had reached the turn in a long life when a man, if he has been prudent, still retains vigor enough for a last flare at the end— just as he had reached this turn in his life, Erminia had died, and release had come like a blow.

She had died, and immediately, so unreasonable are the ways of the heart, he had been overcome by regret. Almost to his astonishment, he had felt her loss, he had grieved for her, he had reproached himself bitterly. Lying in her coffin, with that defenseless smile on her lips and a wisp of tulle hiding her throat, she had appealed to his tenderness more deeply than she had ever appealed to his passion. In the days that followed, he had suffered as a man suffers who loses an aching limb. But regret, he discovered before six months had gone, is not among the enduring realities. "When the year is over," he had told himself, meeting his daughter-in-law's brimming eyes with a shiver of apprehension, "even if I wait until the year is over, I shall be still young enough to find a little happiness at the end." Already, though he had been a faithful husband, he knew where happiness might be found. He had seen the nunlike figure and the dove's eyes of a joy that was young, and yet not too young to be companionable to restful age. Well, a year, even at seventy-one, is not everlasting.

But at the end of the first year, his two daughters were still shrouded in mourning, and poor Etta's reason was almost despaired of; at the end of the second year, his son's widow failed in her endeavor and came with her only child to live in his house; and at the end of the third year, the fatherless little girl had twined herself about the roots of his heart. Even then, with three women and one little girl making a home for him, he had not relinquished the hope of his Indian summer of happiness—that patient hope of the old, so much less elastic and so much more enduring than the hope of the young.

Yet, in the end, this also was slowly strangled by life. By life, and by the suffocating grasp of appearances. How could he spoil the lives of three women and one fatherless little girl? How could he bring his joy with the dove's eyes into a house which was already filled with these three women and one little girl tenderly making a home for him? If they had not been so devoted, it might have been easier; but love, as marriage had taught him (for his wife also had loved him before the end of their honeymoon), is responsible for most of the complications of life.

CLARE BOOTHE   *[1937]*

Clare Boothe (Clare Boothe Luce), who was educated at private schools, is an ex-congresswoman and ex-ambassador as well as a playwright. In her writings, she directs her satiric thrusts chiefly at her own sex, but she knows how different sorts of women feel about straying husbands, as she shows us in the first act of The Women. *That her audience responded to her comments is well attested by the fact that the play ran for 657 performances in New York City.*

The Women, Act One

Scene I

Mary Haines' living room. Today, Park Avenue living rooms are decorated with a significant indifference to the fact that ours is still a bisexual society. Period peacock alleys, crystal-hung prima-donna roosts, they reflect the good taste of their mistresses in everything but a consideration of the master's pardonable right to fit in his own home decor. Mary Haines' living room is not like that. It would be thought a comfortable room by a man. This, without sacrificing its own subtle, feminine charm. Above the fireplace, there is a charming portrait of Mary's children—a girl of 11, a boy of 5 or 6. Right, a door to the living quarters. Left, another to the hall. Center, a sofa, armchair, tea-table group; and in the good light from the window, a bridge-table group.

As the curtain rises, Jane, *a pretty, and quite correct little Irish-American maid, is arranging the tea-table.* Four Women *are playing bridge in a smoking-car cloud of smoke. They are:*

Nancy, *who is sharp, but not acid; sleek but not smart; a worldly and yet virginal 35. And her partner—*

Peggy, *who is pretty, sweet, 25.* Peggy's *character has not, will never quite "jell." And—*

Sylvia, *who is glassy, elegant, feline, 34. And her partner—*

Edith, *who is a sloppy, expensively dressed (currently by Lane Bryant) matron of 33 or 34. Indifferent to everything but self,* Edith *is incapable of either deliberate maliciousness or spontaneous generosity.*

SYLVIA. So I said to Howard, "What do you expect me to do? Stay home and darn your socks? What do we all have money for? Why do we keep servants?"

NANCY. You don't keep them long, God knows—(*Placing the pack of cards.*) Yours, Peggy.

PEGGY. Isn't it Mrs. Potter's? I opened with four spades. (SYLVIA *firmly places the pack before* PEGGY. PEGGY, *wrong again, deals.*)

SYLVIA. Second hand, you did. And went down a thousand. (*Patronizingly.*) Peggy, my pet, you can't afford it.

PEGGY. I can too, Sylvia. I'm not a pauper.

SYLVIA. If your bridge doesn't improve, you soon will be.

NANCY. Oh, shut up, Sylvia. She's only playing till Mary comes down.

SYLVIA (*querulously*). Jane, what's Mrs. Haines doing up there?

JANE (*reproachfully*). It's that lingerie woman *you* sent her, Mrs. Fowler.

SYLVIA. I didn't expect Mrs. Haines to buy anything. I was just trying to get rid of the creature. (JANE *exits.*) Peggy, bid.

PEGGY. Oh, mine? By.

SYLVIA (*looking at* PEGGY). She won't concentrate.

NANCY. She's in love, bless her. After the child's been married as long as you girls, she may be able to concentrate on vital matters like bridge.

SYLVIA (*bored*). Another lecture on the Modern Woman?

NANCY. At the drop of a hat. By.

SYLVIA. I consider myself a perfectly good wife. I've sacrificed a lot for Howard Fowler—two spades. I devote as much time to my children as any of my friends.

NANCY. Except Mary.

SYLVIA. Oh, Mary, of course. Mary is an exception to all of us.

NANCY. Quite right. (*They are waiting for* PEGGY *again.*) Peggy?

PEGGY (*uncertainly*). Two no trumps? (EDITH *rises suddenly. Plainly, she feels squeamish.*)

SYLVIA (*wearily*). Edith, not *again?*

EDITH. I shouldn't have eaten that alligator pear. Morning sickness! I heave the whole darn day. This is positively the last time I go through this lousy business for any man! Four spades. If men had to bear babies, there'd never be—

NANCY.—more than one child in a family. And he'd be a boy. By. (EDITH *sinks on the edge of her chair, lays down her cards.*)

PEGGY. I wish *I* were having a baby. We can't afford one now.

SYLVIA. And you'll never be able to, until you know Culbertson. (*Arranging* EDITH's *cards.*) Honestly, Edith! Why didn't you show a slam?

EDITH (*rising hurriedly*). Oh, I *have* got to unswallow. Wait till you've had three, Peggy. You'd wish you'd never gotten past the bees and flowers. (*Exits precipitously.*)

NANCY (*disgusted*). Poor, frightened, bewildered madonna!

SYLVIA. I'm devoted to Edith Potter. But she does get me down. You'd think she had a hard time. Dr. Briggs says she's like shelling peas. She ought to go through what *I* went through. Nobody *knows!*

NANCY. No clubs, partner?

SYLVIA. So when Cynthia came, I had a Cæsarian. You should see my stomach— It's a slam!

NANCY. Are you sure?

SYLVIA. Got the king, Peggy? (PEGGY *obligingly plays the king.*) Thanks, dear, it's a slam. And the rubber. (*Rises, lights a fresh cigarette, goes to armchair and perches.*) But I've kept my figure. I must say, I don't blame Phelps Potter for playing around.

PEGGY. Oh, does her husband . . . ?

SYLVIA. Oh, Phelps has made passes at all us girls. I do think it's bad taste for a man to try to make his wife's friends, *especially* when he's bald and fat. I told him once, "Phelps Potter," I said, "the next time you grab at me, I'm going straight to Edith."

NANCY. And did you?

SYLVIA. Certainly not. I wouldn't say anything to hurt Edith for the world. Well, you can't blame the men. But I'll say one thing for Edith. She's not as dumb as *some* of my friends. She's on to her husband.

PEGGY *(bravely)*. Do you think *he* is on to her?

SYLVIA. What do you mean?

PEGGY. If he could only hear her talk about him!

SYLVIA. Listen, Peggy, do we know how men talk about us when we're not around?

NANCY. I've heard rumors.

SYLVIA. Exactly. Peggy, you haven't been married long enough to form a private opinion of your husband.

PEGGY. Well, if I had one, I'd keep it to myself. Do you think I'd tell anybody in the world about the quarrels John and I have over money? I'd be too proud! *(Enter* EDITH. *Goes to tea-table, and gathers a handful of sandwiches.)*

SYLVIA. All over, dear?

EDITH. Oh, that was a false alarm. What happened?

SYLVIA. Only a slam, dear. You do underbid.

EDITH. I'll bet you had me on the pan.

SYLVIA. I never say behind my friends' backs what I won't say to their faces. I said you ought to diet.

EDITH. There's no use dieting in my condition. I've got to wait until I can begin from scratch. Besides, I've got the most wonderful cook. She was with Mary. She said Mary let her go because she was too extravagant. I think this cook Mary has is too, too homey. *(Examines sandwich.)* Water cress. I'd just as soon eat my way across a front lawn.

SYLVIA. I think Mary's gone off terribly this winter. Have you noticed those deep lines, here? *(Draws her finger around her mouth.)*

NANCY. Smiling lines. Tragic, aren't they?

SYLVIA. Perhaps they *are*. Maybe a woman's headed for trouble when she begins to get too—smug.

NANCY. Smug? Don't you mean, happy?

PEGGY. Mr. Haines adores her so!

SYLVIA. *(snickering and flashing* EDITH *a significant glance)*. Yes, doesn't he?

NANCY *(coldly)*. You just can't bear it, Sylvia, can you?

SYLVIA. Bear what?

NANCY. Mary's happiness. It gets you down.

SYLVIA. Nancy Blake, if there's one thing I can say for myself, I've never been jealous of another woman. Why should I be jealous of Mary?

NANCY. Because she's contented. Contented to be what she is.

SYLVIA. Which is what?

NANCY. A woman.

EDITH. And what, in the name of my revolting condition, are we?

NANCY. Females.

SYLVIA. Really. And what are you, pet?

NANCY. What nature abhors, I'm—a virgin—a frozen asset.

EDITH. I wish I were a virgin again. The only fun I ever had was holding out on Phelps. Nancy, you ought to thank God every night you don't have to make sacrifices for some man.

PEGGY. I wish I could make a little money, writing the way you do, Miss Blake.

NANCY. If you wrote the way I do, that's just what you'd make.

SYLVIA. You're not exactly a popular author, are you, dear?

NANCY. Not with you. Well, good news, Sylvia. My book is finished and once again I'm about to leave your midst.

PEGGY. Oh, I wish we could afford to travel. Where do you go this time, Miss Blake?

NANCY. Africa, shooting.

SYLVIA. Well, darling, I don't blame you. I'd rather face a tiger any day than the sort of things the critics said about your last book. (*Enter* MARY. *She is a lovely woman in her middle thirties. She is what most of us think our happily married daughters are like. She is carrying several white boxes.*)

MARY. Sorry, girls. (*Teasing.*) Sylvia, must you always send me woebegone creatures like that lingerie woman? It's been a very expensive half hour for me.

PEGGY (*looking at* SYLVIA). For me, too, Mrs. Haines.

MARY (*laughing*). Nonsense, Peggy, you were playing for me. Here. (*Hands* PEGGY *a box.*) Don't open it now. It's a bed-jacket. Or a tea cozy. Or something padded. I wouldn't know. I was crying so hard.

SYLVIA. You didn't believe that woman's sob story?

MARY. Of course I did. (*She really didn't.*) Anyway, she's a lot worse off than you and I. (*Putting down another box.*) Edith, wee garments—

EDITH. Darling, how sweet! (*It comes over her again.*) Oh, my God! I'm sick as a cat. (*Sits.*)

SYLVIA. It's a girl. Girls always make you sicker.

NANCY. Even before they're born?

EDITH. I don't care what it is. I've lost everything including my curiosity. Why did God make it take nine months?

NANCY (*helpfully*). It takes an elephant seven years.

EDITH. I wish I were an elephant. I'll look like one anyway before I'm finished. And it would be heaven not to worry for seven years.

MARY (*laughing*). Oh, Edith, it is rather trying. But when it's all over, isn't it the grandest thing in the world to have them?

EDITH. Well, I'd love mine just as much if they came out of cabbages.

NANCY. And I dare say your husband would hardly notice the difference.

JANE (*entering with teakettle*). Ma'am, Mr. Haines would like to speak to you on the phone.

MARY. Oh, I can feel what it is in my bones, Jane. (*To the others.*) Stephen's going to be kept at the office again tonight. (*Exits.*)

SYLVIA. Give him my love, pet.

MARY (*offstage*). I will.

SYLVIA (*she never lets anything pass*). Nancy, you couldn't be more wrong about me and Mary.

NANCY. Still rankling?

SYLVIA. Jealous? As a matter of fact, I'm sorry for her.

NANCY. Oh-ho? Why?

SYLVIA (*mysteriously*). Well, for all *we* know she may be living in a fool's paradise with Stephen.

NANCY. Let's check that one for a moment, Sylvia. Jane, are the children in?

JANE. Yes. Miss. Just back from the Park. (EDITH *rises*—SYLVIA, *in pantomime, signals her not to leave room. This is not lost on* NANCY. *For a moment she hesitates at the door.*)

PEGGY. Oh, I'd love to see Mrs. Haines' little girl, Miss Blake—

NANCY *(following* PEGGY). Come along, child. Anyway, it's our turn to go on the pan. But we don't have to worry. You've got a poor man. I've got no man at all. *(They exit.)*

EDITH *(goes to tea-table—pours two cups.* JANE *empties ash-trays).* This is positively the last time I play bridge with Nancy. She never misses a chance to get in a dig. What has a creature like her got but her friends? *(*JANE *exits, closing door, left.* SYLVIA *stealthily closes door, right.)* The way she kept at you about Mary made me so nervous, I thought I'd scream. And in my condition—

SYLVIA. Edith, I've got to tell you! I'll burst if I wait!

EDITH. I *knew* you had something! *(She brings her well-laden plate and teacup and settles herself happily beside* SYLVIA *on the sofa.)*

SYLVIA. You'll die!

EDITH. Mary?

SYLVIA. No, Stephen. Guess!

EDITH. You couldn't mean . . . ?

SYLVIA *(nodding)*. Stephen Haines is cheating on Mary!

EDITH. I don't believe you; is it true?

SYLVIA. Wait till you hear. *(Now she is into it.)* You know I go to Michael's for my hair. You ought to go, pet. I despise whoever does yours. Well, there's the most wonderful new manicurist there. *(Shows her scarlet nails.)* Isn't that divine? Jungle Red—

EDITH. Simply divine. Go on.

SYLVIA. It all came out in the most extraordinary way, this morning. I tried to get you on the phone—

EDITH. I was in the tub. Go on.

SYLVIA. This manicurist, she's marvelous, was **doing** my nails. I was looking through *Vogue,* the one with Mary in the Beaux Arts Ball costume—

EDITH. —in that white wig that flattered her so much?

SYLVIA *(nodding)*. Well, this manicurist: "Oh, Mrs. Fowler," she said, "is that that Mrs. Haines who's so awfully rich?"

EDITH. Funny how people like that think people like us are awfully rich.

SYLVIA. I forget what she said next. You know how those creatures are, babble, babble, babble, babble, and never let up for a minute! When suddenly she said: "I know the girl who's being *kept* by Mr. Haines!"

EDITH. No!

SYLVIA. I swear!

EDITH (*thrilled*). Someone *we* know?

SYLVIA. No! That's what's so awful about it. She's a friend of this manicurist. Oh, it wouldn't be so bad if Stephen had picked someone in his own class. But a blond floosie!

EDITH. But how did Stephen ever meet a girl like that?

SYLVIA. How do men ever meet girls like that? That's what they live for, the rats!

EDITH. But—

SYLVIA. I can't go into all the details, now. They're utterly fantastic—

EDITH. You suppose Mary knows?

SYLVIA. Mary's the kind who couldn't help showing it.

EDITH (*nodding, her mouth full of her third cake*). No self-control. Well, she's bound to find out. If a woman's got any instincts, she feels when her husband's off the reservation. I know *I would*.

SYLVIA. Of course you do, darling. Not Mary— (*Rises, and walks about the room, wrestling with* MARY's *sad problem.*) If only there were some way to *warn* her!

EDITH (*horrified, following her*). Sylvia! You're not going to tell her?

SYLVIA. Certainly not. I'd *die* before I'd be the one to hurt her like that!

EDITH. Couldn't someone shut that manicurist up?

SYLVIA. A good story like that? A lot those girls care whose life they ruin.

EDITH. *Isn't* it a dirty trick?

SYLVIA. Isn't it *foul?* It's not as though only Mary's friends knew. We could keep our mouths shut.

EDITH. I know plenty that I never *breathe* about my friends' husbands!

SYLVIA. So do I. *(They exchange a sudden glance of sharp suspicion.)* Anyway, the whole thing's disgustingly unfair to Mary. I feel like a disloyal skunk, just knowing about it—

EDITH. I adore her—

SYLVIA. I *worship* her. She's my dearest friend in all the world— *(Voices, off-stage. They sit down at the card-table and begin to play solitaire hastily. Enter* NANCY *and* PEGGY.*)*

NANCY. Well, Sylvia, feeling better?

SYLVIA *(innocently)*. Meaning what?

NANCY. Must've been choice. You both look so *relaxed.*

SYLVIA. Nancy, were you listening in that door?

PEGGY. Oh, Mrs. Fowler, we were in the nursery. *(MARY enters.)*

SYLVIA *(quickly)*. Well, darling, how is Stephen, the old dear? And did you give him my love?

MARY. I did. Stephen's not so well, Sylvia.

SYLVIA. Oh? What's the trouble?

MARY. Nervous indigestion. That's why I have such a plain cook now.

EDITH. Phelps has had indigestion for years. You should hear that man rumble in the night. Like a truck on cobblestones.

SYLVIA. There's nothing—worrying Stephen?

MARY. Oh, no, he's just been working late. He's not coming home to-night. Oh, I wish—*(Abruptly, with an indulgent laugh.)* Well, man's love is of man's life a thing apart, 'tis woman's whole—et cetera.

SYLVIA. Are you sure it's *work,* darling, and not a beautiful blond?

MARY. Stephen? *(Laughing, and perhaps a little smugly, too.)* Oh, Sylvia.

EDITH *(afraid that* SYLVIA *will go too far)*. Sylvia, let's play!

SYLVIA. Stephen's a very attractive man.

MARY. Isn't he? I can't imagine why he hasn't deserted me for some glamorous creature long ago.

NANCY (*alarmed*). Mary, you *do* sound smug.

MARY. Oh, let me be, Nancy. How can you be too sure of what you believe in most?

SYLVIA. I wouldn't be sure of the Apostle Paul. I always tell Howard, "If you ever manage to make a fool of me, I'll deserve what I get."

NANCY. You certainly will. (*Faces* SYLVIA *squarely*.) Now, Sylvia, let's have it.

SYLVIA. Have what?

NANCY. Just what did you mean when you said Mary was living in a fool's paradise?

MARY. What?

SYLVIA (*angrily*). Nancy, don't be absurd. (*A pause. Then, wriggling out of it.*) Oh, Mary, I was just trying to make a typical Nancy Blake wisecrack about marriage. I said, "A woman's paradise is always a fool's paradise!"

MARY. That's not bad, is it, Nancy? Well, Sylvia, whatever I'm living in, I like it. Nancy, cut.

SYLVIA (SYLVIA *examines her nails minutely, suddenly shows them to* MARY). Mary, how do you like that?

NANCY (*not looking*). Too, too adorable.

SYLVIA. You can't imagine how it stays on. I get it at Michael's—you ought to go, Mary!

EDITH (*protestingly*). Oh, Sylvia—

SYLVIA. A wonderful new manicurist. Olga's her name. She's marvelous.

EDITH. Will you cut, Sylvia?

SYLVIA. Look, Jungle Red.

NANCY. Looks as if you'd been tearing at somebody's throat.

SYLVIA. I'll be damned, Nancy, if I'll let you ride me any more!

MARY. Now, Sylvia, Nancy's just being clever, too.

SYLVIA. She takes a crack at everything about me. Even my nails!

MARY (*laughing*). Well, I like it. I really do! It's new and smart. (*Pats her hand.*) Michael's, Olga, Jungle Red? I'll remember that. (*Cuts cards.*) You and I, Sylvia. I feel lucky today.

SYLVIA (*with a sweet, pitying smile.*) Do you, darling? Well, you know what they say, "Lucky in cards"—

CURTAIN

SCENE II

An afternoon, a few days later. A hairdressing booth in Michael's. An elegantly functional cubbyhole. Right, a recessed mirror in the wall. Left, from the high partition pole, a curtain to the floor. The rear wall is a plain partition. Center, a swivel hairdressing chair. Above it, from an aluminum tree, the hanging thicket of a permanent-wave machine. In the wall, gadgets for curling irons, electric outlets which connect with wires to the drying machines, the hand drier, the manicurists' table-light, stools for the pedicurist, the manicurist, OLGA.

As the curtain rises, the booth is, to put it mildly, full.

MRS. WAGSTAFF, *a fat, elderly woman is in the chair, undergoing the punishment of a permanent. Wires and clamps, Medusa-like, rise from her head, to the cap of the machine.*

OLGA, *at her right, is doing her nails. Her fat bare feet rest in the lap of the* PEDICURIST. *The* FIRST HAIRDRESSER *cools her steaming locks with a hand-drier. The* SECOND HAIRDRESSER, *watch in hand, fiddles with the wires, times the operation. When the machine is working, a small red, light glows among the wires.*

MRS. WAGSTAFF, *apparently inured to public execution, smokes, reads a magazine on her lap, occasionally nibbles a sandwich which the* MANICURIST *passes her from a tray near her instruments. The drier, whenever it is on, makes a loud noise, drowning out voices, which must be harshly raised above it. Now the drier is on, the voices loud.*

MRS. WAGSTAFF. It's burning my neck!

SECOND HAIRDRESSER. Be brave! One minute more!

MRS. WAGSTAFF (*in pain*). O-o-oo!

FIRST HAIRDRESSER. It's going to be so worth it, Mrs. Wagstaff.

MRS. WAGSTAFF. My ears!

SECOND HAIRDRESSER. Be brave!

MRS. WAGSTAFF. O-o-o-o! My nerves— Oo—my God! *(To* PEDICURIST*)* My sandwich—(OLGA *hands her sandwich.)*

SECOND HAIRDRESSER. Ten seconds. We must suffer to be beautiful. *(The curtain parts;* A FIGURE *in flowing white half-enters. It is, judging by the voice, a woman, but its face is completely obliterated by a mud-mask.)*

MUD-MASK. Oh, pardon—I thought I was in here. Why, hello, Mrs. Wagstaff. *(Coyly.)* Guess who I am? *(A second* FACE *appears over this intruder's shoulder. At first, it looks like another mud-mask. It's not. It's the* COLORED MAID, EUPHIE. *She clutches the shoulder of the mud-mask.)*

EUPHIE. Mustn't talk, ma'am. You'll crack yo'self. *(Exit* MUD-MASK *followed by* EUPHIE.*)*

MRS. WAGSTAFF. Who was it?

FIRST HAIRDRESSER. Mrs. Phipps— *(Switches off the drier. Now they all lower their voices to a normal pitch.)* There, dear, the agony's over. *(They take the permanent clamps off* MRS. WAGSTAFF's *hair. A drier is on in the next booth. A voice is heard off-stage, screaming above it.)*

VOICE. —so I feel awful. I ate a lobster at the opening of the Ritz— *(The drier goes off.)*

OLGA *(To* MRS. WAGSTAFF*).* Mrs. Mordie Barnes. She's been in the hospital. It wasn't ptomaine at all. It was a mis—

SECOND HAIRDRESSER. Olga! She'll hear you—

MRS. WAGSTAFF *(thoughtfully).* I think I'll have a mud-mask.

SECOND HAIRDRESSER *(calling outside).* Euphie! Tell the desk Mrs. Wagstaff's working in a mud!

MRS. WAGSTAFF *(enviously).* Mrs. Phipps has such a lovely skin.

FIRST HAIRDRESSER. Not lovelier than yours, Mrs. Wagstaff.

CHORUS (SECOND HAIRDRESSER, OLGA, PEDICURIST). Oh, yours is lovely! Why, not nearly as lovely! Lovelier than yours?

MRS. WAGSTAFF *(coyly).* I do think it's rather good for a woman my age.

FIRST HAIRDRESSER. You talk as if you were an old woman, dear.

MRS. WAGSTAFF *(lying).* I'm 42.

SECOND HAIRDRESSER. Mustn't tell anyone. You don't look a day over 35!

CHORUS (SECOND HAIRDRESSER, PEDICURIST, OLGA). Why, no one would believe it! Why, not a day! Oh, you don't look it!

SECOND HAIRDRESSER. —now you've gotten so much slimmer!

MRS. WAGSTAFF. I have slimmed down, haven't I?

CHORUS (PEDICURIST, OLGA, FIRST HAIRDRESSER). Oh, thin as a shadow! Why, terribly thin! Oh, just right, now!

MRS. WAGSTAFF (*admiring her nail polish*). That's lovely.

OLGA. Jungle Red. Everybody loves it. Do you know Mrs. Howard Fowler?

PEDICURIST (*rising, gathering up her things*). Don't put your stockings on yet, Mrs. Wagstaff, you'll smear your beautiful big toe— (*Exits.*)

OLGA. They say Mr. Fowler made a fortune in some stock. But one of the ladies Mrs. Fowler sent in was telling me Mr. Fowler does like to drink! Only the other day—

FIRST HAIRDRESSER (*sharply*). We're ready now, Mrs. Wagstaff. (*Gets* MRS. WAGSTAFF *up.*) We'll unwind you in the shampoo (*Calling.*) Euphie!

SECOND HAIRDRESSER (*taking* MRS. WAGSTAFF *to door*). This way, dear. How does your permanent feel? And it's going to look lovely, too— (SECOND HAIRDRESSER *herds* MRS. WAGSTAFF *out of the booth,* MRS. WAGSTAFF *walking on her heels, her toes still wadded with cotton. Enter* EUPHIE, *who, during the ensuing dialogue, cleans up the debris on the floor of the booth*).

OLGA. That old gasoline truck! Fifty-two if she's a day!

FIRST HAIRDRESSER. One more permanent and she won't have a hair left on her head.

OLGA. There's plenty on her upper lip.

EUPHIE. She sho' does shed, don't she?

OLGA. Any woman who's fool enough to marry a man ten years younger! Know what a client told me? Her husband's a pansy! (HAIRDRESSER *exits followed by* OLGA.)

SECOND HAIRDRESSER (*entering*). Ready?

EUPHIE. Yes, ma'am. (*The* SECOND HAIRDRESSER *holds back the curtain.*)

MARY (*off-stage*). So I woke up this morning and decided for no reason at all to change the way— (*She enters, followed by* NANCY.) I do my hair. (*Exit* EUPHIE.)

SECOND HAIRDRESSER. Mr. Michaels will be ten minutes, ma'am. Anyone in particular for your manicure?

MARY. Who does Mrs. Fowler's nails?

HAIRDRESSER. Olga. I'll see. (*Exits.*)

NANCY. God, I'd love to do Mrs. Fowler's nails, right down to the wrist, with a nice big buzz saw.

MARY. Sylvia's all right. She's a good friend underneath.

NANCY. Underneath what?

MARY. Nancy, you don't humor your friends enough.

NANCY. So that's the big idea coming here? You're humoring Sylvia?

MARY. Oh, you did hurt her. I had it all over again at lunch. (*She catches a glimpse of herself in the mirror.*) Nancy, am I getting old?

NANCY. Who put that in your head? Sylvia?

MARY. Tell me the truth.

NANCY. Beauty is in the eye of the beholder, and twaddle to that effect.

MARY. But it's such a scary feeling when you see those little wrinkles creeping in.

NANCY. Time's little mice.

MARY. And that first gleam of white in your hair. It's the way you'd feel about autumn if you knew there'd never be another spring—

NANCY (*abruptly*). There's only one tragedy for a woman.

MARY. Growing old?

NANCY. Losing her man.

MARY. That's why we're all so afraid of growing old.

NANCY. Are you afraid?

MARY. Well, I was very pretty when I was young. I never thought about it twice then. Now I know it's why Stephen loved me.

NANCY. Smart girl.

MARY. Now I think about it all the time.

NANCY. Love is not love which alters when it alteration finds. Shakespeare.

MARY. Well, he told me, on my birthday, I'd always look the same to him.

NANCY. Nice present. No jewels?

MARY. It rained that day. He brought me a bottle of perfume called "Summer Rain."

NANCY. How many ounces?

MARY. Nancy, you've never been in love.

NANCY. Says who?

MARY (*surprised*). Have you?

NANCY. Yes.

MARY. You never told me.

NANCY. You never asked— (*Wistfully.*) Neither did *he*. (OLGA *enters with fresh bowl of water.*) Here, innocent. (*Gives a book to* MARY.) The book my readers everywhere have been waiting for with such marked apathy.

MARY. "All the Dead Ladies"?

NANCY. Originally called, "From the Silence of the Womb." My publisher thought that would make too much noise.

MARY. What's it about? (OLGA *begins to file* MARY's *nails.*)

NANCY. Women I dislike: "Ladies"—

MARY. Oh, Nancy!

OLGA. Don't soak it yet. (*Taking* MARY's *hand out of the water.*)

NANCY. No good? Too bad. It's a parting shot. I'm off.

MARY. Off?

NANCY. Africa.

MARY. But not today?

NANCY. I knew if I told you you'd scurry around and do things. A party. Steamer baskets of sour fruit. Not nearly as sour as the witty cables your girl friends would send me— So don't move. No tears. For my sake—just soak it? Good-bye, Mary—

MARY. Good-bye, Nancy. I'll miss you.

NANCY. I doubt it. Practically nobody ever misses a clever woman. (*Exits.*)

OLGA. Funny, isn't she?

MARY. She's a darling.

OLGA (*filing* MARY's *nails*). She's a writer? How do those writers think up those plots? I guess the plot part's not so hard to think up as the end. I guess anybody's life'd make a interesting plot if it had a interesting end— Mrs. Fowler sent you in? (MARY, *absorbed in her book, nods.*) She's sent me three clients this week. Know Mrs. Herbert Parrish that was Mrs. Malcolm Leeds? Well, Mrs. Parrish was telling me herself about her divorce. Seems Mr. Parrish came home one night with lipstick on his undershirt. Said he always explained everything before. But *that* was something he just wasn't going to try to explain. Know Mrs. Potter? She's awful pregnant—

MARY (*she wants to read*). I know.

OLGA. Soak it, please. (*Puts* MARY's *hand in water. Begins on other hand.*) Know Mrs. Stephen Haines?

MARY. What? Why, yes, I—

OLGA. I guess Mrs. Fowler's told you about that! Mrs. Fowler feels awfully sorry for her.

MARY (*laughing*). Oh, she does! Well, I don't. I—

OLGA. You would if you knew this girl.

MARY. What girl?

OLGA. This Crystal Allen.

MARY. Crystal Allen?

OLGA. Yes, you know. The girl who's living with Mr. Haines. (MARY *starts violently.*) Don't you like the file? Mrs. Potter says it sets her unborn child's teeth on edge.

MARY (*indignant*). Whoever told you such a thing?

OLGA. Oh, I thought you knew. Didn't Mrs. Fowler—?

MARY. No—

OLGA. Then you will be interested. You see, Crystal Allen is a friend of mine. She's really a terrible man-trap. Soak it, please. (MARY, *dazed, puts her hand in the dish.*) She's behind the perfume counter at Saks'. So was I before I got fi—left. That's how she met him.

MARY. Stephen Haines?

OLGA. Yeah. It was a couple a months ago. Us girls wasn't busy. It was an awful rainy day, I remember. So this gentleman walks up to the counter. He was the serious type, nice-looking, but kind of thin on top. Well, Crystal nabs him. "I want some perfume," he says. "May I awsk what type of woman for?" Crystal says, very ritzy. That didn't mean a thing. She was going to sell him Summer Rain, our feature, anyway. "Is she young?" Crystal says. "No," he says, sort of embarrassed. "Is she the glamorous type?" Crystal says. "No, thank God," he says. "Thank God?" Crystal says and bats her eyes. She's got those eyes which run up and down a man like a searchlight. Well, she puts perfume on her palm and in the crook of her arm for him to smell. So he got to smelling around and I guess he liked it. Because we heard him tell her his name, which one of the girls recognized from Cholly Knickerbocker's column—Gee, you're nervous—Well, it was after that I left. I wouldn't of thought no more about it. But a couple of weeks ago I stopped by where Crystal lives to say hello. And the landlady says she'd moved to the kind of house where she could entertain her gentleman friend—"What gentleman friend?" I says. "Why, that Mr. Haines that she's had up in her room all hours of the night," the landlady says—Did I hurt? (MARY *draws her hand away.*) One coat, or two? (*Picks up a red bottle.*)

MARY. None. (*Rises and goes to the chair, where she has left her purse.*)

OLGA. But I thought that's what you came for? All Mrs. Fowler's friends—

MARY. I think I've gotten what all Mrs. Fowler's friends came for. (*Puts coin on the table.*)

OLGA (*picks up coin*). Oh, thanks—Well, good-bye. I'll tell her you were in, Mrs. —?

MARY. Mrs. Stephen Haines.

OLGA. Mrs. —? Oh, gee, gee! Gee, Mrs. Haines—I'm sorry! Oh, isn't there something I can do?

MARY. Stop telling that story!

OLGA. Oh, sure, sure, I will!

MARY. And please, don't tell anyone— (*Her voice breaks*) that you told it to *me*—

OLGA. Oh, I won't, gee, I promise! Gee, that would be kind of humiliating for you! (*Defensively.*) But in a way, Mrs. Haines, I'm kinda *glad* you know. Crystal's a terrible girl—I mean, she's terribly clever. And she's terribly pretty, Mrs. Haines—I mean, if I was you I wouldn't waste no time getting Mr. Haines away from her— (MARY *turns abruptly away.*) I mean, now you *know*, Mrs. Haines!

(OLGA *eyes the coin in her hand distastefully, suddenly puts it down on the table and exits.* MARY, *alone, stares blankly in the mirror, then suddenly focusing on her image, leans forward, searching her face between her trembling hands. A drier goes on in the next booth. A shrill voice rises above its drone.*)

VOICE. —Not too hot! My sinus! So *she* said: "I wouldn't want anybody in the world to know," and *I* said: "My dear, you know you can trust *me!*"

CURTAIN

SCENE III

An hour later. MARY's *boudoir. Charming, of course. A door to bedroom, right. A door to the hall, left. A chaise-longue; next to it, a table with books, flowers, a telephone. A dressing table.*

As the curtain rises, MARY *is discovered on the chaise-longue, trying to read.* JANE *enters from the hall. She is upset about something. She keeps daubing at her eyes.*

MARY. Tea, Jane?

JANE. It's coming, ma'am.

MARY. My mother will be here in a few minutes. A cup for her.

JANE. Yes, ma'am. (*Sniffling.*) Ma'am—

MARY. And tell Cook please, dinner on time. We're going to the theater. Mr. Haines likes to be there for the curtain. I'll wear my old black, Jane.

JANE (*looking nervously at the door behind her*). Yes, ma'am.

MARY. No, I'll wear my new blue, Jane.

JANE. Ma'am, it's Cook. She wants to see you. (*Defensively.*) It's about *me*. She says I—

MARY. Later, Jane.

JANE. Don't you believe a word she says, ma'am. It's all his fault.

MARY (*aware of* JANE's *distress for the first time*). Whose fault?

JANE. Her husband's. Ford's.

MARY (*surprised*). What's the matter with Ford? He's a very good butler.

JANE. Oh, he does his work, ma'am. But you don't know how he is in the pantry. Always kidding around with us girls. He don't mean any harm, but Cook— (*Enter* COOK *abruptly with* MARY's *tea tray. She is a fat, kind woman, with a strong Scandinavian accent. At the moment she is very mad.*)

COOK. Afternoon, ma'am. (*Glaring at* JANE.) I'd like to talk to you alone, ma'am.

JANE. I told you, it isn't my fault.

COOK. You led him on!

JANE. I didn't. (*Bursting into tears.*) I've been with Mrs. Haines seven years. She knows I never make trouble downstairs. (*Exits to hall.*)

MARY. Yes, Ingrid?

COOK. Ma'am, you're the nicest I ever had. But I go. I got to get Ford away from that bad girl.

MARY (*very firmly*). Jane is not a bad girl.

COOK (*bursts into tears*). Oh, course she ain't. He was always like that! Sometimes I could die, for the shame!

MARY (*kindly*). I'll send him away. You can stay.

COOK (*more soberly*). No, I don't do that, ma'am.

MARY. I'll give you a hundred dollars. That's more than half of what you make together.

COOK. Thank you, ma'am. We both go.

MARY. Is that sensible?

COOK. No. It's plain dumb.

MARY. Then why?

COOK (*she pauses, rocking from foot to foot*). I guess nobody under-stand. Sure it was no good to marry him. My mother told me he's a lady-killer. Don't marry them, she said. His wife is the lady he kills. Oh, he's terrible. But except for women he's a good man. He always says, "Ingrid, you take the money. You manage good." Oh, he don't want nobody but me for his wife! That's an awful big thing, ma'am.

MARY. Is that the thing that really matters?

COOK. With women like us, yes, ma'am—You give us references? (MARY *nods.*) And don't say nothing about his ways?

MARY. I won't.

COOK (*moving to the door*). Black bean soup, a fricasse, fried sweets and apple pie for dinner, ma'am—(*She opens the door.* JANE *has been eavesdropping.*)

COOK (*in a low, fierce voice*). Slut! (*Exit* COOK.)

JANE (*entering with extra cup on tray*). Did you hear what she called me, Mrs. Haines?

MARY. Please, Jane.

JANE (*cheerfully*). I'd rather be that any day than have some man make a fool of me! (*Enter* MISS FORDYCE. *She is a raw-boned, capable English spinster of 32.*)

MISS FORDYCE. May I see you, Mrs. Haines?

MARY. Of course, Miss Fordyce.

MISS FORDYCE. It's about little Mary—Really, Mrs. Haines, you'll have to talk to your child. She's just smacked her little brother, hard. Pure temper.

MARY. What did little Stevie do to her, Miss Fordyce?

MISS FORDYCE. Well, you see, it happened while I was down getting my tea. When I came up, she'd had such a tantrum, she'd made herself ill. She positively refuses to discuss the incident with me. But I'm quite sure the dear boy hadn't done a thing.

MARY. You're very apt to take the boy's side, Miss Fordyce.

MISS FORDYCE. Not at all. But in England, Mrs. Haines, our girls are not so wretchedly spoiled. After all, this *is* a man's world. The sooner our girls are taught to accept the fact *graciously*—

MARY (*gently*). Send her in to me, Miss Fordyce. (*Exit* MISS FORDYCE.) Oh, Jane, I don't understand it. Miss Fordyce really prefers Mary, but she insists we all make a little god of Stevie. (*Exits to bedroom, leaving the door open.*)

JANE. Them English ones always hold out for the boys. But they say since the War, ma'am, there's six women over there to every man. Competition is something fierce! Over here, you can treat the men the way they deserve—Men aren't so scarce. (*Enter* LITTLE MARY. *She is a broad-browed, thoughtful, healthy, little girl, physically well developed for her age.*)

LITTLE MARY. Where's Mother?

JANE. You're going to catch it. Smacking your little brother. (*Mimicking* MISS FORDYCE.) Such a dear, sweet little lad—shame. (LITTLE MARY *does not answer.*) I'll bet you wish you were Mother's girl, instead of Daddy's girl today, don't you? (LITTLE MARY *doesn't answer.*) What's the matter, the cat got your tongue? (*Enter* MARY, *wearing a negligee.*)

MARY. Hello, darling—Aren't you going to kiss me? (LITTLE MARY *doesn't move.*) What red eyes!

LITTLE MARY. I was mad. I threw up. When you throw up, doesn't it make you cry?

MARY (*smiling*). Stevie tease you? (LITTLE MARY, *embarrassed, looks at* JANE. JANE *snickers, takes the hint and goes out.*) Well, darling?

LITTLE MARY. Mother, I don't know how to begin.

MARY (*sitting on the chaise-longue, and putting out her hand*). Come here. (LITTLE MARY *doesn't budge.*) Would you rather wait until tonight and tell Dad?

LITTLE MARY (*horrified*). Oh, Mother, I couldn't tell him! (*Fiercely.*) And I'd be killed to death before I'd tell skinny old Miss Fordyce—

MARY. That's not the way for my dear little girl to talk.

LITTLE MARY (*setting her jaw*). I don't want to be a dear little girl. (*She suddenly rushes to her mother's outstretched arms in tears.*) Oh, Mother dear, Mother dear!

MARY. Baby, what?

LITTLE MARY. What brother said!

MARY. What did he say, the wretched boy?

LITTLE MARY (*disentangling herself*). He said I had bumps!

MARY. Bumps? You don't mean mumps?

LITTLE MARY. No, bumps. He said I was covered with disgusting bumps!

MARY (*alarmed*). Mary, *where?*

LITTLE MARY (*touching her hips and breasts with delicate, ashamed finger tips*). *Here* and *here!*

MARY. Oh—(*Controlling her relieved laughter, and drawing her daughter to her side.*) Of course you have bumps, darling. Very pretty little bumps. And you have them because—you're a little girl.

LITTLE MARY (*wailing*). But, Mother dear, I don't want to be a little girl. I hate girls! They're so silly, and they tattle, tattle—

MARY. Not really, Mary.

LITTLE MARY. Yes, Mother, I know. Oh, Mother, what *fun* is there to be a lady? What can a lady do?

MARY (*cheerfully*). These days, darling, ladies do all the things men do. They fly airplanes across the ocean, they go into politics and business—

LITTLE MARY. You don't, Mother.

MARY. Perhaps I'm happier doing just what I do.

LITTLE MARY. What do you do, Mother?

MARY. Take care of you and Stevie and Dad.

LITTLE MARY. You don't, Mother. Miss Fordyce and the servants do.

MARY (*teasing*). I see. I'm not needed around here.

LITTLE MARY (*hugging her*). Oh, Mother, I don't mean that. It wouldn't be any fun at all without *you*. But, Mother, even when the ladies *do* do things, they stop it when they get the lovie-dovies.

MARY. The what?

LITTLE MARY. Like in the movies, Mother. Ladies always end up so *silly*. (*Disgusted.*) Lovey-dovey, lovey-dovey all the time!

MARY. Darling, you're too young to understand—

LITTLE MARY. But, Mother—

MARY. "But Mother, but Mother!" There's one thing a woman can do, no man can do.

LITTLE MARY (*eagerly*). What?

MARY. Have a child. (*Tenderly.*) Like you.

LITTLE MARY. Oh, that! Everybody knows that. But is that any fun, Mother dear?

MARY. Fun? No. But it is—joy. (*Hugging her.*) Of a very special kind.

LITTLE MARY (*squirming away*). Well, it's never sounded specially exciting to me—I love you, Mother. But I bet you anything you like, Daddy has more *fun* than you! (*She slips away from* MARY. *Then sees her mother's dispirited face, turns and kisses her warmly.*) Oh, I'm sorry, Mother. But you just *don't understand!* (*A pause.*) Am I to be punished, Mother?

MARY (*she is thinking about something else*). What do you think?

LITTLE MARY. I smacked him awful hard—Shall I punish myself?

MARY. It will have to be pretty bad.

LITTLE MARY (*solemnly*). Then I won't go down to breakfast with Daddy tomorrow, or the next day—O.K., Mother?

MARY. O.K. (LITTLE MARY *walks, crestfallen, to the door as* JANE *enters.* LITTLE MARY *sticks out her tongue.*)

LITTLE MARY. There's my tongue! So what? (*Exits skipping.*)

JANE (*laughing*). She never lets anybody get the best of her, does she, Mrs. Haines?

MARY. My poor baby. She doesn't want to be a woman, Jane.

JANE. Who does?

MARY. Somehow, I've never minded it, Jane. (*Enter* MRS. MOREHEAD. *She is a bourgeois aristocrat of 55.* MARY *rises, kisses her.*)

MRS. MOREHEAD. Hello, child. Afternoon, Jane.

JANE. Afternoon, Mrs. Morehead. (*Exits to bedroom.*)

MARY. Mother, dear! (*She walks slowly to the dressing table.*)

MRS. MOREHEAD (*cheerfully*). Well, what's wrong? (*Sits.*)

MARY (*turning*). How did you know something's wrong?

MRS. MOREHEAD. Your voice on the phone. Is it Stephen?

MARY. How did you know?

MRS. MOREHEAD. You sent for *Mother*. So it must be he. (*A pause.*)

MARY. I don't know how to begin, Mother.

MRS. MOREHEAD (*delighted to find that her instincts were correct*). It's a woman! Who is she?

MARY. Her name is Crystal Allen. She—she's a salesgirl at Saks'. (*Her mother's cheerful and practical manner discourages tears, so she begins to cream and tonic her face instead.*)

MRS. MOOREHEAD. She's young and pretty, I suppose.

MARY. Well, yes. (*Defensively.*) But common.

MRS. MOREHEAD (*soothingly*). Of course—Stephen told you?

MARY. No. I—I found out—this afternoon.

MRS. MOREHEAD. How far has it gone?

MARY. He's known her about three months.

MRS. MOREHEAD. Does Stephen know you know?

MARY (*shaking her head*). I—I wanted to speak to you first. (*The tears come anyway.*) Oh, Mother dear, what am I going to say to him?

MRS. MOREHEAD. *Nothing.*

MARY. Nothing? (*Enter* JANE *with the new dress.*)

JANE. I'll give it a touch with the iron.

MARY. Look, Schiaparelli—(JANE *holds dress up.*) It's rather trying, though, one of those tight skirts with a flared tunic—

MRS. MOREHEAD. Personally, I always thought you looked best in things not too extreme. (*Exit* JANE.)

MARY. But, Mother, you don't really mean I should say nothing?

MRS. MOREHEAD. I do.

MARY. Oh, but Mother—

MRS. MOREHEAD. My dear, I felt the same way twenty years ago.

MARY. Not Father?

MRS. MOREHEAD. Mary, in many ways your father was an exceptional man. (*Philosophically.*) That, unfortunately, was not one of them.

MARY. Did you say nothing?

MRS. MOREHEAD. Nothing. I had a wise mother, too. Listen, dear, this is not a new story. It comes to most wives.

MARY. But Stephen—

MRS. MOREHEAD. Stephen is a man. He's been married twelve years—

MARY. You mean, he's tired of me!

MRS. MOREHEAD. Stop crying. You'll make your nose red.

MARY. I'm not crying. (*Patting tonic on her face.*) This stuff stings.

MRS. MOREHEAD (*going to her*). Stephen's tired of himself. Tired of feeling the same things in himself year after year. Time comes when every man's got to feel something new—when he's got to feel young again, just because he's growing old. Women are just the same. But when *we* get that way we change our hair dress. Or get a new cook. Or redecorate the house from stem to stern. But a man can't do over his office, or fire his secretary. Not even change the style of his hair. And the urge usually hits him hardest just when he's beginning to lose his hair. No, dear, a man has only one escape from his old self: to see a different self—in the mirror of some woman's eyes.

MARY. But, Mother—

MRS. MOREHEAD. This girl probably means no more to him than that new dress means to you.

MARY. But, Mother—

MRS. MOREHEAD. "But Mother, but Mother!" He's not giving anything to her that belongs to you, or you would have felt that yourself long ago.

MARY (*bewildered*). Oh, I always thought I would. I love him so much.

MRS. MOREHEAD. And he loves you, baby. (*Drawing* MARY *beside her on the chaise-longue.*) Now listen to me: Go away somewhere for a month or two. There's nothing like a good dose of another woman to make a man appreciate his wife. Mother knows!

MARY. But, there's never been a lie between us before.

MRS. MOREHEAD. You mean, there's never been a *silence* between you before. Well, it's about time. Keeping still, when you *ache* to talk, is about the only sacrifice spoiled women like us ever have to make.

MARY. But, I'd forgive him—

MRS. MOREHEAD. Forgive him? (*Impatiently.*) For what? For being a man? Accuse him, and you'll never get a chance to forgive him. He'd have to justify himself—

MARY. How can he!

MRS. MOREHEAD (*sighing*). He can't and he *can*. Don't make him try. Either way you'd lose him. And remember, dear, it's being together at the *end* that really matters. (*Rising.*) One more piece of motherly advice: Don't confide in your girl friends!

MARY. I think they all know.

MRS. MOREHEAD. They think you don't? (MARY *nods.*) Leave it that way. If you let them advise you, they'll see to it, in the name of friendship, that you lose your husband and your home. I'm an old woman, dear, and I know my sex. (*Moving to the door.*) I'm going right down this minute and get our tickets.

MARY. Our—tickets?

MRS. MOREHEAD. You're taking me to Bermuda, dear. My throat's been awfully bad. I haven't wanted to worry you, but my doctor says—

MARY. Oh, Mother darling! Thank you!

MRS. MOREHEAD. Don't thank me, dear. It's rather—*nice* to have you need Mother again. (*Exits. The telephone rings.* MARY *answers it.*)

MARY. Yes?—Oh, Stephen—Yes, dear?— (*Distressed.*) Oh, Stephen! Oh, no—I'm not angry. It's—it's just that I wanted to see the play. Yes, I can get Mother. Stephen, will you be very—late? (*It's a bit of a struggle, but she manages a cheerful voice.*) Oh, it's—all right. Have a good time. Of course, I know it's just business—No, dear—I won't wait up—Stephen. I love— (*A click. The other end has hung up.* JANE *enters.* MARY *turns her back. Her face would belie the calmness of her voice.*) Jane—The children and I will have dinner alone—

CURTAIN

MARGARET FARRAND THORP   [1939]

Margaret Farrand Thorp, who was born in New Jersey in 1891, graduated from Smith College in 1914 and received her Ph.D. from Yale. Besides teaching at Smith College from 1926 to 1929, she has filled a variety of positions as editor, publicity director, and writer. The present selection is from America at the Movies.

A Cinema Husband

There is social and psychological significance in the fact that 70 percent of Gary Cooper's fan mail comes from women who write that their husbands do not appreciate them. Their ideal is still the ideal husband of the Victorian era who told his wife at breakfast every morning how much she meant to him, but that husband is not a type which the postwar American man has any interest in emulating. He prefers to conceal his deeper emotions at breakfast, and during the rest of the day as well. His wife, consequently, has to spend her afternoons at the movies.

In the movies a wife finds it quite worthwhile to get into a new evening frock for a tête-à-tête dinner at home because her husband is sure, by dessert time at least, to take her hand across the intimately small and inconvenient table and say, "Darling, you get lovelier every day." When a cinema husband comes home from a business trip he dashes from room to room in the ultra-modern apartment or even up and down stairs if they live in a colonial cottage in Connecticut, frantic if his wife is not on hand to greet him. If she is away for a week-end he makes fabulously expensive long-distance calls without inquiring the toll rate, or boards a transcontinental airplane because he cannot exist any longer without speaking to her. Of course all this is very often the prelude to a murder but it is on the whole rather less humiliating to be murdered than to be taken for granted.

KATHERINE ANNE PORTER [1940]

Katherine Anne Porter, author of Noon Wine *and* Ship of Fools, *describes herself in childhood as "precocious, nervous, rebellious, unteachable." Born in Texas in 1890, she was educated at what she describes as "small southern convent schools." She has lectured at universities, although she never attended one.*

A Day's Work

The dull scrambling like a giant rat in the wall meant the dumbwaiter was on its way up, the janitress below hauling on the cable. Mrs. Halloran paused, thumped her iron on the board, and said, "There it is. Late. You could have put on your shoes and gone around the corner and brought the things an hour ago. I can't do everything."

Mr. Halloran pulled himself out of the chair, clutching the arms and heaving to his feet slowly, looking around as if he hoped to find crutches standing near. "Wearing out your socks, too," added Mrs. Halloran. "You ought either go barefoot outright or wear your shoes over your socks as God intended," she said. "Sock feet. What's the good of it, I'd like to know? Neither one thing nor the other."

She unrolled a salmon-colored chiffon nightgown with cream-colored lace and broad ribbons on it, gave it a light flirt in the air, and spread it on the board. "God's mercy, look at that indecent thing," she said. She thumped the iron again and pushed it back and forth over the rumpled cloth. "You might just set the things in the cupboard," she said, "and not leave them around on the floor. You might just."

Mr. Halloran took a sack of potatoes from the dumb-waiter and started for the cupboard in the corner next the icebox. "You might as well take a load," said Mrs. Halloran. "There's no need on earth making a half-dozen trips back and forth. I'd think the poorest sort of man could well carry more than five pounds of potatoes at one time. But maybe not."

Her voice tapped on Mr. Halloran's ears like wood on wood. "Mind your business, will you?" he asked, not speaking to her directly. He carried on the argument with himself. "Oh, I couldn't do that, Mister Honey," he answered in a dull falsetto. "Don't ever ask me to think of such a thing, even. It wouldn't be right," he said, standing still with his knees bent, glaring bitterly over the potato sack at the scrawny strange woman he had never liked, that one standing there ironing clothes with a dirty look on her whole face like a suffering saint. "I may not be much good any more," he told her in his own voice, "but I still have got wits enough to take groceries off a dumb-waiter, mind you."

"That's a miracle," said Mrs. Halloran. "I'm thankful for that much."

"There's the telephone," said Mr. Halloran, sitting in the armchair again and taking his pipe out of his shirt pocket.

"I heard it as well," said Mrs. Halloran, sliding the iron up and down over the salmon-colored chiffon.

"It's for you, I've no further business in this world," said Mr. Halloran. His little greenish eyes glittered; he exposed his two sharp dogteeth in a grin.

"You could answer it. It could be the wrong number again or for somebody downstairs," said Mrs. Halloran, her flat voice going flatter, even.

"Let it go in any case," decided Mr. Halloran, "for my own part, that is." He struck a match on the arm of his chair, touched off his pipe, and drew in his first puff while the telephone went on with its nagging.

"It might be Maggie again," said Mrs. Halloran.

"Let her ring, then," said Mr. Halloran, settling back and crossing his legs.

"God help a man who won't answer the telephone when his own daughter calls up for a word," commented Mrs. Halloran to the ceiling. "And she in deep trouble, too, with her husband treating her like a dog about the money, and sitting out late nights in saloons with that crowd from the Little Tammany Association. He's getting into politics now with the McCorkery gang. No good will come of it, and I told her as much."

"She's no troubles at all, her man's a sharp fellow who will get ahead if she'll let him alone," said Mr. Halloran. "She's nothing to complain of, I could tell her. But what's a father?" Mr. Halloran cocked his head toward the window that opened on the brick-paved areaway and crowed like a rooster. "What's a father these days and who would heed his advice?"

"You needn't tell the neighbors, there's disgrace enough already," said Mrs. Halloran. She set the iron back on the gas ring and stepped out to the telephone on the first stair landing. Mr. Halloran leaned forward, his thin, red-haired hands hanging loosely between his knees, his warm pipe sending up its good decent smell right into his nose. The woman hated the pipe and the smell; she was a woman born to make any man miserable. Before the depression, while he still had a good job and prospects of a raise, before he went on relief, before she took in fancy washing and ironing, in the Good Days Before, God's pity, she didn't exactly keep her mouth shut, there wasn't a word known to man she couldn't find an answer for, but she knew which side her bread was buttered on, and put up with it. Now she was, you might say, buttering her own bread and she never forgot it for a minute. And it's her own fault we're not riding round today in a limousine with ash trays and a speaking tube and a cut-glass vase for flowers in it. It's what a man gets for marrying one of these holy women. Gerald McCorkery had told him as much, in the beginning.

"There's a girl will spend her time holding you down," Gerald had told him. "You're putting your head in a noose will strangle the life out of you. Heed the advice of one who wishes you well," said Gerald McCorkery. This was after he had barely set eyes on Lacey Mahaffy one Sunday morning in Coney Island. It was like McCorkery to see that in a flash, born judge of human nature that he was. He could look a man over, size him up, and there was an end to it. And if the man didn't pass muster, McCorkery could ease him out in a way that man would never know how it happened. It was the secret of McCorkery's success in the world.

"This is Rosie, herself," said Gerald that Sunday in Coney Island. "Meet the future Mrs. Gerald J. McCorkery." Lacey Mahaffy's narrow face had gone sour as whey under her big straw hat. She barely nodded to Rosie, who gave Mr. Halloran a look that fairly undressed him right there. Mr. Halloran had thought, too, that McCorkery was picking a strange one; she was good-looking all right, but she had the smell of a regular little Fourteenth Street hustler if Halloran knew anything about women. "Come on," said McCorkery, his arm around Rosie's waist, "let's all go on the roller coaster." But Lacey would not. She said, "No, thank you. We didn't plan to stay, and we must go now." On the way home Mr. Halloran said, "Lacey, you judge too harshly. Maybe that's a nice girl at heart; hasn't had your opportunities." Lacey had turned upon him a face ugly as an angry cat's, and said, "She's a loose, low woman, and 'twas an insult to introduce her to me." It was a good while before the pretty fresh face that Mr. Halloran had fallen in love with returned to her.

Next day in Billy's Place, after three drinks each, McCorkery said, "Watch your step, Halloran; think of your future. There's a straight good girl I don't doubt, but she's no sort of mixer. A man getting into politics needs a wife who can meet all kinds. A man needs a woman knows how to loosen her corsets and sit easy."

Mrs. Halloran's voice was going on in the hall, a steady dry rattle like old newspapers blowing on a park bench. "I told you before it's no good coming to me with your troubles now. I warned you in time but you wouldn't listen. . . . I told you just how it would be, I tried my best. . . . No, you couldn't listen, you always knew better than your mother. . . . So now all you've got to do is stand by your married vows and make the best of it. . . . Now listen to me, if you want himself to do right you have to do right first. The woman has to do right first, and then if the man won't do right in turn it's no fault of hers. You do right whether he does wrong or no, just because he does wrong is no excuse for you."

"Ah, will you hear that?" Mr. Halloran asked the areaway in an awed voice. "There's a holy terror of a saint for you."

". . . the woman has to do right first, I'm telling you," said Mrs. Halloran into the telephone, "and then if he's a devil in spite of it, why she has to do right without any help from him." Her voice rose so the neighbors could get an earful if they wanted. "I know you from old, you're just like your father. You must be doing something wrong yourself or you wouldn't be in this fix. You're doing wrong this minute, calling over the telephone when you ought to be getting your work done. I've got an iron on, working over the dirty nightgowns of a kind of woman I wouldn't soil my foot on if I'd had a man to take care of me. So now you do up your housework and dress yourself and take a walk in the fresh air. . . ."

"A little fresh air never hurt anybody," commented Mr. Halloran loudly through the open window. "It's the gas gets a man down."

"Now listen to me, Maggie, that's not the way to talk over the public wires. Now you stop that crying and go and do your duty and don't be worrying me any more. And stop saying you're going to leave your husband, because where will you go, for one thing? Do you want to walk the streets or set up a laundry in your kitchen? You can't come back here, you'll stay with your husband where you belong. Don't be a fool, Maggie. You've got your living, and that's more than many a woman better than you has got. Yes, your father's all right. No, he's just sitting here, the same. God knows what's to become of us. But you know how he is, little he cares. . . . Now remember this, Maggie, if anything goes wrong with your married life it's your own fault and you needn't come here for sympathy. . . . I can't waste any more time on it. Good-bye."

Mr. Halloran, his ears standing up for fear of missing a word, thought how Gerald J. McCorkery had gone straight on up the ladder with Rosie; and for every step the McCorkerys took upward, he, Michael Halloran, had taken a step downward with Lacey Mahaffy. They had started as greenhorns with the same chances at the same time and the same friends, but McCorkery had seized all his opportunities as they came, getting in steadily with the Big Shots in ward politics, one good thing leading to another. Rosie had known how to back him up and push him onward. The McCorkerys for years had invited him and Lacey to come over to the house and be sociable with the crowd, but Lacey would not.

"You can't run with that fast set and drink and stay out nights and hold your job," said Lacey, "and you should know better than to ask your wife to associate with that woman." Mr. Halloran had got into the habit of dropping around by himself, now and again, for McCorkery still liked him, was still willing to give him a foothold in the right places, still asked him for favors at election time. There was always a good lively crowd at the McCorkerys, wherever they were; for they moved ever so often to a better place, with more furniture. Rosie helped hand around the drinks, taking a few herself with a gay word for everybody. The player piano or the victrola would be going full blast, with everybody dancing, all looking like ready money and a bright future. He would get home late these evenings, back to the same little cold-water walk-up flat, because Lacey would not spend a dollar for show. It must all go into savings against old age, she said. He would be full of good food and drink, and find Lacey, in a bungalow apron, warming up the fried potatoes once more, cross and bitterly silent, hanging her head and frowning at the smell of liquor on his breath. "You might at least eat the potatoes when I've fried them and waited all this time," she would say. "Ah, eat them yourself, they're none of mine," he would snarl in his disappointment with her, and with the life she was leading him.

He had believed with all his heart for years that he would one day be manager of one of the G. and I. chain grocery stores he worked

for, and when that hope gave out there was still his pension when
they retired him. But two years before it was due they fired him,
on account of the depression, they said. Overnight he was on the
sidewalk, with no place to go with the news but home. "Jesus," said
Mr. Halloran, still remembering that day after nearly seven years of
idleness.

The depression hadn't touched McCorkery. He went on and on
up the ladder, giving beefsteaks and beanfests and beer parties for
the boys in Billy's Place, standing in with the right men and never
missing a trick. At last the Gerald J. McCorkery Club chartered a
whole boat for a big excursion up the river. It was a great day, with
Lacey sitting at home sulking. After election Rosie had her picture
in the papers, smiling at McCorkery; not fat exactly, just a fine figure of a woman with flowers pinned on her spotted fur coat, her
teeth as good as ever. Oh, God, there was a girl for any man's
money. Mr. Halloran saw out of his eye-corner the bony stooped
back of Lacey Mahaffy, standing on one foot to rest the other like a
tired old horse, leaning on her hands waiting for the iron to heat.

"That was Maggie, with her woes," she said.

"I hope you gave her some good advice," said Mr. Halloran. "I
hope you told her to take up her hat and walk out on him."

Mrs. Halloran suspended the iron over a pair of pink satin panties.
"I told her to do right and leave wrongdoing to the men," she said,
in her voice like a phonograph record running down. "I told her to
bear with the trouble God sends as her mother did before her."

Mr. Halloran gave a loud groan and knocked out his pipe on the
chair arm. "You would ruin the world, woman, if you could, with
your wicked soul, treating a new-married girl as if she had no home
and no parents to come to. But she's no daughter of mine if she sits
there peeling potatoes, letting a man run over her. No daughter of
mine and I'll tell her so if she—"

"You know well she's your daughter, so hold your tongue," said
Mrs. Halloran, "and if she heeded you she'd be walking the streets
this minute. I brought her up an honest girl, and an honest woman
she's going to be or I'll take her over my knee as I did when she
was little. So there you are, Halloran."

Mr. Halloran leaned far back in his chair and felt along the shelf
above his head until his fingers touched a half-dollar he had noticed
there. His hand closed over it, he got up instantly and looked about
for his hat.

"Keep your daughter, Lacey Mahaffy," he said, "she's none of mine but the fruits of your long sinning with the Holy Ghost. And now I'm off for a little round and a couple of beers to keep my mind from dissolving entirely."

"You can't have that dollar you just now sneaked off the shelf," said Mrs. Halloran. "So you think I'm blind besides? Put it back where you found it. That's for our daily bread."

"I'm sick of bread daily," said Mr. Halloran, "I need beer. It was not a dollar, but a half-dollar as you know well."

"Whatever it was," said Mrs. Halloran, "it stands instead of a dollar to me. So just drop it."

"You've got tomorrow's potatoes sewed up in your pocket this minute, and God knows what sums in that black box wherever you hide it, besides the life savings," said Mr. Halloran. "I earned this half-dollar on relief, and it's going to be spent properly. And I'll not be back for supper, so you'll save on that, too. So long, Lacey Mahaffy, I'm off."

"If you never come back, it will be all the same," said Mrs. Halloran, not looking up.

"If I came back with a pocket full of money, you'd be glad to see me," said Mr. Halloran.

"It would want to be a great sum," said Mrs. Halloran.

Mr. Halloran shut the door behind him with a fine slam.

He strolled out into the clear fall weather, a late afternoon sun warming his neck and brightening the old red-brick, high-stooped houses of Perry Street. He would go after all these years to Billy's Place, he might find some luck there. He took his time, though, speaking to the neighbors as he went. "Good afternoon, Mr. Halloran." "Good afternoon to you, Missis Caffery." . . . "It's fine weather for the time of year, Mr. Gogarty." "It is indeed, Mr. Halloran." Mr. Halloran thrived on these civilities, he loved to flourish his hat and give a hearty good day like a man who has nothing on his mind. Ah, there was the young man from the G. and I. store around the corner. He knew what kind of job Mr. Halloran once held there. "Good day, Mr. Halloran." "Good day to you, Mr. McInerny, how's business holding up with you?" "Good for the times, Mr. Halloran, that's the best I can say." "Things are not getting any better, Mr. McInerny." "It's the truth we are all hanging on by the teeth now, Mr. Halloran."

Soothed by this acknowledgment of man's common misfortune Mr. Halloran greeted the young cop at the corner. The cop, with his quick eyesight, was snatching a read from a newspaper on the stand across the sidewalk. "How do you do, Young O'Fallon," asked Mr. Halloran, "is your business lively these days?"

"Quiet as the tomb itself on this block," said Young O'Fallon. "But that's a sad thing about Connolly, now." His eyes motioned toward the newspaper.

"Is he dead?" asked Mr. Halloran; "I haven't been out until now, I didn't see the papers."

"Ah, not yet," said Young O'Fallon, "but the G-men are after him, it looks they'll get him surely this time."

"Connolly in bad with the G-men? Holy Jesus," said Mr. Halloran, "who will they go after next? The meddlers."

"It's that numbers racket," said the cop. "What's the harm, I'd like to know? A man must get his money from somewhere when he's in politics. They oughta give him a chance."

"Connolly's a great fellow, God bless him, I hope he gives them the slip," said Mr. Halloran, "I hope he goes right through their hands like a greased pig."

"He's smart," said the cop. "That Connolly's a smooth one. He'll come out of it."

Ah, will he though? Mr. Halloran asked himself. Who is safe if Connolly goes under? Wait till I give Lacey Mahaffy the news about Connolly, I'll like seeing her face the first time in twenty years. Lacey kept saying, "A man is a downright fool must be a crook to get rich. Plenty of the best people get rich and do no harm by it. Look at the Connollys now, good practical Catholics with nine children and more to come if God sends them, and Mass every day, and they're rolling in wealth richer than your McCorkerys with all their wickedness." So there you are, Lacey Mahaffy, wrong again, and welcome to your pious Connollys. Still and all it was Connolly who had given Gerald McCorkery his start in the world; McCorkery had been publicity man and then campaign manager for Connolly, in the days when Connolly had Tammany in the palm of his hand and the sky was the limit. And McCorkery had begun at the beginning, God knows. He was running a little basement place first, rent almost nothing, where the boys of the Connolly Club and the Little Tammany Association, just the mere fringe of the district, you might say, could drop in for quiet evenings for a game and a drink along with the talk. Nothing low, nothing but what was customary, with the house taking a cut on the winnings and a fine profit on the liquor, and holding the crowd together. Many was the big plan hatched there came out well for everybody. For everybody but myself, and why was that? And when McCorkery says to me, "You can take over now and run the place for the McCorkery Club," ah, there was my chance and Lacey Mahaffy wouldn't hear of it, and with Maggie coming on just then it wouldn't do to excite her.

Mr. Halloran went on, following his feet that knew the way to Billy's Place, head down, not speaking to passers-by any more, but talking it out with himself again, again. What a track to go over seeing clearly one by one the crossroads where he might have taken a different turn that would have changed all his fortunes; but no, he had gone the other way and now it was too late. She wouldn't say a thing but "It's not right and you know it, Halloran," so what could a man do in all? Ah, you could have gone on with your rightful affairs like any other man, Halloran, it's not the woman's place to decide such things; she'd have come round once she saw the money, or a good whack on the backsides would have put her in her place. Never had mortal woman needed a good walloping worse than Lacey Mahaffy, but he could never find it in his heart to give it to her for her own good. That was just another of your many mistakes, Halloran. But there was always the lifelong job with the G. and I. and peace in the house more or less. Many a man envied me in those days I remember, and I was resting easy on the savings and knowing with that and the pension I could finish out my life with some little business of my own. "What came of that?" Mr. Halloran inquired in a low voice, looking around him. Nobody anwered. You know well what came of it, Halloran. You were fired out like a delivery boy, two years before your time was out. Why did you sit there watching the trick being played on others before you, knowing well it could happen to you and never quite believing what you saw with your own eyes? G. and I. gave me my start, when I was green in this country, and they were my own kind or I thought so. Well, it's done now. Yes, it's done now, but there was all the years you could have cashed in on the numbers game with the best of them, helping collect the protection money and taking your cut. You could have had a fortune by now in Lacey's name, safe in the bank. It was good quiet profit and none the wiser. But they're wiser now, Halloran, don't forget; still it's a lump of grief and disappointment to swallow all the same. The game's up with Connolly, maybe; Lacey Mahaffy had said, "Numbers is just another way of stealing from the poor, and you weren't born to be a thief like that McCorkery." Ah, God, no, Halloran, you were born to rot on relief and maybe that's honest enough for her. That Lacey— A fortune in her name would have been no good to me whatever. She's got all the savings tied up, such as they are, she'll pinch and she'll starve, she'll wash dirty clothes first, she won't give up a penny to live on. She has stood in my way, McCorkery, like a skeleton rattling its bones, and you were right about her, she has been my ruin. "Ah, it's not too late yet, Halloran," said McCorkery, appearing plain as day inside Mr. Halloran's head with the same old face and way with him. "Never say die, Halloran. Elections are coming on again, it's a busy time for all, there's work to be done and you're the very man I'm looking for. Why didn't you come to me sooner, you know I never forget an old friend. You don't deserve your ill fortune, Halloran," McCorkery told him; "I said so to others and I say it now to your face, never did man deserve more of the world than you, Halloran, but the truth is, there's not always enough good luck to go round; but it's your turn now, and I've got a job for you up to your abilities at last. For a man like you, there's nothing to it at all, you can toss it off with one hand tied, Halloran, and good money in it. Organization work, just among your own neighbors, where you're known and respected for a man of your word and an old friend of Gerald McCorkery. Now look, Halloran," said Gerald McCorkery, tipping him the wink, "do I need to say more? It's voters in large numbers we're after, Halloran, and you're to bring them in, alive or dead. Keep your eye on the situation at all times and get in touch with me when necessary. And name your figure in the way of money. And come up to the house sometimes, Halloran, why don't you? Rosie has asked me a hundred times, 'Whatever went with Halloran, the life of the party?' That's the way you stand with Rosie, Halloran. We're in a two-story flat now with green velvet curtains and carpets you can sink to your shoetops in, and there's no reason at all why you shouldn't have the same kind of place if you want it. With your gifts, you were never meant to be a poor man."

Ah, but Lacey Mahaffy wouldn't have it, maybe. "Then get yourself another sort of woman, Halloran, you're a good man still, find yourself a woman like Rosie to snuggle down with at night." Yes, but McCorkery, you forget that Lacey Mahaffy had legs and hair and eyes and a complexion fit for a chorus girl. But would she do anything with them? Never. Would you believe there was a woman wouldn't take off all her clothes at once even to bathe herself? What a hateful thing she was with her evil mind thinking everything was a sin, and never giving a man a chance to show himself a man in any way. But she's faded away now, her mean soul shows out all over her, she's ugly as sin itself now, McCorkery. "It's what I told you would happen," said McCorkery, "but now with the job and the money you can go your ways and let Lacey Mahaffy go hers." I'll do it, McCorkery. "And forget about Connolly. Just remember I'm my own man and always was. Connolly's finished, but I'm not. Stronger than ever, Halloran, with Connolly out of the way. I saw this coming long ever ago, Halloran, I got clear of it. They don't catch McCorkery with his pants down, Halloran. And I almost forgot. . . . Here's something for the running expenses to start. Take this for the present, and there's more to come. . . ."

Mr. Halloran stopped short, a familiar smell floated under his nose: the warm beer-and-beefsteak smell of Billy's Place, sawdust and onions, like any other bar maybe, but with something of its own besides. The talk within him stopped also as if a hand had been laid on his mind. He drew his fist out of his pocket almost expecting to find green money in it. The half-dollar was in his palm. "I'll stay while it lasts and hope McCorkery will come in."

The moment he stepped inside his eye lighted on McCorkery standing at the bar pouring his own drink from the bottle before him. Billy was mopping the bar before him idly, and his eye, swimming toward Halloran, looked like an oyster in its own juice. McCorkery saw him too. "Well, blow me down," he said, in a voice that had almost lost its old County Mayo ring, "if it ain't my old sidekick from the G. and I. Step right up, Halloran," he said, his poker face as good as ever, no man ever saw Gerald McCorkery surprised at anything. "Step up and name your choice."

Mr. Halloran glowed suddenly with the warmth around the heart he always had at the sight of McCorkery, he couldn't put a name on it, but there was something about the man. Ah, it was Gerald all right, the same, who never forgot a friend and never seemed to care whether a man was rich or poor, with his face of granite and his eyes like blue agates in his head, a rock of a man surely. There he was, saying "Step right up," as if they had parted only yesterday; portly and solid in his expensive-looking clothes, as always; his hat a darker gray than his suit, with a devil-may-care roll to the brim, but nothing sporting, mind you. All first-rate, well made, and the right thing for him, more power to him. Mr. Halloran said, "Ah, McCorkery, you're the one man on this round earth I hoped to see today, but I says to myself, maybe he doesn't come round to Billy's Place so much nowadays."

"And why not?" asked McCorkery, "I've been coming around to

Billy's Place for twenty-five years now, it's still headquarters for the old guard of the McCorkery Club, Halloran." He took in Mr. Halloran from head to foot in a flash of a glance and turned toward the bottle.

"I was going to have a beer," said Mr. Halloran, "but the smell of that whisky changes my mind for me." McCorkery poured a second glass, they lifted the drinks with an identical crook of the elbow, a flick of the wrist at each other.

"Here's to crime," said McCorkery, and "Here's looking at you," said Mr. Halloran, merrily. Ah, to hell with it, he was back where he belonged, in good company. He put his foot on the rail and snapped down his whisky, and no sooner was his glass on the bar than Mc-Corkery was filling it again. "Just time for a few quick ones," he said, "before the boys get here." Mr. Halloran downed that one, too, before he notice that McCorkery hadn't filled his own glass. "I'm ahead of you," said McCorkery, "I'll skip this one."

There was a short pause, a silence fell around them that seemed to ooze like a fog from somewhere deep in McCorkery, it was suddenly as if he had not really been there at all, or hadn't uttered a word. Then he said outright: "Well, Halloran, let's have it. What's on your mind?" And he poured two more drinks. That was McCorkery all over, reading your thoughts and coming straight to the point.

Mr. Halloran closed his hand round his glass and peered into the little pool of whisky. "Maybe we could sit down," he said, feeling weak-kneed all at once. McCorkery took the bottle and moved over to the nearest table. He sat facing the door, his look straying there now and then, but he had a set, listening face as if he was ready to hear anything.

"You know what I've had at home all these years," began Mr. Halloran, solemnly, and paused.

"Oh, God, yes," said McCorkery with simple good-fellowship. "How is herself these days?"

"Worse than ever," said Mr. Halloran, "but that's not it."

"What is it, then, Halloran?" asked McCorkery, pouring drinks. "You know well you can speak out your mind to me. Is it a loan?"

"No," said Mr. Halloran. "It's a job."

"Now that's a different matter," said McCorkery. "What kind of a job?"

Mr. Halloran, his head sunk between his shoulders, saw McCork-ery wave a hand and nod at half a dozen men who came in and ranged themselves along the bar. "Some of the boys," said Mc-

Corkery. "Go on." His face was tougher, and quieter, as if the drink gave him a firm hold on himself. Mr. Halloran said what he had planned to say, had said already on the way down, and it still sounded reasonable and right to him. McCorkery waited until he had finished, and got up, putting a hand on Mr. Halloran's shoulder. "Stay where you are, and help yourself," he said, giving the bottle a little push, "and anything else you want, Halloran, order it on me. I'll be back in a few minutes, and you know I'll help you out if I can."

Halloran understood everything but it was through a soft warm fog, and he hardly noticed when McCorkery passed him again with the men, all in that creepy quiet way like footpads on a dark street. They went into the back room, the door opened on a bright light and closed again, and Mr. Halloran reached for the bottle to help himself wait until McCorkery should come again bringing the good word. He felt comfortable and easy as if he hadn't a bone or muscle in him, but his elbow slipped off the table once or twice and he upset his drink on his sleeve. Ah, McCorkery, is it the whole family you're taking on with the jobs? For my Maggie's husband is in now with the Little Tammany Association. "There's a bright lad will go far and I've got my eye on him, Halloran," said the friendly voice of McCorkery in his mind, and the brown face, softer than he remembered it, came up clearly behind his closed eyes.

"Ah, well, it's like myself beginning all over again in him," said Mr. Halloran, aloud, "besides my own job that I might have had all this time if I'd just come to see you sooner."

"True for you," said McCorkery in a merry County Mayo voice, inside Mr. Halloran's head, "and now let's drink to the gay future for old times' sake and be damned to Lacey Mahaffy." Mr. Halloran reached for the bottle but it skipped sideways, rolled out of reach like a creature, and exploded at his feet. When he stood up the chair fell backward from under him. He leaned on the table and it folded up under his hands like cardboard.

"Wait now, take it easy," said McCorkery, and there he was, real enough, holding Mr. Halloran braced on the one side, motioning with his hand to the boys in the back room, who came out quietly and took hold of Mr. Halloran, some of them, on the other side. Their faces were all Irish, but not an Irishman Mr. Halloran knew in the lot, and he did not like any face he saw. "Let me be," he said with dignity, "I came her to see Gerald J. McCorkery, a friend of mine from old times, and let not a thug among you lay a finger upon me."

"Come on, Big Shot," said one of the younger men, in a voice like a file grating, "come on now, it's time to go."

"That's a fine low lot you've picked to run with, McCorkery," said Mr. Halloran, bracing his heels against the slow weight they put upon him toward the door, "I wouldn't trust one of them far as I could throw him by the tail."

"All right, all right, Halloran," said McCorkery. "Come on with me. Lay off him, Finnegan." He was leaning over Mr. Halloran and pressing something into his right hand. It was money, a neat little roll of it, good smooth thick money, no other feel like it in the world, you couldn't mistake it. Ah, he'd have an argument to show Lacey Mahaffy would knock her off her feet. Honest money with a job to back it up. "You'll stand by your given word, McCorkery, as ever?" he asked, peering into the rock-colored face above him, his feet weaving a dance under him, his heart ready to break with gratitude.

"Ah, sure, sure," said McCorkery in a loud hearty voice with a kind of curse in it. "Crisakes, get on with him, do." Mr. Halloran found himself eased into a taxicab at the curb, with McCorkery speaking to the driver and giving him money. "So long, Big Shot," said one of the thug faces, and the taxicab door thumped to. Mr. Halloran bobbed about on the seat for a while, trying to think. He leaned forward and spoke to the driver. "Take me to my friend Gerald J. McCorkery's house," he said, "I've got important business. Don't pay any attention to what he said. Take me to his house."

"Yeah?" said the driver, without turning his head. "Well, here's where you get out, see? Right here." He reached back and opened the door. And sure enough, Mr. Halloran was standing on the sidewalk in front of the flat in Perry Street, alone except for the rows of garbage cans, the taxicab hooting its way around the corner, and a cop coming toward him, plainly to be seen under the street light.

"You should cast your vote for McCorkery, the poor man's friend," Mr. Halloran told the cop, "McCorkery's the man who will get us all off the spot. Stands by his old friends like a maniac. Got a wife named Rosie. Vote for McCorkery," said Mr. Halloran, working hard at his job, "and you'll be Chief of the Force when Halloran says the word."

"To hell with McCorkery, that stooge," said the cop, his mouth square and sour with the things he said and the things he saw and did every night on that beat. "There you are drunk again, Halloran, shame to you, with Lacey Mahaffy working her heart out over the washboard to buy your beer."

"It wasn't beer and she didn't buy it, mind you," said Mr. Halloran, "and what do you know about Lacey Mahaffy?"

"I knew her from old when I used to run errands for St. Veronica's Altar Society," said the cop, "and she was a great one, even then. Nothing good enough."

"It's the same today," said Mr. Halloran, almost sober for a moment.

"Well, go on up now and stay up till you're fit to be seen," said the cop, censoriously.

"You're Johnny Maginnis," said Mr. Halloran, "I know you well."

"You should know me by now," said the cop.

Mr. Halloran worked his way upstairs partly on his hands and knees, but once at his own door he stood up, gave a great blow on the panel with his fist, turned the knob and surged in like a wave after the door itself, holding out the money toward Mrs. Halloran, who had finished ironing and was at her mending.

She got up very slowly, her bony hand over her mouth, her eyes starting out at what she saw. "Ah, did you steal it?" she asked. "Did you kill somebody for that?" the words grated up from her throat in a dark whisper. Mr. Halloran glared back at her in fear.

"Suffering Saints, Lacey Mahaffy," he shouted until the whole houseful could hear him, "haven't ye any mind at all that you can't see your husband has had a turn of fortune and a job and times are changed from tonight? Stealing, is it? That's for your great friends the Connollys with their religion. Connolly steals, but Halloran is an honest man with a job in the McCorkery Club, and money in pocket."

"McCorkery, is it?" said Mrs. Halloran, loudly too. "Ah, so there's the whole family, young and old, wicked and innocent, taking their bread from McCorkery, at last. Well, it's no bread of mine, I'll earn my own as I have, you can keep your dirty money to yourself, Halloran, mind you I mean it."

"Great God, woman," moaned Mr. Halloran, and he tottered from the door to the table, to the ironing board, and stood there, ready to weep with rage, "haven't you a soul even that you won't come along with your husband when he's riding to riches and glory on the Tiger's back itself, with everything for the taking and no questions asked?"

"Yes, I have a soul," cried Mrs. Halloran, clenching her fists, her hair flying. "Surely I have a soul and I'll save it yet in spite of you. . . ."

She was standing there before him in a kind of faded gingham winding sheet, with her dead hands upraised, her dead eyes blind but fixed upon him, her voice coming up hollow from the deep tomb, her throat thick with grave damp. The ghost of Lacey Mahaffy was threatening him, it came nearer, growing taller as it came, the face changing to a demon's face with a fixed glassy grin. "It's all that drink on an empty stomach," said the ghost, in a hoarse growl. Mr. Halloran fetched a yell of horror right out of his very boots, and seized the flatiron from the board. "Ah, God damn you, Lacey Mahaffy, you devil, keep away, keep away," he howled, but she advanced on air, grinning and growling. He raised the flatiron and hurled it without aiming, and the specter, whoever it was, whatever it was, sank and was gone. He did not look, but broke out of the room and was back on the sidewalk before he knew he had meant to go there. Maginnis came up at once. "Hey there now, Halloran," he said, "I mean business this time. You get back upstairs or I'll run you in. Come along now, I'll help you get there this time, and that's the last of it. On relief the way you are, and drinking your head off."

Mr. Halloran suddenly felt calm, collected; he would take Maginnis up and show him just what had happened. "I'm not on relief any more, and if you want any trouble, just call on my friend, McCorkery. He'll tell you who I am."

"McCorkery can't tell me anything about you I don't know already," said Maginnis. "Stand up there now." For Halloran wanted to go up again on his hands and knees.

"Let a man be," said Mr. Halloran, trying to sit on the cop's feet. "I killed Lacey Mahaffy at last, you'll be pleased to hear," he said, looking up into the cop's face. "It was high time and past. But I did not steal the money."

"Well, aint' that just too bad," said the cop, hauling him up under the arms. "Chees, why'n't you make a good job while you had the chance? Stand up now. Ah, hell with it, stand up or I'll sock you one."

Mr. Halloran said, "Well, you don't believe it so wait and see."

At that moment they both glanced upward and saw Mrs. Halloran coming downstairs. She was holding to the rail, and even in the speckled hall-light they could see a great lumpy clout of flesh standing out on her forehead, all colors. She stopped, and seemed not at all suprised.

"So there you are, Officer Maginnis," she said. "Bring him up."

"That's a fine welt you've got over your eye this time, Mrs. Halloran," commented Officer Maginnis, politely.

"I fell and hit my head on the ironing board," said Mrs. Halloran. "It comes of overwork and worry, day and night. A dead faint, Officer Maginnis. Watch your big feet there, you thriving, natural fool," she added to Mr. Halloran. "He's got a job now, you mightn't believe it, Officer Maginnis, but it's true. Bring him on up, and thank you."

She went ahead of them, opened the door, and led the way to the bedroom through the kitchen, turned back the covers, and Officer Maginnis dumped Mr. Halloran among the quilts and pillows. Mr. Halloran rolled over with a deep groan and shut his eyes.

"Many thanks to you, Officer Maginnis," said Mrs. Halloran.

"Don't mention it, Mrs. Halloran," said Officer Maginnis.

When the door was shut and locked, Mrs. Halloran went and dipped a large bath towel under the kitchen tap. She wrung it out and tied several good hard knots in one end and tried it out with a whack on the edge of the table. She walked in and stood over the bed and brought the knotted towel down in Mr. Halloran's face with all her might. He stirred and muttered, ill at ease. "That's for the flat-iron, Halloran," she told him, in a cautious voice as if she were talking to herself, and whack, down came the towel again. "That's for the half-dollar," she said, and whack, "that's for your drunken-ness—" Her arm swung around regularly, ending with a heavy thud on the face that was beginning to squirm, gasp, lift itself from the pillow and fall back again, in a puzzled kind of torment. "For your sock feet," Mrs. Halloran told him, whack, "and your laziness, and this is for missing Mass and—" here she swung half a dozen times— "that is for your daughter and your part in her. . . ."

She stood back breathless, the lump on her forehead burning in its furious colors. When Mr. Halloran attempted to rise, shielding his head with his arms, she gave him a push and he fell back again. "Stay there and don't give me a word," said Mrs. Halloran. He pulled the pillow over his face and subsided again, this time for good.

Mrs. Halloran moved about very deliberately. She tied the wet towel around her head, the knotted end hanging over her shoulder. Her hand ran into her apron pocket and came out again with the money. There was a five-dollar bill with three one-dollar bills rolled in it, and the half-dollar she had thought spent long since. "A poor start, but something," she said, and opened the cupboard door with a long key. Reaching in, she pulled a loosely fitted board out of the wall, and removed a black-painted metal box. She unlocked this, took out one five-cent piece from a welter of notes and coins. She then placed the new money in the box, locked it, put it away, replaced the board, shut the cupboard door and locked that. She went out to the telephone, dropped the nickel in the slot, asked for a number, and waited.

"Is that you, Maggie? Well, are things any better with you now? I'm glad to hear it. It's late to be calling, but there's news about your father. No, no, nothing of that kind, he's got a job. I said a *job*. Yes, at last, after all my urging him onward. . . . I've got him bedded down to sleep it off so he'll be ready for work tomorrow. . . . Yes, it's political work, toward the election time, with Gerald McCorkery. But that's no harm, getting votes and all, he'll be in the open air and it doesn't mean I'll have to associate with low people, now or ever. It's clean enough work, with good pay; if it's not just what I prayed for, still it beats nothing, Maggie. After all my trying . . . it's like a miracle. You see what can be done with patience and doing your duty, Maggie. Now mind you do as well by your own husband."

PHYLLIS MCGINLEY *[1951]*

Phyllis McGinley, who was born in Oregon in 1905, writes often about men. One of her books is actually entitled Husbands Are Difficult. *She attended the universities of Utah and California, was married in 1937, and now lives in Larchmont, New York. Larchmont, or its equivalent, is the setting of "The 5:32," which shows that husbands are not really so difficult—or at least not all of the time.*

The 5:32

She said, if tomorrow my world were torn in two,
Blacked out, dissolved, I think I would remember
(As if transfixed in unsurrendering amber)
This hour best of all the hours I knew:

When cars come backing into the shabby station
Children scuffing the seats, and the women driving
With ribbons around their hair, and the trains arriving,
And the men getting off with tired but practiced motion.

Yes, I would remember my life like this, she said:
Autumn, the platform red with Virginia creeper,

And a man coming toward me, smiling, the evening paper
Under his arm, and his hat pushed back on his head;
And wood smoke lying like haze on the quiet town,
And dinner waiting, and the sun not yet gone down.

SIGRID DE LIMA   *[1951]*

*Sigrid de Lima, who was born in 1921 and graduated from Barnard
College in 1942, received her MS in journalism from Columbia in 1944.
For her first two novels,* Captain's Beach *and* The Swift Cloud, *she was
awarded the Prix de Rome in 1953. Her portrait in* Captain's Beach *of
Mr. Mortlock slopping up the floor represents the seediest kind of husband, a man who becomes senile, as "helpless as a baby," before the book
ends.*

A Seedy Husband

"When I wake up and want a drink of water, I always get up and get
it from the bathroom," said Mortlock. He put his finger next to the
faucet, and the water sprayed all over the kitchen floor.

"Look out what you're doing!" exclaimed Mrs. Mortlock.

"I'm sorry. I'll take care of it. I'm real sorry."

All the sorriness came rushing out of him. But he wasn't just sorry
about the splatters of water on the floor, or even that the little dog
was sick in the corner, or that, well, that he'd got a load on, the way
a fellow will sometimes, or that he did pretty often, and that things,
well, everything hadn't worked out so; and he was pretty much of
a bum, he'd admit that, his own fault, too, though, a lot of things,
and he was sorry. "I'm sorry. I'm real sorry." She'd have to understand that. And she probably did.

But she'd look at him and say being sorry don't make the splatters
come off the floor or make the dog any better or help any of the
other things, and she'd be right. She'd be perfectly right. "I'll get a
rag and clean that mess up," he said.

"Not the dish towel," said Mrs. Mortlock. He was reaching for it.

"One of them rags under the sink," suggested Mrs. Cassidy. "I
always say," she continued, "a man is more trouble around the house
than doing things yourself. They don't never catch on."

Mortlock dabbed away at the floor, turning the rag over, leaving sloppy wet streaks. His wife watched him and his aunt watched him.

"Leave it," said Mrs. Mortlock finally, "that's good enough."

"It's **not very good, though,** but for a man it's good enough, I suppose."

All men, thought Mortlock wretchedly. He filled the dog's pan now with water and tried very carefully to carry it across the room. It slopped a little, and he noticed that it slopped.

"Here you are, Schnitzel."

From the minute you're born you're doing things you're not supposed to do. Even little tiny babies messing and puking all over the place and when you get older the things you do are worse and worse. Girls do things sometimes that they're ashamed of, but, well, it's different and they're always the ones that do the cleaning up afterwards anyways.

He looked at his wife. She was standing at the sink washing the vegetables, and all he could see was her back. After he'd gone she'd get out the mop and fix up the floor. He knew that.

He got a mixed-up tender feeling for her, looking at her like that and at the wrinkled gray cotton stockings she was wearing, and the old worn-out shoes, and the great big blue cotton skirt that hiked up a little bit in back. Then she leaned over to put something into the garbage can and her skirt hiked up even farther, up over the place where her stockings were rolled, and he could see the back space of her knees, bare like that, with a kind of long dimple in it.

In a way it's the women's fault for having us in the first place. . . .

ADRIENNE CECILE RICH   *[1951]*

Adrienne Cecile Rich has had an opportunity to apply the theory she expresses in this early poem, published in 1951 while she was still attending Radcliffe College. She carries a husband through his "estranged intensities," meanwhile raising her three sons and writing more poetry.

An Unsaid Word

She who has power to call her man
From that estranged intensity

Where his mind forages alone,
Yet keeps her peace and leaves him free,
And when his thoughts to her return
Stands where he left her, still his own,
Knows this the hardest thing to learn.

SAMPLER: Helpmates

Women of the type I was at that time like to have men sick in bed.
Then a truce is declared. An illusion of complete possession takes
the place of the feeling of strain that one has all the time that one
is trying to hold the whole attention of a man. Temporarily he is
ours without a chance to escape, without even the desire for escape.
Delivered into one's hands, he is helpless as a baby—dependent upon
us for everything, dependent upon our sympathy, our judgment,
and our love. Ceasing to try and maintain his separate individuality
by assertion of opinion or by independent action, a man sick in bed
reverts to an undifferentiated infantilism.

—MABEL DODGE LUHAN, in
Intimate Memories, 1936

After all, marriage is not a natural state. Or let us put it another
way: marriage isn't natural for men, though it is for women. A man
doesn't have to be actually married. After a fashion, he *is* married,
always, even when he isn't. He has all the advantages of the state;
women look after him whether or not they are married to him—the
landlady, the cleaning woman, the waitress, the girl at the drug-
store. They love him instinctively. They spoil him. One or another
of them will certainly go to bed with him if so requested, no matter
how unappetizing he may be. There is always a girl. The bachelor
may find life complicated in other ways, but he is not frustrated
when it comes to women.

A woman, on the other hand, has a rougher time of it—until she has
roped, tied and branded her man and made a comfortable home for
the children. Necessity, as well as instinct, sends the ladies pell-mell
to the altar; it is only the secondary things, social pressure or conscience, that send the men. All this being so, I find it wonderful and
beautiful that two such opposite sorts of creatures, who really have

nothing in common except their species, should so often manage to get together and acquire the technique of marriage.

—EMILY HAHN, in *Spousery*, 1956

Once I'd put my mind to it, I was sure I could make my man happy. Would he make me happy? I thought so. I knew exactly what I wished and would make it very clear to him. I wanted someone who would love me and find me passionately desirable as well as droll; someone who would think I was a genius and cherish my whims and preoccupations; and someone who would follow my rehearsals and wait backstage and take me out to eat when I was tired and applaud my performances with zest and delight and also, of course, with discrimination, but never with just discrimination alone. If I were late from rehearsals, he would, of course, cook dinner—or he would hire a maid to cook. He would consider my taste in household furniture and clothes sound; nobody ever had before, but he would. He would do work that interested him and I would naturally be interested in it too. After the war he would be free to take vacations whenever it suited me and we would travel and work and be enthusiastic together. If any of this seems preposterous or even pitiful, consider the attitude of any male artist toward his bride.

—AGNES DE MILLE, in her autobiography,
And Promenade Home, 1958

My husband gave me a broom one Christmas. This wasn't right. No one can tell me it was meant kindly.

—GRACE PALEY, in a short story,
"An Interest in Life," 1959

LAEL TUCKER WERTENBAKER   *[1957]*

Lael Tucker Wertenbaker, who was foreign correspondent for Time *and* Life *from 1940 to 1946, was born in Pennsylvania in 1909 and graduated from the University of Kentucky. Her book about her husband's death is an agonizing but splendid portrait of a man who could love and could die. Mrs. Wertenbaker, who now lives in New York City, is a novelist and free-lance writer.*

This Is How He Was

Our marriage had survived all that it had to survive, including the high ideal we set for it from the first intensely romantic moments when we fell in love, at the ages of thirty-four and forty-two, in London, in wartime. By this I mean it survived deviations from the ideal and the ideal survived and we never settled for less.

It survived wartime separations in wartime capitals and the first winter months in Ciboure when we saw no one else at all, before we had learned how to live that way. It survived an inexcusable and neurotic piece of behavior on my part in our second year of marriage; the seventy-six hours we went without sleep or an instant's separation violently settling with it; and the months when Wert continued to punish me after he had forgiven me and I continued to seek absolution after I had received it. It survived the year he took a job as an executive which he did not want and commuted to New York from its suburbs which he did not like and we spent too much money and lived badly and went into debt and he was at his sullenest and I was at my sloppiest. It survived a Little Toidey which I bought for Chris and Wert burned.

This last-mentioned incident was both comic and cosmic. All three of us lost our formidable tempers at once. I felt that I was defending women and children against the age-old tyranny of man and Wert felt that he was defending man against modern enslavement by women, children, and offensive gadgets. Chris was defending his selfish comfort in a universe still scaled too big for him. When the dust, or rather the ashes, of that battle settled, an enduring family peace was established, with Wert as undisputed head of his family. Later I got a china pot with roses on it for Chris, which Chris loved and his father admired. I found that the delight of yielding to a demanding man was great. I make no moral of this. You can only yield with such pride to a man whose respect for what he gets is as great as his desire to have it. I can only comment, in this short homily from a preacher's daughter, that a chain of command in a functioning unit of uncowed and contributing individuals operates better than a constant struggle for authority or what is sometimes called equality.

Wert made one note among many others for the book he was going to write called *The Time of Enchantment*, the middle book of the Barons trilogy, of which *The Barons* and *The Death of Kings* were the first and third volumes:

In all large organizations where one man is at the top, the others near the top will fight to get there, and so the morality of that organization will be conditioned by the struggle for power, and that morality will determine the organization's external, as well as its internal, dealings. The only way to avoid this power complex, this power struggle, is by keeping the organization small and powerless (as in a very small business or a very small kingdom) or by curbing the power of the top man by vesting power in other—and frequently hostile—organizations (as in checks and balances of U.S. Government or kingship in Britain). Let loose the struggle for power anywhere, and it will destroy all other concepts.

In the small and powerless kingdom of our family, the amount of power retained in each pair of hands was early defined. This reduced considerably the turbulence generated by four positive personalities adjusting to each other within a succession of places and years and circumstances.

We were always at economic peace with each other, and this is rarer than it sounds. I don't think Wert and I in twelve years ever had a quarrel based on money, who spent it for what, who made it or did not make it, and certainly not whose it was. When we married, I owned some clothes, household furnishings, and a typewriter. He had just paid off old debts, had a small amount of furniture, and five thousand dollars, with which we inexplicably bought land in Virginia, which we later inexplicably sold for no profit. We both had jobs. We found ourselves at the time in the middle-income middle class. Later we trespassed in the domain of the very, very rich on the unlimited expense accounts allowed by corporations to employees in wartime Europe. Later still we were dependent on our wildly fluctuating separate fortunes as writers. I always took a sensuous pleasure in being with Wert in luxurious surroundings. It was partly because he fitted so comfortably into them and, through luck or legerdemain, often managed to achieve them; it was partly for the feeling, derived from the proudly impecunious Southern heritage we shared, of trespassing where we claimed more right than many on whom we trespassed. This feeling was in no wise diminished by our disapproval, on the simplest principles, of the social bases of excessive luxuriousness. We were not solemn about it, but laughed at our own complacency. "Change your social status today, lady?" Wert asked me, as we dressed in our tourist cabin for dinner with first-class diplomatic friends on the S.S. *America* in 1952. "Are we rich or poor right now?" the children were apt to inquire before making a demand, without considering that the answer measured either our stability or our social standing. "They prided themselves," Wert wrote in his shelved and uncompleted novel about a married couple, "that they could move from ease to simplicity with simplicity and ease."

"Being reconstructed doesn't change us from being Southerners, and there's a lot we'll never have to explain to each other," Wert said, the second time we met. If it had not been for all that hadn't had to be explained, including a sense of physical integrity that had survived earlier casual relationships, and two previous marriages apiece, the hazards would have been greater. If it had not been for all that, I should have had more difficulty in understanding his conscience and his carelessness, his intolerance and his kindness, his silent moods and sudden joys, his perfectionism and his pleasure in getting drunk. He was a difficult man, but a most rewarding one.

"Tell it as a search . . ." and it was.

We shared like forebears and cheerful childhoods in different parts of the small-town South. We had both emerged into confused and partial adulthood in the twenties, combated the depression in Manhattan, separated only by streets, and we had finally met against the background of England at war, with Wert as my editor and me as his reporter on the same publication. Often we were bemused by the parallels of our pasts and the unlikely miracle of our meeting at all, and would think we understood each other better than we did. Uncovering misunderstanding, we would stand aghast in sudden loneliness the sharper because we had thought that with this marriage we had achieved unloneliness.

What else can I call it? It is a positive state of being, resulting from a negative one: the absence of loneliness.

Perhaps what we accomplished in twelve years, in spite of all our lapses—which were always succeeded by progressions—was simply the "good marriage" that almost every couple strives for; and what made it an accomplishment was, simply again, its rarity.

One brilliant spring morning at Sneden's Landing, I tried to express my delight in us after more than ten years together by making water-ground corn-meal pancakes for Wert's breakfast and by putting beside the plate as valentine a poem of Blake's, tampering only with two pronouns.

> Love and harmony combine,
> And around our souls entwine
> While thy branches mix with mine,
> And our roots together join.

Joys upon our branches sit
Chirping loud and singing sweet;
Like gentle streams beneath our feet
Innocence and virtue meet.

I the golden fruit do bear,
Thou art clad in flowers fair;
Thy sweet boughs perfume the air,
And the turtle buildeth there.

But he was cannier than I about the maintenance of what we so valued, beyond love expressed by poetry. Several days later that spring of 1953 he told me that I was trying too hard to meet the whole challenge—of life in the United States, motherhood, writing . . . and him. Fortunately, he could take me back to Europe in a month, where I couldn't cook or wash socks or worry about the community or the schools or anything but him, our children, and writing. "I haven't had a whole wife for several months, and to hell with it," he said. I had balanced things well for a long time, but now I was allowing the parts to add up to more than a whole, the pressures to press, the worthwhile causes to take more and more time. I realized that I was weary and diffuse and neglecting all by cutting down none of what I felt to be obligations. So, also, when we had been too long alone in Ciboure and had begun to acquire, even though together, some of the insidious laziness of hermits, he would rise one day in flight and we would go off to a capital.

Being together can be like a party where you forget for a while that you are or ever were lonely. Total revelation of yourself to another is, I suppose, possible, but I would not like to so reveal myself. It seems to me something you would have to be lonely for a while afterwards to get over. I value the deep core of my own privacy and respect that of others. "Oneness" of two people is a poet's notion. What I use the made word "unloneliness" to try to describe is ineffable—two individuals in profound comfort together—and is, to me, the finest relationship of all.

Now, in the face of the two loneliest acts of all, dying and being left living, we tried to hold this feeling, to stay in this state.

"Dying is the last thing I'll have a chance to do well," Wert said. "I hope to hell I can."

I have a childlike, as Wert had an adult and analytical, acceptance of reality. Resignation is no part of such acceptance. I had checked and rechecked the medical questions involved in Wert's fate, and I found disagreement with Jim's [Dr. James Danielson] psychological attitudes, but no responsible area of doubt as to his medical conclusion. So by the time Wert had returned to himself from the semi-submersion of surgery, death had moved into the middle foreground of our lives, like a mountain, as a fact. From then on we never denied or even forgot its presence, never had to return to its existence with a sense of shock. It was no longer merely an inevitability, over the horizon, or just the possibility it had been as soon as we knew he had cancer. We used blunt, simple words when we talked about it. Wert never became obsessed with death, any more than he ever had been. It was the end of himself as he knew himself, and it became the most important thing in his life, in ours, because it was to be soon. Everything happened in this perspective. Nothing essential had changed except the perspective. Wert did not change. Since he did not change and there was no more time to grow, he consolidated, made larger, purer, all he already was as an adult in the time he had left.

This is how he was. There is neither judgment nor conclusion in what I am writing now. Any profound experience brings you new kin. Many people have talked to me since about the dying of others. People die in as many ways as they live. Montaigne said also, in an essay called "Men by Various Ways Arrive at the Same End": "Truly man is a marvelously vain, diverse, and fluctuating subject. It is hard to found a certain and uniform judgment on him." Many die of sicknesses that directly affect the brain and the will. A doing man, in contrast to a contemplative man, may, like one I know, deliberately prefer to live his last days as if he were going to live forever. Such a man has as much right to refuse to know his fate as my man had to know his.

It is an immense subject, touching everyone. I approach writing about even the death of one man with terrified humility. Can I even convey the laughter we laughed and some of our absurd fumblings? Very few men and no women I have read think well in the abstract. There is only one piece of broad wisdom I feel justified in trying to communicate, if I can, later on. Otherwise I can only tell this story as it happened to us.

The hospital staff reacted to Wert's behavior, which changed in no particular from his normal behavior, with awe and awkwardness. They knew the result of the operation, which was on his record, and I told the friends I had made among them that he knew it, too. I hoped they would react with easy frankness toward him. Instead the opaqueness of the relationship between patient and medical attendants seemed to increase. Maybe the bell tolled too insistently on that floor. Maybe the "croakers" and "stiffs" of medical neophytes are as much fearful euphemisms as "pass on" and "gone to his reward on high."

One very pretty young nurse who believed firmly in the theory of telling patients "the worst," and with whom Wert had flirted from the beginning, with his charming Southern outrageousness, said to me, "But he's so *natural*." And Jim, shaking his head in wonder, said, "Wert hasn't changed at all. He's just exactly the same."

I began to suspect that of all attitudes the rarest is simple acceptance. It is easier perhaps to be noble than natural in the face of death.

"If *you* had been skittish—if you had lied to me by one word, by one intonation, that morning, I'd be a sniveling paranoiac by now, suspicious of everything and everybody," Wert said. It was on Friday, I think, when he marked in his *carnet,* "Better."

"You mean on Tuesday?" I asked, trying to remember what phrase I had used then to put to him the truth without a lot of words or emphasis, not even sure how conscious he was.

"No. You said 'It's not too bad' then, which was fairly ambiguous. It was enough for right then. I knew what you meant. At the time. I think I knew then anyway. It was too soon when I saw the clock, and I was conscious that stinking as I felt and much as I hurt not enough had been done to me inside. You're so far down at that point, you're pretty clear about yourself. It's later on you get confused. I was full of tubes and needles in the arm and things were being said that I couldn't hear—that whispering outside the door—and you came and stood by the bed—that was on Wednesday morning—and you said to me, 'You're going to die, but you're going to have a piece of good time first.' The truth is the whole truth as you know it and nothing else sounds the same. You were telling it and I knew it and so I felt fine. It would be no damn good for me if you hadn't. I'm a suspicious son of a bitch by nature and afraid of fooling myself or being fooled."

We decided at the time, however, to fool other people. Later we were rather sorry. It was unfair, especially to a few of them, and not Wert's way. I wish I could have been more honest with more of the people who loved Wert. It would have honored them and given them a chance to know they were saying good-bye.

Wert's strength was the kind that could only be undermined or rotted away. Mine was a kind of toughness, resilient rather than resistant, and it sprang back in response to his. Alone, or with other people, it bent under the strain. Acceptance does not obviate strain, only simplifies it. I could neither give nor accept comfort. And I was terrified of tears.

There were warning signs that I could fail Wert and then he would have to die alone. To sleep I took pills for the first time in my life. I woke up at three in the mornings, sobbing, and had to wring myself dry and take another pill. The one evening I cried in front of Suzie, who loved Wert, she immediately burst into such a flood of loving tears I realized what a mean restraint it had imposed that I had not let her weep sooner by refusing to weep myself, and that I must not get started. Later, when I had to tell three people the truth, I came out all over with hives, as I had done during the first days when I was asking for medical information on the basis of the facts.

So, for the rest, I told the whopping social lie: giving out that the operation as planned had been successfully performed. And most people believed me and those who did not most kindly did not let on. It was very restful, actually, to act out now and then the part I should have liked to be living. I'm a poor liar as a rule. Wert laughed at me for being so convincing.

"Protect yourself, honey," said Wert. "This one's on you. I need you and I'm a selfish bastard."

ELLEN CURRIE   *[1958]*

Ellen Currie, who was born in New York City in 1930 and graduated from Adelphi College, has published stories in The New Yorker *and in* Accent. *She is now at work on a novel to be published by The Dial Press.*

Moses Supposes

The first thing Patrick heard that morning, in his mother-in-law's damp, cold, closed-up beach house, was the crash and stammer of the air-locked shower on the floor beneath his room. He lay catty-corner on an iron bed, more or less under a sandy and dilapidated quilt. He was sunburned and gloomy and twenty years old. There were no sheets on the bed and neither it nor the quilt was adequate to his length. He was freezing.

The person taking the shower was Patrick's wife, Mona. He had met her the summer before last in this same seaside village, where he'd worked as a waiter at the Balmy Days Hotel. Since he had no money and no daring, considered himself to be low on charm, and came equipped with a record of debacle in dealings with children, small animals and girls, he'd thought for awhile that being in love with Mona was the worst thing that ever hit him. They made a ludicrous couple. She was a little, noisy, pretty girl; a sort of bluejay, heretical, put together by a reckless hand. He was peripheral—horribly tall, ferocious and shy. He knew that he didn't have a chance. But then one winter night, in the Lion's Den back at Columbia, she'd said rather tragically over a grilled cheese sandwich that she thought they'd better get married; so they had. Eight months later she surreptitiously departed from their "studio" apartment on 115th Street, taking with her the dress she was married in and nearly all the joy he had ever known.

That had been on Monday. Her mother called Patrick Monday night, to tell him that Mona was perfectly fine, but incommunicado. By Tuesday he was breathing fast and had managed to loosen all his lower front teeth. On Wednesday his mother-in-law, who had an aptitude for intrigue, threw out a tip that enabled him to track Mona. But here it was Thursday, and he had yet to set eyes on her.

He'd walked up from the station on Wednesday afternoon with his hands in his pockets and his heart in his mouth. He found the door unlocked and the house deserted. It was a peculiar house, a partly dismantled shrine to a former owner, a man named Dizzy Bailey, who seemed to have been a comedian of the baggy-pants school. Now and then Mona's mother carted away some of the theatrical memorabilia and stowed it in a closet underneath the stairs, but for the most part she contented herself with supplementing the decor—she ran to bathrooms papered with *Punch* covers, pieces of batik tacked up on walls, and lamps converted from champagne jeroboams. The living room was two stories high and in addition to it the first floor contained a kitchen, a bedroom and a bath. Patrick went into that bedroom. A few of Mona's things were there. On the second floor, five more bedrooms opened off a mezzanine. Distributed among them, in a fairly carefree fashion, were seventeen uncomfortable beds, several of them double-deckers. Dizzy Bailey had liked to have people around him, and so did Mona's mother.

Patrick had sat around for a while—stranded in the godforsaken whimsicality of the living room, having a crisis of nerves and sweating forlornly in the Indian summer heat. Then he hung the ninety-dollar suit his father had bought him for a trousseau proprietorially in Mona's closet. He'd discovered a derelict pair of bathing trunks on the porch, and he put them on. The weather was freakish—too warm for fall, but never quite as warm as you'd thought it was, and far too cold for bathing trunks.

Stippled with gooseflesh and rejoicing in his own discomfort, Patrick toured the beach front, searching for Mona. He didn't find her. In fact, he didn't see anyone at all, and he was in no mood for looking at oceans. The houses he could see were shuttered and desolate. There was no one fishing in the surf. There was no girl sitting out on the end of the jetty, where he'd first seen Mona, alone and cross-legged, her face toward Spain.

He plowed along through the soft sand of the dunes, exploring his character. He had it in for himself and he didn't see why Mona shouldn't too. He drafted quite a bill of particulars: he decided it was high time he figured out whether he was going to be St. Francis or a man of steel; he decided he wasn't either—he was just a leftover altar boy with invisible scapulars strung all over him. He decided that although he was six feet four inches tall, he was skinny as a rail and astigmatic and probably not even, if you could believe what people told you, very virile. He was a prig and a grind; he was sulky; he was sentimental. All the A's and 99's and Excellent's and Splendid's he'd ever aspired to, ever won, were tattooed on his chest. He belonged in skirts, a sprig of lilac pinned to his collar, tears in his eyes. He saw right through himself, and he didn't see why Mona shouldn't.

By the time he'd gotten it all worked out, he was a million miles from nowhere. When he got back to the house, Mona's door was on the hook and his clothes were on the floor outside it. If he was any kind of a man, he said to himself as he stamped upstairs, he'd break down that door and swarm all over her. But it simply wasn't in him. He lay down on the first bed he came to. The last thing that assailed him before he fell almost instantly asleep was the terrible knowledge that his whole life, up to and including that day, had been a washout.

He had no real hopes for this chilly Thursday morning, either, but the disadvantages of his situation, plus the fact that he was hungry, changed yesterday's anguish to a kind of noble pessimism. Somewhat stiffened by it, he got up.

When he went downstairs and into the kitchen, Mona was scouring the sink. She was wearing an outside track sweater and a pair of faded jeans. It was Patrick's track sweater. This circumstance so cheered him that he had the sensation of having been dropped, upright, several feet through space.

"Hello," he said politely.

"Hello, morose," Mona said without turning. She sluiced water around the sink, squinted at it, and went to work with the scouring powder again. All of this rub-a-dub-dub looked awfully out of character to him.

He hooked his bare foot around the leg of an old bridge chair painted turquoise and dragged it out from the table. It made a satisfactory noise on the gritty floor. Mona didn't look up. Patrick sat down, feeling conspicuous and unsightly, but attracting remarkably little attention. He sneezed.

Mona looked at him then. "Is that sunburn?" she asked, in a tone that played off scorn against repulsion.

"No," Patrick said. "That was a sneeze."

"Is that sunburn all over you?"

"No," Patrick said, which was a lie. He was susceptible to scrofulous, peeling sunburns, of the type that never turned to tan. This condition called up in him a disproportionate sense of shame. He sneezed again.

"Have you got a cold too?" Mona wanted to know. She was taking on a certain air of menace.

"Yes, I have a cold too," Patrick said. "It's all part of my death wish."

Mona put the can of scouring powder down on the table beside him. It was called Bon Ami. He was moved almost to tears.

"I'm sort of hungry," he said pitifully.

"You can't feel too bad if you're hungry."

"Since when did you know how I feel? You never know how I feel."

"You never know how I feel, either," Mona said. "You only know how *you* feel; you never know how *I* feel."

"That's true," Patrick said. The conversation appeared to him to be going into a skid. He propped his elbows on the table and his head on his hands. He was cold, feverish, sore, miserable. He cared more about this girl than anything he could think of, and he couldn't even talk to her. She jogged his elbows off the table and swabbed it with a damp cloth. He sat with his clasped hands caught between his bare and hairy knees and inventoried, bleakly, the shelf above the kitchen table. He counted three different brands of oregano, all of the possible permutations of garlic, a corkscrew, a bottle of bitters, some smelling salts, and a jar of face cream which numbered among its ingredients not only estrogenic hormones but royal gélé, right, so to speak, out of the mouth of the queen bee. All those things reminded him of his mother-in-law. His mother-in-law had married four times. He reflected that Mona had a dreadful heredity. And her environment had been nothing to brag about.

"You don't need hormones, kiddy," Patrick said mournfully.

"What is that supposed to mean?" Mona said. She was busy with a broom now. She'd been holding it like a hockey stick but she switched her grip, the better, possibly, to swat him with it.

"You swing that thing at me and I'll smack you so hard you'll fly up to the ceiling," he warned her.

"If you think I came out here with somebody else, you're out of your mind," Mona said. "Try that on for size."

It was a thought that hadn't crossed his mind, but it did so now, with painful heat. "I know you from the old country," he shouted. "Try that on for size!"

"I just want to tell you one thing," Mona said, poking her head at him and leaning tensely on her broom. "I came out here to get my mind off my mind, that's the only reason. And I was doing all right until you showed up. Now put your *clothes* on and don't keep *shivering.*"

"Not me," Patrick said. His clothes were still in a heap before her bedroom door; he'd seen them.

"If I make some scrambled eggs, will you put your clothes on?" Mona said blackly.

"No," Patrick said, after thinking it over.

"I suppose you came out here for a serious talk. Well, I can't have a serious talk with anybody that looks the way you do."

The wall behind Patrick had been covered, in a wayward decorative impulse, with straw hats hung on nails. Hats of all shapes and sizes hung there, in various colors and stages of decrepitude—hats that might have struck the taste of coolie laborers, Calvin Coolidge, members of Calypso bands, middle-aged ladies on Caribbean cruises. Patrick selected a thing with a floppy fringed brim and a pink felt octopus wearing sunglasses fixed to its crown. Mona's mother had brought it home from Nassau. She thought it was a riot. Patrick stood up, bowed, clapped the hat on his head, brushed off his trunks and generally put himself in order, all with a tight smile for his wife.

"Very funny," Mona said.

He suspected that she did think he was funny. He didn't think he was funny at all. He stalked into the living room and lay down on his back on the rattan couch. He pulled one of the loose cushions from the back of the couch and folded his arms across it. The cushion was lumpy and smelled of damp. He hugged it against the chill in the room, determined not to think about anything. He would not hold two opposing points of view at once; he would not examine both sides of any question; he would be stoic, ruthless and hard.

Autographed photographs, programs, caricatures, cartoons, almost obliterated the board walls of the living room. They dated from Dizzy Bailey's time. Patrick studied them, prostrate. He was full of tender feelings as a rule, and chance mementos of other people's lives inflamed in him a counterfeit nostalgia—they seemed to offer hints of something panoramic, something poignant, meaningful and large. Today, for no very clear reason, all that salvage, growing yearly more distant and irrelevant in its frames, disgusted him. He loathed it. Patrick looked up at the more-than-life-sized portrait of Dizzy Bailey that hung, suspended on lengths of cable, from the peak of the roof. It showed him, grinning, mugging, very ocher in complexion, behind bars. He was wearing a broadly striped convict's suit and a little round pillbox hat and a ball and chain on his ankle. Outside of the cell, taking stock of him, sat a tiny marcelled pompon of a dog. According to the written testimony of all these people in these glossy photographs, all these people who had licked their lips and smiled, Dizzy Bailey was a great little guy. For the first time, Patrick was prepared to doubt it. Dizzy Bailey looked pretty sinister, if you really looked at him. He looked sly. That dog, Patrick saw, bellied down in a pose he had mistaken for fidelity and trust, had Dizzy Bailey's number. That dog was wasting for a chance to sink its teeth in Dizzy Bailey. On the other hand, it knew, ball and chain or no, that Dizzy Bailey still had one free foot. Dizzy Bailey'd been kicking that dog around for many a moon. Maybe. On the third hand, maybe not. If you looked at things one way, they were one thing. If you looked at them another way, they turned into something else. The force of this encounter with truth made Patrick's face hot, and he pulled his hat brim down over his eyes, groaning. He listened to Mona banging things out in the kitchen. Misery sat on his chest.

Then it began to rain, with a spatter like a handful of pebbles flung against the house. He reached out and plucked the string of an old standard lamp that stood behind the couch. The room was suddenly cozy, even warmer, lighted in the rain. In his present temper he was inclined to regret this. It happened that Mona thought that the use of electricity during rainstorms invited catastrophe, though, and he hoped to lure her into the living room to turn the lamp off. He latched his fingers across his eyes and watched the doorway to the kitchen through them. Before very long, Mona appeared there.

"Are you going to put on your clothes like a human being, or not?" she said aloofly.

"Not," Patrick said. She didn't look grieved, especially. "I'm not a human being, kiddy," Patrick said. "I'm just an old bone that's been thrown out of the cage."

"I don't mind it so much when you're just maladjusted," Mona said. "But when you're melancholy, that I resent." She wandered over to the lamp and made a fleeting pass at it, before she caught herself and put her hands behind her for a stroll around the room. "Raining," she announced, lighting on a window seat.

"You're uncannily correct," Patrick said. "Uncannily."

"It's cold in here," Mona said.

"Check," Patrick said.

Mona went over to his clothes, piled helter-skelter on the floor, and swung her foot in an arc across them. "I see you wore your blue shirt."

"So?" Patrick said.

"I happen to know you think you look pretty cute in your blue shirt."

"You don't know half what you think you know," Patrick said.

"I don't know anything, to hear you tell it," Mona said without rancor. "I don't know anything, I don't feel anything. Except the wrong things, of course." She stirred his clothes gingerly with the toe of her sneaker.

"Not at all," Patrick said, speaking up at the roof, "not at *all*. I know you're a fine type. Sensitive. I know you won that poetry prize at the Greek Games last year. I read that Lyric to Athena, boy. I'm familiar with that picture of a clown you painted in your senior year at Music and Art."

"What's the matter with my clown?" Mona asked dangerously.

"Nothing's the matter with him. He's smashing. He's posh. I'm crazy about him myself. I just hate pictures of clowns, that's all. They're what everybody paints when they get their first insight."

"Thanks a big bunch," Mona said. She was considering his clothes, bent with her legs apart in a stance she might as well have employed to inspect a dead bat on a back road somewhere.

"I thought you were a truth seeker," Patrick said. "Or I wouldn't have brought it up."

She picked up his shirt by one cuff, swept it along the floor and tossed it at him. It missed the couch and fell on the floor beside him with a light clatter of buttons against boards. He paid it no attention. She tossed his trousers at him too, and they sailed completely over the couch, raining change, and landed on the other side. She dusted her hands and went back into the kitchen. He heard her thumping around out there. After a while she brought in a tumbler of orange juice and put it down on a battered table covered with snapshots of Dizzy Bailey, under glass. The orange juice was just out of reach. He left it there. She brought in a tray with a plate of scrambled eggs and some silver on it and put it beyond the orange juice.

"Just sit up and eat like a human being, will you," she said. "I don't want egg all over everywhere."

"I believe I can be trusted to eat a few scrambled eggs," Patrick said grandly, "without littering the whole countryside."

She went back into the kitchen and stayed there. He held his straw hat on his head with one hand and his cushion on his chest with the other and, with difficulty, raised the upper half of his body to shout: "Come in here!" Nothing happened. He sat up and swallowed two enormous forkfuls of scrambled eggs, rearranging the rest to conceal the dent he'd made in them. Then he went into the kitchen, wearing his hat and carrying his cushion. Mona was standing by the stove, holding a piece of toast between her teeth and taking off her jeans. She'd already taken off her sweater. She was wearing a lavender bathing suit, not her own. He could see on her shoulders the pale familiar streaks where last year's straps had crossed and these straps didn't. She folded the jeans and put them, with the sweater, on a chair. Then she took a big red dunce cap off the wall and put it on her head. Her hair was straight and fair and, he thought, pastoral. It stuck out from under the pointed hat in wisps, though, and she resembled an eighteen-year-old, inexperienced witch. She took a bite out of her toast and stood looking at him, not very friendly.

"Where's *my* toast?" Patrick said.

"I'm not using any toaster in this storm," Mona said. "I'm not electrocuting myself just to stuff you full of toast. This is yesterday's toast."

He knew her habit of saving scraps and dabs of this and that and consuming them, dutifully, days later. It made him uncomfortable, but it made him feel at home. His mother did it too. He thought it was something basic in the female character. Something a little bit admirable and a little bit corrupt. Mona looked pathetic standing there, chewing on her old abandoned toast. Her summer tan was going fast and the cold brought a chalky bloom to her skin. She was also slightly bowlegged.

"I forgot my eggs," he said. He went into the living room, dropped his cushion on the couch, picked up his eggs and his orange juice and stood in the doorway to bolt his breakfast while he watched her. He thought she looked unhappy and cold.

"Let's light the oven," he said.

"What for?"

"For the sport of the thing," he said. "Maybe we'll make a few loaves of toast. A lifetime supply of secondhand toast, wouldn't you like that?"

"Sure I would," Mona said. "Wouldn't anybody?"

"Anybody with his wits about him," Patrick said. He put down his empty plate and knelt in front of the stove. There was no pilot light for the oven and he had to light the gas with a match. He did this with considerable trepidation, half-expecting to ignite the octopus on his hat and turn himself into a human torch. The gas caught with a pop, though, and no damage. He straightened up, leaving the oven door open. Mona was huddled on one of the turquoise bridge chairs. She had her heels on the seat and her chin rested on her right knee. There was a big yellow bruise on her left shin and the area around her eyes was smudged with violet. She looked starved and fugitive in the darkening kitchen, like an underprivileged raccoon. Patrick wanted to turn on the overhead light, but in another way he didn't. He didn't want to affront her in any way, suddenly. He'd have gone, for the moment, away out of his way not to cause her any pain. It was raining very hard.

"Why don't you move your chair out into the middle of the room, baby," he said tenderly. "It'd be warmer."

"Don't call me that," Mona said.

"Listen, Mona," he began fretfully.

"Screw you," Mona said.

"What'd *I* do?" Patrick shouted. "What'd I *do?* I come home from a three-hour lab and you're gone. I find a note on the lampshade. 'There's a lamb chop in the refrigerator'—I need a lamp chop like I need a third leg. How would you like it?"

"I guess I wouldn't like it," Mona said.

"I wouldn't do it to you," Patrick said.

"Well, I would do it to you and I did do it to you, so shut up."

"Everything was cotton candy and all of a sudden I'm no place. That's a fine way to treat me!"

"I'm sorry if I hurt your feelings," Mona said courteously. "I didn't mean it that way."

"Feelings, *feelings,*" Patrick bellowed. "Aren't you happy, or what?"

"The next son of a bitch that asks me am I happy, I'm going to spit in his eye," Mona said.

"I'd like to know where you got all this language," Patrick said, infuriated, "that's what I'd like to know."

"I'm a married woman and I can use any language I feel like," Mona told him. "I can use Esperanto if I feel like it. I can say any words I feel like." She gave him samples of words she felt like saying at the moment.

"Your mother should get a load of that," Patrick said.

"My mother," Mona said. She put her hands in the hair that straggled from under her hat and gave it a pull.

"Your mother's all right," Patrick said. "I don't like you when you act that way. Your mother's a great old girl."

"She walks, she talks, she crawls on her belly like a reptile," Mona said. "She's a great old girl."

"She figured out where you were, anyway."

"She figured out where I was because I told her. That's how smart she is. I told her not to tell you, of course. But she has no conception of honor whatsoever. What else did she tell you?"

"Plenty," Patrick said grimly, lying.

"Like what, for instance?" Mona asked, looking at him.

"Are you alone out here?" he said, feeling sick.

"In my estimation that's an extremely vile thing for you to say to me," Mona said haughtily. "And my mother never said anything like that to you, either. And you don't even believe it, which makes it worse."

"I don't know what all she said to me," Patrick said. "She said not to worry. That was pretty funny. She said men were different from women, which wasn't exactly news. She kept kissing me and crying and getting philosophical. I think she's reading Ouspensky again, she's all muddled up. I mean more than always."

"Oh, the poor thing," Mona said.

"What about me? I'm the poor thing in this scenario."

"You're just so pure you could die of it, Tiger."

"Why are you so mad at me?"

"Don't be wistful, you crumb," Mona said. "That's not significant." She picked up a waxed paper carton that had held orange juice, drained the last quarter-inch into a glass and shied the carton at a brown paper bag full of trash. The whole business toppled, dumping eggshells on the floor. "My garbage runneth over," she said sadly.

"*Our* garbage," Patrick said. He went over and cleaned up the mess.

"Pardon me," Mona said. "Togetherness. I forgot."

"I love you," Patrick said dismally, on his knees among the eggshells.

"I know it," Mona said, drinking her orange juice.

"Well, then, don't you? I mean, love me?"

Mona shrugged. "That's not terribly significant, as I see it."

"If you run across anything that's significant," Patrick said, "I hope to Christ you'll let me know!" The kitchen was getting very dark, despite the glow drifting in from the other room. He found two candle stubs set in clamshells on the drainboard of the sink. He lighted them and brought them over to the table. They made for a queer, rather ritual atmosphere. He sat down opposite Mona, scowling at her lack of appreciation of his efforts at homemaking. "Listen, Mona," he said, clearing his throat, "just tell me one thing. Don't get mad, now, just tell me one thing. Where were you yesterday when I was looking for you?"

"It's none of your business where I was. You have a dirty mind. I climbed a tree, if it's any of your business."

"A tree."

"You know what a tree is, Tiger. With leaves on. Not that this was much of a tree, but it was all I could find on short notice. I just felt like sitting in a tree. Like I'd led a wasted life on account of not having sat in enough trees, or like I might not get another chance, or I don't know, something wiggy. I was looking at bark. I hope you realize you're embarrassing me."

"Bark."

"You're acquainted with bark?"

"Bark," Patrick said, as though a great many things had straightened out for him. "I used to eat it." He put his hand across his eyes and squeezed them.

"Verree funnee," Mona said.

"I did," Patrick said guiltily. "We had a sweet cherry tree in the yard and I ate off all the bark as high as I could reach and then I piled stones around the trunk and ate more. It died, the tree."

"Are you riddled with remorse, by any chance?"

Patrick looked at her with real dislike. "I killed that tree. If that tree had been a man, they'd have hung me."

"I think that's pretty cute," Mona said in a nasty way.

"It doesn't exactly haunt me night and day."

"I think it's pretty cute the way your eyelids puff up when you look at those pictures of baskets of kittens."

"Carry on," Patrick said.

"I like the way you get religious when you see those old raggedy women raiding trash cans on Broadway. I like the way it makes you think of your mother and my mother and me. And all the time you know darn well your mother's playing mah-jongg in the Bronx and I'm eating sugar doughnuts in the snack bar at Barnard. And my mother, beloved wife of Tom, Dick, Harry and Max, is over on the couch on Park Avenue, giving her analyst an earful."

"You have a deep understanding of my character," Patrick said unpleasantly. "You have some terrific insights at times."

"That's right."

"O.K.," Patrick said. "If you want to be that way, *be* that way."

"If I gave you half a chance you'd be one of those people who's always hauling other people around to look at sunsets and expecting them to vibrate when you vibrate. You're a truth and beauty monger, and I hate them all."

"Well, I'm very sorry," Patrick said formally, making wet, interesting circles with the bottom of her glass, "but that's the way I am."

"I know how you are. I don't have to *like* it. I like the kind of people that keep a tommy gun in their violin case. That's the kind of people I like."

"Well, you married me," Patrick said bravely, "so you better get used to me."

"I'm no good at this married business, I'm very sorry but I don't know the first thing about it. It was all a big mistake. One time after we got married I brought home some strawberries, regular strawberries in a box. And after I got them home, I didn't know *what* I was supposed to do with them. Do you *cut* the green things off, or do you *pull* the green things off? I had to call my mother up and ask her what to do with strawberries. She gave me a whole lot of chatter, but you think she knew? Some authority. If I told *you* I didn't know what to do with strawberries, you'd start sobbing, you'd think it was so great. Or else you'd give me that holy look all night that makes me want to retch."

"So I cry in the movies," Patrick said irritably, "put a bullet in my heart."

"Two years ago I was sixteen and I didn't even know you," Mona said, sounding rattled. "I was sixteen years old and I was having a very good time. What did I have to meet you for? I was learning to drink beer. Every afternoon we'd all go over to the Alcove and Archie Beaufort would feed me a teaspoonful of beer. He was my boy friend. And every once in a while he'd kiss me on the ear. I can see his big white face. That was probably the last good year I'll ever have."

"You should have married Archie Beaufort," Patrick said.

"Archie Beaufort was a goon."

Patrick tried to take her hand and she rapped his knuckles with the handle of a knife. He groaned. "There's just one thing you seem to be forgetting."

"Don't tell me, let me guess," Mona said. "You love me—yes?"

Patrick took a breath, groaned again, and went back to making circles with the glass.

"I'm sorry if I hurt your feelings," Mona said, "but it makes me nervous to hear people say that. I've been hearing it for ten thousand years. Like one time before my father died he lost all his money. More than one time, but one time in particular. And we all had to stay in one room in some ratty hotel near Forty-second Street. I slept with my mother and him. Gordon and Monroe slept—I don't know—in a shoebox on the window sill; in a bureau drawer, like Kayo. Anyway, in the middle of the night the phone would ring and he'd get up cursing and put his clothes on and they'd fight awhile and he'd go out. And right in the middle of the action, the whole time, they'd both keep screaming, 'I love you, I love you.' And the people next door would hammer on the walls and they'd scream it out louder, 'I love you.' Especially my mother, she's very big on that."

"Did she?" Patrick asked.

"Did she love him? My father? Sure. She didn't know him from Adam, but she was all over him, like ivy. He was nice all right. He used to shave my eyebrows."

"Off?" Patrick said in horror.

"No, no, the in-between part. I happened to be a very hairy child. My brother Gordon didn't like my father terribly well," she went on, dreamy and detached. "He liked his own father. He used to carry around a big slate with MY FATHER'S NAME WAS SANDERS CAREW written on it, until my mother made him cut it out. She thought it hurt my father's feelings, which I doubt. My father couldn't stand Gordon. He was always knocking Gordon's teeth out or what not, by accident. Playing baseball. Gordon detested baseball. Gordon was pretty nice about it, except for the slate."

"And what about Monroe?" Patrick said.

"Monroe's father was another father altogether," Mona said. "You know that. Those two were before my time, Gordon's father and Monroe's father."

"Did Monroe like your father?"

"I don't think so. Once he threw a roll at him."

"Holy hat," Patrick said. "It sounds awful." He was distressed. He disapproved of Mona's mother and her brothers because he thought they were not serious; but he liked them. They were gaudy —all fuss and feathers and bounce. Now they'd been jarred out of focus. They were mortal, guilty. They were strangers.

"I guess," Mona said. "And then she married What's-his-name, and it was more of the same, only he had lots of cash. We went to live in France for a while and it was all very chic in a downtrodden way. They planted the boys in some terrible school and What's-his-name's sousy old French aunt was supposed to keep me out of their hair. We all used to eat dinner at a big long table under a chandelier made out of glass morning glories. We were about a mile away from each other. And What's-his-name would sit at one end of the table and give my mother the blast. And she'd blot herself on her napkin and give it back from the other end, the counterblast. But anyway, what I started to say, they'd both stick in all these 'I love you's'— their veins would be bulging, that didn't stop them—'I love you, I love you.' And they did. In a manner of speaking."

"What *was* his name?" Patrick asked nervously. He and Mona were strangers. There was nothing between them but a kitchen table, they had no points of reference but a candle in a clamshell apiece and a couple of cockeyed hats. It was intolerable, shameful,

He didn't want to be married to this girl. He couldn't think how it had happened.

"Jacques," Mona said. "Moldy. Was he moldy! He was always leaning on me. That type." She put her forefingers on her eyelids and pressed them closed. "This world isn't set up just the way I'd have done it myself," she said, and her voice cracked. "No kidding."

"Don't cry," Patrick said. He was afraid to touch her.

"Did you ever see me cry? I never cry." She was trembling. She spread her fingers to cover her face, and Patrick looked at her hands and at her wedding ring. "The afternoon I came out here—well, here's how I happened to come out here, I'll give you the whole Gestalt: After you left for your nine-o'clock class I cleaned up the apartment and I got dressed and I went to the doctor. I cut my Milton and Abnormal. I hate Abnormal anyhow."

"You went to the *doctor?*" said Patrick, all alarm. "Are you sick?"

"I'm not sick; be quiet. So then afterwards I took the subway back up to 116th Street and I went to the market and I bought some lamb chops. And I was debating whether I should go home and get rid of my lamb chops and maybe be late for my Shakespeare, or go straight to my Shakespeare and take my lamb chops with me. I was standing on the corner there pondering this big problem and waiting for the light to change. My hair was combed and I looked, you know, I looked all right. Nice. I had my navy blue suit on. Navy blue. And I started to cross the street and a man came across. He looked all right. I hardly noticed him. But then he said in some very affected voice, 'My, what an attractive girl!' So I looked down. And then, when he got right beside me, he said, right *at* me, right into my face, 'You *bum.*'" She stared at Patrick through her fingers; she looked stricken and very, very scared.

"He was drunk," Patrick said.

"No."

Patrick got up and went around to squat on the floor next to her chair. He circled her wrists with his fingers. "That guy sounds to me like nothing but a very sick person," he said gently. "But I know how you feel."

"You don't know how I feel. All this rapport junk is junk. My mother was in gorgeous rapport with every junky husband she ever had. And in the middle of her chest she thought they were crumbs."

"That's different," Patrick said. "We're altogether different."

"What are you holding my hand for?" Mona said crabbily. "Stop holding my hand! I'm pregnant."

"For Pete *sake*," Patrick said. He was astounded. "Imagine that!" He let go of her abruptly and sat hard on the floor.

"Imagine that, imagine that," Mona said despondently. "I'm having a baby and it could look like you. It could scratch its head the way you do. You scratch the left side of your head with your right hand and the right side of your head with your left hand. If I have a baby and it scratches its head like that, I'll kill myself, I mean it."

"I won't do it anymore," Patrick promised.

"I *like* it. You don't understand. I was walking up Broadway and I was shaking. You don't know how bad you'd feel. I felt as if somebody'd spat on me. Somebody who knew what he was spitting on. And all of a sudden I had a feeling—I could have a little child by the hand and be walking up Broadway and all the people on Broadway would look at us and they'd have wolf's heads instead of people's heads. They'd have fangs and little flickering glittering eyes and they'd be slavering and looking at me and this child that was just the way you were when you were a little boy and you ate that bark. Oh, it was awful!"

"And then what? Where was I all this time?"

"Well, that's the thing. I didn't want to go to my Shakespeare and first I thought I'd go over to the College and look for you. But you'd have been at work by then, in Admissions, and I didn't want to go there. And then I realized something I never realized before. If you saw a lot of people on Broadway, Patrick, with wolf's heads and fangs and things, you'd say to yourself, 'Goodness gracious mercy me, look at all those poor people with wolf's heads, those poor sick people they must feel terrible about it.' And then you'd go look up the name of a specialist. You'd be very tactful and sweet about it and you wouldn't let on you'd noticed anything, but you'd get them all to the specialist. And then you'd sell your socks to pay the bill."

"I really don't think I would," Patrick said.

"Yes. It's your tragic flaw. And when they ripped off your arms and they ripped off your legs and you were just a bloody piece of meat on the pavement on Broadway your silly voice that's just like Mickey Rooney's would float around in the air saying, 'Those poor poor people, they were even sicker than I thought.'" She took one hand away from her face and clutched her throat.

"I don't sound a bit like Mickey Rooney," Patrick said resentfully.

"Moses supposes his toeses are roses," Mona said wearily, "but Moses supposes erroneously. You sound more like Mickey Rooney than Mickey Rooney does." She sighed and put her face down on her arms on the table, turned away from him so that all he got was a view of her red straw hat and the babyish downy look of the back of her neck. "So then I called my friendly neighborhood mother," she said in a tired-out voice, "and gave her the word. She said 'Mona! Oh, my baby' and wept till I just about had tears running down my arm from the telephone. Then she said she'd sell a bond."

"She doesn't have to sell a bond," Patrick said. "I'll quit school."

"You would, too, you *boob*," Mona said, with no breath to spare. "You would. Don't be so boring. My father left me lots of jack and once I get my hands on it I'll buy my mother off."

"And what about me?" Patrick said. "It's my child too, isn't it, what about me, I'm responsible."

"Don't be so boring," Mona begged. "And that's how I happened to come out here. I wanted to look at things and think and be all by myself and not near you."

"For how long?" Patrick asked anxiously. "Not for long? Not forever?"

Mona didn't answer him. "All I can think about is how awful everything is. Take my mother. I like her quite a lot. I like her very well, to be frank with you. And I shouldn't. Old Creeping Jane, she's awful. She took every one of us kids aside—Monroe, then Gordon, then me—and told every single one of us that our own particular father was the only man she ever loved. She doesn't even know the difference, Patrick. I shouldn't like her at all, don't you think? She's awful. Things are *awful*, don't you think? Take my brother Gordon, for example. He gets fruitier every minute." She lifted her head and looked at him, pinched and frightened. "If I saw Gordon and I didn't know he was Gordon, I'd look at something else, so I wouldn't have to look at him. But just the same, I like him very well. And Monroe is mean, he's as mean as anything, and the trouble is, he's got a conscience. When Gordon was a baby, Monroe hated Gordon's father so much that he used to pick Gordon right up from the floor by the rims of his ears. That's how Gordon got so deaf. Monroe told me that, and he told Gordon and my mother and God knows who all, probably perfect strangers. And he hates himself for it, he flails himself for it, and do you know what? The whole time, if Gordon wasn't two feet taller than Monroe, Monroe would still be picking him up by his ears. The whole time. And still and all, I like Monroe. A lot."

"Don't you like me any more?" Patrick said.

"Sure I do. I never said I didn't," she said faintly. "It's just that everything's so awful, Patrick. Don't you think everything's awful?" She put her cold hands on the nape of his neck and rammed his face against the stiff, faded bodice of her bathing suit. His hat fell off. "Don't you think it's awful?" she moaned into his hair, hanging on to him and kissing his ears and his forehead in a transport of despair. "Isn't life crummy, though, isn't it low?"

"Yes," he said happily, kissing her chest, wondering if she'd broken his nose, "I guess it is. I guess it's pretty bad."

EMILIE BIX BUCHWALD   [1961]

Emilie Bix Buchwald, who was born in Austria in 1935, has published stories, poems, and articles since her graduation from Barnard College in 1957. She is now raising her family, teaching at the University of Minnesota, and working toward a Ph.D.

Jupiter and Io: These Older Nights

These older nights you look more closely at your lover,
Dis: -interestedly, -passionately, -cover
The fact he's getting old and fat all over.
No more the God—but still, no more the rover.

And in the bathroom mirror lurks another,
A queer resemblance, at first glance, a bother,
To one not you and young, nor quite that scold, your mother;
A something in between—with something, still, not either.

The Argus eyes that watched the gentle heifer,
The jealous eyes that made the creature suffer,
They're shut, and we are meadowed peacefully forever,
I, old cow, and you, by Jove, a duffer.

SHEILA CUDAHY [1961]

Sheila Cudahy was born in Chicago in 1920, graduated from Barnard College in 1943, and received her Master of Arts from Columbia in 1944. For many years she was a publisher, first with Pellegrini and Cudahy and subsequently with Farrar, Straus and Cudahy. Like most publishers, she has done more editing than writing of her own. Poems is her first book.

They Met by Chance

They met by chance in the park at the zoo
A chill spring day
    new grass and puddles patterned with children
    and pull toys and pigeons
    waddling erratically on the walk,
    deflecting his thoughts induced by talks
    he had had with his atheist friend, a
    mortician, on the relevance of religion.

And the spring sent the lake scudding
    like an ecstatic glass bubble
    reflecting the zoo and the temple of love, and the bench
    where she unemployed, a dietician dismissed with two weeks'
      pay,
    enjoyed the spring grass day askew
    in a weather of children and jingling toys
    and love-bent pigeons sleek as doves
    on the walk to the zoo
    where suddenly he and she were aware
that a single caged eagle held them together in its agate stare.

A middle-aged fool, a messianic incompetent
devoted to drubbing abstract dichotomies
which she coolly noted meet in life;
in fact, their couplings produce a supple breed
of possible alternatives and viable accidents.

More concrete evidence was needed to seduce the sage.
She became his wife, his penitent in residence.

Married
Irreconcilable

They find they most enjoy the city zoo
Where bright with wings the beasts confined
    renew her sentimental appetites:
    Please do not feed the animals
He sees the creatures of his prophecies reborn.
    The lion speaks.
    The bull ablaze casts off thorn-harried flesh and flies.
    Rhinoceros turns unicorn and feasts on fresh spring flowers

He cries a warning as the regal bird descends
and with a fixed and lidless gaze devours eyes.

Absurd, she says.
It sings.

About the Editors

JOHN A. KOUWENHOVEN is a Professor of English at Barnard College, a trustee of the Rhode Island School of Design, a member of the executive council of the Society for the History of Technology, and a member of the editorial boards of *American Quarterly* and *Technology and Culture*. Formerly an editor of *Harper's Magazine*, Mr. Kouwenhoven is the author of *The Beer Can by the Highway* (1961), *The Columbia Historical Portrait of New York* (1953) and *Made in America* (1948).

JANICE FARRAR THADDEUS was born in 1933 in New York City and educated in private schools and at Radcliffe and Barnard Colleges, graduating from the latter in 1955. She received her Master of Arts degree from Columbia University in 1959 and is currently working on her Ph.D. Since 1956 she has taught at Barnard College, where she now holds the position of Instructor of English. She is married to Patrick Thaddeus, an astrophysicist.

Format by Sidney Feinberg
Set in Linotype Caledonia
Composed, printed and bound by American Book-Stratford Press, Inc.
HARPER & ROW, PUBLISHERS, INCORPORATED